Lister's Antiseptic Principle of the
Practice of Surgery

Harvey's Motion of the Heart and Blood

Auenbrugger's Percussion of the Chest

Laënnac's Auscultation and the Stethoscope

Jenner's Inquiry into Smallpox Vaccine;
Further Observations;
Continuation of Observations

Morton's Administering Sulphuric Ether;
Physiology of Ether

Simpson's A New Anaesthetic Agent

Holmes's Contagiousness of Puerperal Fever

CLASSICS OF
MEDICINE AND
SURGERY

(formerly titled: *Epoch-making Contributions to Medicine,
Surgery and the Allied Sciences*)

Collected by

C. N. B. CAMAC

DOVER PUBLICATIONS, INC.
NEW YORK

HENRY SCHUMAN
NEW YORK

Published in Canada by General Publishing Company, Ltd., 30 Lesmill Road, Don Mills, Toronto, Ontario.
Published in the United Kingdom by Constable and Company, Ltd., 10 Orange Street, London WC 2.

This Dover edition, first published in 1959, is an unabridged and unaltered republication of the work originally published by W. B. Saunders Company in 1909 under the title *Epoch-making Contributions to Medicine, Surgery and the Allied Sciences*.

Library of Congress Catalog Card Number: 59-16811

Manufactured in the United States of America
Dover Publications, Inc.
180 Varick Street
New York, N. Y. 10014

INTRODUCTION

In the mass of scientific literature which appears year after year there occurs, very occasionally, an article which presents the results of experiment or investigation that prove epoch-making. These articles, though recording masterpieces of scientific research, are buried with valueless or ephemeral writings.

Certain of my teachers, in presenting a subject at clinics and lectures, had, for the inspection of the students, the article which communicated such observations as first placed the subject upon a sound scientific basis. Subsequently, in my own teaching I followed this custom. There has thus resulted a collection, begun some twelve years ago, of epoch-making articles, a part of which is gathered into the present volume.

Upon first thought one is disposed to conclude that to-day such communications would be obsolete and of historic value only, but on reading the articles the fact becomes evident that the work and observations were so thoroughly and accurately done in the first instance that the teaching, practice, and terminology of to-day are either the same as when first communicated or based directly on these foundations. In many instances, subsequent writers have merely paraphrased the statements of the original observers. Indeed, one may go further and say that some of the errors of to-day are the result of disregarding or misquoting the facts clearly set forth in these original treatises. As an example, Jenner's definite direction regarding the technique of vaccination, if adhered to, would prevent many of the infections and shocking ulcerations seen even in our own day. Again, in Laënnec's writings is to be found much that would clear the confusion regarding physical signs which teachers to-day discuss without even referring to the observations of this master-mind. In other branches of science, as physics and chemistry, in law and in art, the teachings of great authorities are familiarly quoted and used as guides.

There is no reason why in medicine such familiarity should not be considered requisite to a proper education.

Professor Ostwald's estimate of Original Literature

Professor Ostwald, in writing of his student days at the University of Dorpat, speaks of his "wolfish hunger" for more than the text-book, and how "ravenously" he devoured the original treatises by the recognized masters when, as a senior, he was admitted into the University library. He says:

Reading the Original Articles

" * * * * At first, as a result of my earlier training, I read only text-books and monographs. But when I began my preparatory work the professor * * * * directed me to look up in the old volumes * * * * the descriptions which the discoverers of the required substances had given of their original experiments. * * * * I had learned that every scientific discovery is the result of a natural process of development, which leads through more or less numerous errors and misconceptions to a definite and lasting result."

Evolution of Scientific Discovery

He goes on to say:

Youthful impressions the Warp upon which is woven the intellectual life

" * * * * It is well known to what a degree a man's life is influenced by the impressions gained in youth; these are, as it were, the warp upon which the intellectual life of a man is woven. So, after those years in Dorpat, it has been absolutely necessary for me to have free access to original literature, and in all other places where I have worked it has been my first concern to place this indispensable aid at the disposal of my colleagues and myself. For I had learned that the inclination and ability to view a question from historical standpoint is of the same importance in the education of the chemist (and of every other investigator) as is the inclination and ability to do careful and conscientious experimental work.

How the Teacher obtains suggestions for Laboratory research

"Later, I was led to notice another characteristic feature of such a library. This early acquired inclination to read the old literature in the original * * * * had from the very beginning suggested all kinds of scarcely obvious thoughts and experiments. This habit proved of great value to me when in the course of time the number of investigators working with me increased and the demand for themes became greater."

I venture to quote still further from this valuable source; he says:

" *   *   *   * It is not alone the requirements of the pro- Scientific
fessor which are satisfied by this study of the old literature. By disputes
following the scientific disputes of the past (and indeed no period
has been free from these disputes), a kind of personal acquaintance Personal
with the character and manner of thought of the writers is in- acquaintance with the
voluntarily obtained, along with a practical experience of the prob- Writers and the
lems of science. *   *   *   * The reader acquires a lively sense Problems of
of scientific and personal style; at times, he is annoyed by the Science
prolixity and vagueness of one writer or pleased by the concise Style
clearness of another, and endeavors to attain in his own works that
which has been so pleasing in the works of others. In short, a Intercourse
large part of that gain which accompanies regular intercourse with with Talented and Learned
talented and learned men may be obtained by such an intimate ac- Men
quaintance with a collection of old scientific journals.

*   *   *   * Thus the journals with their long and tiresome
rows of uniform volumes   *   *   *   * have proved to be a most Long and tire-
useful, and at the same time a most interesting, aid for all kinds of some rows of uniform
work in any way connected with science. In our age, which is turn- Volumes
ing so energetically from a narrow specialism to a broader conception of all scientific problems, the use of this aid will become more
and more general; and what up to the present has been a luxury A necessity for
for a few will become a necessity for everybody. *   *   *   *" everybody

In the arrangement of this volume no effort has been made,
either to include all articles on the subject which appeared at the
time of the epoch-making one, or to present the subjects in chrono- Plan of this
logical order.   The main object is to take the article out of that Volume
"long and tiresome row of uniform volumes" and to place it within
the reach of the student.   The best English translation has been
selected for articles appearing in a foreign tongue, but reference
to the original as well as to other writings by the same author is
given. These lists of writings are biographical sketches, as it The lists of
were, of the scientific side of the investigator's mind.   In them we writings are evidences of
see the breadth of his interests, the studies which led up to his great the Writers'
work, and the number and character of his contributions.   It has intellectual interests
also been thought best to give a sketch only regarding the biog- The Biograph-
raphy of each writer, as there are now numerous works on the lives ical Sketches
of all those whose writings would entitle them to a place among the
epoch-makers.   What appears in these sketches, however, has
been written after consulting the most authoritative sources.   In

one instance, that of Morton, I have been able to find but one satisfactory source regarding this observer's personal history; reference to this is made in the sketch. Portraits also appear with each article, and in some instances facsimiles of the title-pages. For the portrait of Dr. O. W. Holmes I am indebted to Dr. J. W. Farlow, of the Boston Medical Library; for that of Auenbrugger I am indebted to Sidney Colvin, Esq., Keeper of Department of Prints and Drawings of the British Museum, who kindly sent me a copy from the source mentioned under the portrait. After careful search it would seem that this is the only portrait of Auenbrugger in existence.

The Portraits and Facsimiles

I wish to acknowledge my indebtedness to "The British Medical Journal," "The Boston Medical and Surgical Journal," to Messrs. George Bell and Co., London, and to Messrs. Houghton, Mifflin and Co., Boston, for permission to reprint the articles which first appeared from their publishing houses. To Professors Welch and Osler, to whom I first submitted the plan of such a volume, I wish to express my appreciation of their advice and encouragement. From Professors Musser and Barker and Dr. C. G. L. Wolf I have received valuable suggestions from time to time. Mr. Browne, Librarian of the New York Academy of Medicine, has, as on many former occasions, rendered me practical assistance.

C. N. B. C.

108 East 65th Street,
New York.

CONTENTS

Antisepsis

London
18 Sept 1906

My dear Sir

Professor Osler
has sent me your
most kind letter.

I feel that you do me
very great honour in
proposing to publish my
first paper on the Antiseptic
Principle in company with
works of men so highly
distinguished. Professor Osler's
recommendation removes

any hesitation I might
otherwise have felt in giving
my cordial assent to your
proposal.

Believe me
My dear Sir
very sincerely yours

Lister

C. N. B. Carmac Esq᷑

LORD LISTER, O.M., F.R.S., F.R.C.S.

1867

ON THE ANTISEPTIC PRINCIPLE OF THE PRACTICE OF SURGERY

By JOSEPH LISTER, F.R.S.,

PROF. OF SURGERY IN THE UNIVERSITY OF GLASGOW

Read in the Surgical Section before the Annual Meeting of the British Medical Association in Dublin, on August 9th, 1867

Copied from The British Medical Journal, September 21st, 1867

EXPLANATORY NOTE

In the Lancet for March 16, 1867, Lister published the first of a series of articles entitled "On a new Method of Treating Compound Fracture, Abscess, etc., with Observation on the Condition of Suppuration." This series antedates the one here reprinted, but is made up almost entirely of reports of cases which are summarized and commented upon in this one. The reports on these cases, like those of Jenner's in the vaccination studies, show the gradual revelation of the truths regarding antisepsis.

The article from the British Med. Jour., for Aug. 9, 1867, selected for this volume, may be considered as a part of and conclusion to this detailed report, the first of which appeared in the Lancet for March 16, 1867. In the first article of the Lancet series, which strictly marks the first of Lister's publications on antisepsis the following statements appear:

" * * * * * Turning now to the question how the atmosphere produces decomposition of organic substances, we find that a flood of light has been thrown upon this most important subject by the philosophic researches of M. Pasteur, who has demonstrated by thoroughly convincing evidence that it is not to its oxygen or to any of its gaseous constituents that the air owes this property, but to minute particles suspended in it, which are the germs of various low forms of life, long since revealed by the microscope, and regarded as merely accidental concomitants of putrescence, but now shown by Pasteur to be its essential cause, resolving the complex organic compounds into substances of simpler chemical constitution, just as the yeast plant converts sugar into alcohol and carbonic acid.

" * * * Applying these principles to the treatment of compound fracture, bearing in mind that it is from the vitality of the atmospheric particles that all the mischief arises, it appears that all that is requisite is to dress the wound with some material capable of killing these septic germs, provided that any substance can be found reliable for this purpose, yet not too potent as a caustic.

"In the course of the year 1864 I was much struck with an account of the remarkable effects produced by carbolic acid upon the sewage of the town of Carlisle, the admixture of a very small proportion not only preventing all odour from the lands irrigated with the refuse material, but, as it was stated, destroying the entozoa which usually infest cattle fed upon such pastures.

"My attention having for several years been directed to the subject of suppuration, more especially in its relation to decomposition, I saw that such a powerful antiseptic was peculiarly adapted for experiments with a view to elucidating that subject, and while I was engaged in the investigation the applicability of carbolic acid for the treatment of compound fracture naturally occurred to me.

"My first attempt of this kind was made in Glasgow Royal Infirmary in March, 1865, in a case of compound fracture of the leg.   It proved unsuccessful, in consequence, as I now believe, of improper management; but subsequent trials have more than realised my most sanguine anticipations   *   *   *   "

A large number of cases reported in detail through several issues of the Lancet here follow.

ON THE ANTISEPTIC PRINCIPLE OF THE PRACTICE OF SURGERY

By JOSEPH LISTER, F.R.S.

In the course of an extended investigation into the nature of inflammation, and the healthy and morbid conditions of the blood in relation to it, I arrived several years ago at the conclusion that the essential cause of suppuration in wounds is decomposition, brought about by the influence of the atmosphere upon blood or serum retained within them, and, in the case of contused wounds, upon portions of tissue destroyed by the violence of the injury.

To prevent the occurrence of suppuration with all its attendant risks was an object manifestly desirable, but till lately apparently unattainable, since it seemed hopeless to attempt to exclude the oxygen which was universally regarded as the agent by which putrefaction was effected. But when it had been shown by the researches of Pasteur that the septic properties of the atmosphere depended not on the oxygen, or any gaseous constituent, but on minute organisms suspended in it, which owed their energy to their vitality, it occurred to me that decomposition in the injured part might be avoided without excluding the air, by applying as a dressing some material capable of destroying the life of the floating particles. Upon this principle I have based a practice of which I will now attempt to give a short account.

The material which I have employed is carbolic or phenic acid, a volatile organic compound, which appears to exercise a peculiarly destructive influence upon low forms of life, and hence is the most powerful antiseptic with which we are at present acquainted.

The first class of cases to which I applied it was that of compound fractures, in which the effects of decomposition in the injured part

9

were especially striking and pernicious. The results have been such as to establish conclusively the great principle that all local inflammatory mischief and general febrile disturbances which follow severe injuries are due to the irritating and poisonous influence of decomposing blood or sloughs. For these evils are entirely avoided by the antiseptic treatment, so that limbs which would otherwise be unhesitatingly condemned to amputation may be retained, with confidence of the best results.

In conducting the treatment, the first object must be the destruction of any septic germs which may have been introduced into the wounds, either at the moment of the accident or during the time which has since elapsed. This is done by introducing the acid of full strength into all accessible recesses of the wound by means of a piece of rag held in dressing forceps and dipped into the liquid.* This I did not venture to do in the earlier cases; but experience has shown that the compound which carbolic acid forms with the blood, and also any portions of tissue killed by its caustic action, including even parts of the bone, are disposed of by absorption and organisation, provided they are afterwards kept from decomposing. We are thus enabled to employ the antiseptic treatment efficiently at a period after the occurrence of the injury at which it would otherwise probably fail. Thus I have now under my care, in Glasgow Infirmary, a boy who was admitted with compound fracture of the leg as late as eight and one-half hours after the accident, in whom, nevertheless, all local and constitutional disturbance was avoided by means of carbolic acid, and the bones were soundly united five weeks after his admission.

The next object to be kept in view is to guard effectually against the spreading of decomposition into the wound along the stream of blood and serum which oozes out during the first few days after the accident, when the acid originally applied has been washed out or dissipated by absorption and evaporation. This part of the treatment has been greatly improved during the past few weeks. The method which I have hitherto published (see Lancet for Mar.

---

* The addition of a few drops of water to a considerable quantity of the acid, induces it to assume permanently the liquid form.

16th, 23rd, 30th, and April 27th of the present year)* consisted in the application of a piece of lint dipped in the acid, overlapping the sound skin to some extent and covered with a tin cap, which was daily raised in order to touch the surface of the lint with the anti-septic. This method certainly succeeded well with wounds of moderate size; and indeed I may say that in all the many cases of this kind which have been so treated by myself or my house-sur-geons, not a single failure has occurred. When, however, the wound is very large, the flow of blood and serum is so profuse, especially during the first twenty-four hours, that the antiseptic application cannot prevent the spread of decomposition into the interior unless it overlaps the sound skin for a very considerable distance, and this was inadmissible by the method described above, on account of the extensive sloughing of the surface of the cutis which it would involve. This difficulty has, however, been overcome by employing a paste composed of common whiting (carbonate of lime), mixed with a solution of one part of carbolic acid in four parts of boiled linseed oil so as to form a firm putty. This application contains the acid in too dilute a form to excoriate the skin, which it may be made to cover to any extent that may be thought desirable, while its sub-stance serves as a reservoir of the antiseptic material. So long as any discharge continues, the paste should be changed daily, and, in order to prevent the chance of mischief occurring during the process, a piece of rag dipped in the solution of carbolic acid in oil is put on next the skin, and maintained there permanently, care being taken to avoid raising it along with the putty. This rag is always kept in an antiseptic condition from contact with the paste above it, and destroys any germs which may fall upon it during the short time that should alone be allowed to pass in the changing of the dressing. The putty should be in a layer about a quarter of an inch thick, and may be advantageously applied rolled out between two pieces of thin calico, which maintain it in the form of a continuous sheet, which may be wrapped in a moment round the whole circumference of a limb if this be thought desirable, while

* See explanatory note, pp. 7–3 (N. B. C.).

the putty is prevented by the calico from sticking to the rag which is next the skin.*   When all discharge has ceased, the use of the paste is discontinued, but the original rag is left adhering to the skin till healing by scabbing is supposed to be complete.   I have at present in the hospital a man with severe compound fracture of both bones of the left leg, caused by direct violence, who, after the cessation of the sanious discharge under the use of the paste, without a drop of pus appearing, has been treated for the last two weeks exactly as if the fracture was a simple one.   During this time the rag, adhering by means of a crust of inspissated blood collected beneath it, has continued perfectly dry, and it will be left untouched till the usual period for removing the splints in a simple fracture, when we may fairly expect to find a sound cicatrix beneath it.

We cannot, however, always calculate on so perfect a result as this.   More or less pus may appear after the lapse of the first week, and the larger the wound, the more likely this is to happen.   And here I would desire earnestly to enforce the necessity of persevering with the antiseptic application in spite of the appearance of suppuration, so long as other symptoms are favorable.   The surgeon is extremely apt to suppose that any suppuration is an indication that the antiseptic treatment has failed, and that poulticing or water dressing should be resorted to.   But such a course would in many cases sacrifice a limb or a life.   I cannot, however, expect my professional brethren to follow my advice blindly in such a matter, and therefore I feel it necessary to place before them, as shortly as I can, some pathological principles intimately connected, not only with the point we are immediately considering, but with the whole subject of this paper.

If a perfectly healthy granulating sore be well washed and covered with a plate of clean metal, such as block tin, fitting its surface pretty accurately, and overlapping the surrounding skin an inch or so in

---

* In order to prevent evaporation of the acid, which passes readily through any organic tissue, such as oiled silk or gutta percha, it is well to cover the paste with a sheet of block tin, or tinfoil strengthened with adhesive plaster.   The thin sheet lead used for lining tea chests will also answer the purpose, and may be obtained from any wholesale grocer.

every direction and retained in position by adhesive plaster and a bandage, it will be found, on removing it after twenty-four or forty-eight hours, that little or nothing that can be called pus is present, merely a little transparent fluid, while at the same time there is an entire absence of the unpleasant odour invariably perceived when water dressing is changed. Here the clean metallic surface presents no recesses like those of porous lint for the septic germs to develope in, the fluid exuding from the surface of the granulations has flowed away undecomposed, and the result is the absence of suppuration. This simple experiment illustrates the important fact that granulations have no inherent tendency to form pus, but do so only when subjected to preternatural stimulus. Further, it shows that the mere contact of a foreign body does not of itself stimulate granulations to suppurate; whereas the presence of decomposing organic matter does. These truths are even more strikingly exemplified by the fact that I have elsewhere recorded (Lancet, March 23rd, 1867), that a piece of dead bone free from decomposition may not only fail to induce the granulations around it to suppurate, but may actually be absorbed by them; whereas a bit of dead bone soaked with putrid pus infallibly induces suppuration in its vicinity.

Another instructive experiment is, to dress a granulating sore with some of the putty above described, overlapping the sound skin extensively; when we find, in the course of twenty-four hours, that pus has been produced by the sore, although the application has been perfectly antiseptic; and, indeed, the larger the amount of carbolic acid in the paste, the greater is the quantity of pus formed, provided we avoid such a proportion as would act as a caustic. The carbolic acid, though it prevents decomposition, induces suppuration—obviously by acting as a chemical stimulus; and we may safely infer that putrescent organic materials (which we know to be chemically acrid) operate in the same way.

In so far, then, carbolic acid and decomposing substances are alike; viz., that they induce suppuration by chemical stimulation, as distinguished from what may be termed simple inflammatory suppuration, such as that in which ordinary abscesses originate—

where the pus appears to be formed in consequence of an excited action of the nerves, independently of any other stimulus. There is, however, this enormous difference between the effects of carbolic acid and those of decomposition; viz., that carbolic acid stimulates only the surface to which it is at first applied, and every drop of discharge that forms weakens the stimulant by diluting it; but decomposition is a self-propagating and self-aggravating poison, and, if it occur at the surface of a severely injured limb, it will spread into all its recesses so far as any extravasated blood or shreds of dead tissue may extend, and lying in those recesses, it will become from hour to hour more acrid, till it requires the energy of a caustic sufficient to destroy the vitality of any tissues naturally weak from inferior vascular supply, or weakened by the injury they sustained in the accident.

Hence it is easy to understand how, when a wound is very large, the crust beneath the rag may prove here and there insufficient to protect the raw surface from the stimulating influence of the carbolic acid in the putty; and the result will be first the conversion of the tissues so acted on into granulations, and subsequently the formation of more or less pus. This, however, will be merely superficial, and will not interfere with the absorption and organisation of extravasated blood or dead tissues in the interior. But, on the other hand, should decomposition set in before the internal parts have become securely consolidated, the most disastrous results may ensue.

I left behind me in Glasgow a boy, thirteen years of age, who, between three and four weeks previously, met with a most severe injury to the left arm, which he got entangled in a machine at a fair. There was a wound six inches long and three inches broad, and the skin was very extensively undermined beyond its limits, while the soft parts were generally so much lacerated that a pair of dressing forceps introduced at the wound and pushed directly inwards appeared beneath the skin at the opposite aspect of the limb. From this wound several tags of muscle were hanging, and among them was one consisting of about three inches of the triceps in almost its entire thickness; while the lower fragment of the bone, which was broken high up, was protruding four inches and a half, stripped of muscle, the skin being tucked in under it.   Without the assistance of the antiseptic treatment, I should certainly have thought of nothing else but amputation at the shoulder-joint; but, as the radial pulse could be felt and the fingers had sensation, I did not hesitate to try to save the limb and adopted the plan of treatment above described, wrapping the arm from the shoulder to below the elbow in the antiseptic application, the whole interior of the wound, together with the protruding bone, having previously been freely treated with strong carbolic acid.   About the tenth day, the discharge, which up to that time had been only sanious and serous, showed a slight admixture of slimy pus; and this increased till (a few days before I left) it amounted to about three drachms in twenty-four hours.   But the boy continued as he had been after the second day, free from unfavorable symptoms, with pulse, tongue, appetite, and sleep natural and strength increasing, while the limb remained as it had been from the first, free from swelling, redness, or pain. I, therefore, persevered with the antiseptic dressing; and, before I left, the discharge was already somewhat less, while the bone was becoming firm.   I think it likely that, in that boy's case, I should have found merely a superficial sore had I taken off all the dressings at the end of the three weeks; though, considering the extent of the injury, I thought it prudent to let the month expire before disturbing the rag next the skin.   But I feel sure that, if I had resorted to ordinary dressing when the pus first appeared, the progress of the case would have been exceedingly different.

The next class of cases to which I have applied the antiseptic treatment is that of abscesses.   Here also the results have been extremely satisfactory, and in beautiful harmony with the pathological principles indicated above.   The pyogenic membrane, like the granulations of a sore, which it resembles in nature, forms pus, not from any inherent disposition to do so, but only because it is subjected to some preternatural stimulation.   In an ordinary abscess, whether acute or chronic, before it is opened the stimulus which maintains the suppuration is derived from the presence of pus pent up within the cavity.   When a free opening is made in the ordinary

way, this stimulus is got rid of, but the atmosphere gaining access
to the contents, the potent stimulus of decomposition comes into
operation, and pus is generated in greater abundance than before.
But when the evacuation is effected on the antiseptic principle, the
pyogenic membrane, freed from the influence of the former stimulus without the substitution of a new one, ceases to suppurate (like
the granulations of a sore under metallic dressing), furnishing merely
a trifling amount of clear serum, and, whether the opening be dependent or not, rapidly contracts and coalesces.   At the same time
any constitutional symptoms previously occasioned by the accumulation of the matter are got rid of without the slightest risk of the
irritative fever or hectic hitherto so justly dreaded in dealing with
large abscesses.

In order that the treatment may be satisfactory, the abscess must
be seen before it is opened.   Then, except in very rare and peculiar
cases,* there are no septic organisms in the contents, so that it is
needless to introduce carbolic acid into the interior.   Indeed, such
a procedure would be objectionable, as it would stimulate the pyogenic membrane to unnecessary suppuration.   All that is requisite
is to guard against the introduction of living atmospheric germs
from without, at the same time that free opportunity is afforded
for the escape of the discharge from within.

I have so lately given elsewhere a detailed account of the method
by which this is effected (Lancet, July 27th, 1867), that I shall not
enter into it at present further than to say that the means employed
are the same as those described above for the superficial dressing
of compound fractures; viz., a piece of rag dipped into the solution
of carbolic acid in oil to serve as an antiseptic curtain, under cover
of which the abscess is evacuated by free incision, and the antiseptic
paste to guard against decomposition occurring in the stream of pus
that flows out beneath it; the dressing being changed daily until
the sinus is closed.

---

* As an instance of one of these exceptional cases, I may mention that of
an abscess in the vicinity of the colon, and afterwards proved by postmortem examination to have once communicated with it.   Here the pus was extremely offensive when evacuated, and exhibited vibrios under the microscope.

The most remarkable results of this practice in a pathological point of view have been afforded by cases where the formation of pus depended on disease of bone. Here the abscesses, instead of forming exceptions to the general class in the obstinacy of the suppuration, have resembled the rest in yielding in a few days only a trifling discharge, and frequently the production of pus has ceased from the moment of the evacuation of the original contents. Hence it appears that caries, when no longer labouring as heretofore under the irritation of decomposing matter, ceases to be an opprobrium of surgery, and recovers like other inflammatory affections. In the publication before alluded to, I have mentioned the case of a middle-aged man with a psoas abscess depending in diseased bone, in whom the sinus finally closed after months of patient perseverance with the antiseptic treatment. Since that article was written I have had another instance of abscess equally gratifying, but differing in the circumstance that the disease and the recovery were more rapid in their course. The patient was a blacksmith, who had suffered four and a half months before I saw him from symptoms of ulceration of cartilage in the left elbow. These had latterly increased in severity so as to deprive him entirely of his night's rest and of appetite. I found the region of the elbow greatly swollen, and on careful examination found a fluctuating point at the outer aspect of the articulation. I opened it on the antiseptic principle, the incision evidently penetrating to the joint, giving exit to a few drachms of pus. The medical gentleman under whose care he was (Dr. Macgregor, of Glasgow) supervised the daily dressing with the carbolic acid paste till the patient went to spend two or three weeks at the coast, when his wife was entrusted with it. Just two months after I opened the abscess, he called to show me the limb, stating that the discharge had been, for at least two weeks, as little as it was then, a trifling moisture upon the paste, such as might be accounted for by the little sore caused by the incision. On applying a probe guarded with an antiseptic rag, I found that the sinus was soundly closed, while the limb was free from swelling or tenderness; and, although he had not attempted to exercise it much, the joint could already be moved through a con-

siderable angle. Here the antiseptic principle had effected the
restoration of a joint, which, on any other known system of treatment, must have been excised.

Ordinary contused wounds are, of course, amenable to the same
treatment as compound fractures, which are a complicated variety
of them. I will content myself with mentioning a single instance
of this class of cases. In April last, a volunteer was discharging
a rifle when it burst, and blew back the thumb with its metacarpal
bone, so that it could be bent back as on a hinge at the trapezial
joint, which had evidently been opened, while all the soft parts
between the metacarpal bones of the thumb and forefinger were
torn through. I need not insist before my present audience on the
ugly character of such an injury. My house-surgeon, Mr. Hector
Cameron, applied carbolic acid to the whole raw surface, and completed the dressing as if for compound fracture. The hand remained free from pain, redness or swelling, and with the exception
of a shallow groove, all the wound consolidated without a drop of
matter, so that if it had been a clean cut, it would have been regarded
as a good example of primary union. The small granulating
surface soon healed, and at present a linear cicatrix alone tells of
the injury he has sustained, while his thumb has all its movements
and his hand a fine grasp.

If the severest forms of contused and lacerated wounds heal thus
kindly under the antiseptic treatment, it is obvious that its application to simple incised wounds must be merely a matter of detail.
I have devoted a good deal of attention to this class, but I have not
as yet pleased myself altogether with any of the methods I have
employed. I am, however, prepared to go so far as to say that a
solution of carbolic acid in twenty parts of water, while a mild and
cleanly application, may be relied on for destroying any septic
germs that may fall upon the wound during the performance of an
operation; and also that, for preventing the subsequent introduction
of others, the paste above described, applied as for compound fractures, gives excellent results. Thus I have had a case of strangulated inguinal hernia in which it was necessary to take away half a
pound of thickened omentum, heal without any deep-seated sup-

puration or any tenderness of the sac or any fever; and amputations, including one immediately below the knee, have remained absolutely free from constitutional symptoms.

Further, I have found that when the antiseptic treatment is efficiently conducted, ligatures may be safely cut short and left to be disposed of by absorption or otherwise. Should this particular branch of the subject yield to all that it promises, should it turn out on further trial that when the knot is applied on the antiseptic principle, we may calculate as securely as if it were absent on the occurrence of healing without any deep-seated suppuration, the deligation of main arteries in their continuity will be deprived of the two dangers that now attend it, viz., those of secondary hæmorrhage and an unhealthy state of the wound. Further, it seems not unlikely that the present objection to tying an artery in the immediate vicinity of a large branch may be done away with; and that even the innominate, which has lately been the subject of an ingenious experiment by one of the Dublin surgeons, on account of its well-known fatality under the ligature for secondary hæmorrhage, may cease to have this unhappy character when the tissues in the vicinity of the thread, instead of becoming softened through the influence of an irritating decomposing substance, are left at liberty to consolidate firmly near an unoffending though foreign body.

It would carry me far beyond the limited time which, by the rules of the Association, is alone at my disposal, were I to enter into the various applications of the antiseptic principle in the several special departments of surgery.

There is, however, one point more that I cannot but advert to, viz., the influence of this mode of treatment upon the general healthiness of an hospital. Previously to its introduction the two large wards in which most of my cases of accident and of operation are treated were among the unhealthiest in the whole surgical division of the Glasgow Royal Infirmary, in consequence apparently of those wards being unfavorably placed with reference to the supply of fresh air; and I have felt ashamed when recording the results of my practice, to have so often to allude to hospital gangrene or pyæmia. It was interesting, though melancholy, to observe that whenever all or nearly all the beds contained cases with open sores, these grievous complications were pretty sure to show themselves; so that I came to welcome simple fractures, though in themselves of little interest either for myself or the students, because their presence diminished the proportion of open sores among the patients. But since the antiseptic treatment has been brought into full operation, and wounds and abscesses no longer poison the atmosphere with putrid exhalations, my wards, though in other respects under precisely the same circumstances as before, have completely changed their character; so that during the last nine months not a single instance of pyæmia, hospital gangrene, or erysipelas has occurred in them.

As there appears to be no doubt regarding the cause of this change, the importance of the fact can hardly be exaggerated.

LIST OF WRITINGS *

Observations on the Muscular Tissue of the Skin, 7 pp., 1 pl., octavo, London, W. Clowes and Sons, 1853 (P., v, 1046).

Observations on the Contractile Tissue of the Iris, 3–11 pp., 1 pl., octavo, London, W. Clowes and Sons, (1853); also in P., v, 1046; repr. from Quart. Jour. Mic. Soc., London, 1853.

On the Minute Structure of Involuntary Muscular Fibre, pp. 549–557, 1 pl., quarto, Edinburgh, Neill and Co., 1857; repr. from Trans. Roy. Soc. Edinb., 1857, xxi, pt. 4.

On the Early Stages of Inflammation (Abstr.), 7 pp., octavo, London, 1857; also in P., v, 1025.

On Spontaneous Gangrene from Arteritis and the Causes of Coagulation of the Blood in Diseases of the Blood-vessels, 16 pp., octavo, Edinburgh, Murray and Gibb, 1858; repr. from Edinb. Med. Jour., 1857–58, iii.

Preliminary Account of an Inquiry into the Functions of the Visceral Nerves, with Special Reference to the So-called Inhibitory System, pp. 367–380, octavo, London, 1858, cutting from Proc. Roy. Soc. London.

Contributions to Physiology and Pathology (An Inquiry Regarding the Parts of the Nervous System which regulate the Contractions of the Arteries), pp. 607–702, 2 pl., quarto; London, Taylor and Francis, 1859; cutting from Phil. Trans. Lond., 1858, cxlviii, pt. 2.

On the Coagulation of the Blood, the Croonian Lecture delivered June 11, 1863, 31 pp., octavo; London, Taylor and Francis, 1863.

* As they appear in the Surgeon-General's Library Index Catalogue (Washington) and the Index Medicus.

Introductory Lecture Delivered in the University of Edinburgh, November 8, 1869, 22 pp., octavo; Edinburgh, Edmonston and Douglas, 1869.

Observations on Ligature of Arteries on the Antiseptic System, 16 pp., 2 pl., roy. octavo; Edinburgh, Edmonston and Douglas, 1869-70; also in P., v, 217; repr. from Lancet, London, 1869, i.

Remarks on a Case of Compound Dislocation of the Ankle with Other Injuries, Illustrating the Antiseptic System of Treatment, 35 pp., octavo, Edinburgh, Edmonston and Douglas, 1870.

On the Effects of the Antiseptic System of Treatment Upon the Salubrity of a Surgical Hospital, 19 pp., octavo, Edinburgh, Edmonston and Douglas, 1870.

On Some Cases Illustrating the Result of Excision of the Wrist for Caries, Treatment of Deformity from Contracted Cicatrix, and Antiseptic Dressing Under Circumstances of Difficulty, Including Amputation at the Hip-joint, 7 pp. octavo, Edinburgh, Oliver and Boyd, 1871.

A Further Contribution to the Natural History of Bacteria and the Germ Theory of Fermentative Changes, 31 pp., 3 pl., octavo, London, J. E. Alard and B. Close, 1873; repr. from Quart. Jour. Mic. Soc., London, 1873, n. s. xiii.

A Contribution to the Germ Theory of Putrefaction and Other Fermentative Changes, and to the Natural History of Torulæ and Bacteria, pp. 313-344, 5 pl., quarto, Edinburgh, Neill and Co., 1875; repr. from Trans. Roy. Soc. Edinb., xxvii.

On the Relation of Micro-organisms to Disease; an Address, 10 pp., octavo, London, J. E. Adlard, 1881; repr. from Quart. Jour. Mic. Soc., London, 1881, n. s. xxi.

Chirurgie Antiseptique et théorie des Germes. Œuvres réunies de...Traduction du Dr. Gustave Borginon, xvi, 5-635 pp., octavo, Paris, A. Delahaye and E. Lecrosuier, 1882.

On the Present Position of Antiseptic Surgery, in Wood's Med. and Surg. Monograph, New York, 1890, viii, 551-562.

On the Antiseptic Principle in the Practice of Surgery, Brit. Med. Jour., London, 1867, ii, 246-248; also Lancet, London, 1867, ii, 353-668.

On a New Method of Treating Compound Fractures, Abscesses, etc., with Observations on the Condition of Suppuration, *ibid.*, 326, 357, 387, 507.

An Address on the Antiseptic System of Treatment in Surgery, Brit. Med. Jour., London, 1868, ii, 53, 101, 461, 515; 1869, i, 301-304.

A Method of Antiseptic Treatment Applicable to Wounded Soldiers in the Present War, *ibid.*, 1870, ii, 243.

The Glasgow Infirmary and the Antiseptic Treatment, Lancet, London, 1870, i, 210.

Further Evidence Regarding Effects of the Antiseptic System of Treatment upon the Salubrity of a Surgical Hospital, *ibid.*, ii, 287-289.

Address on Surgery (Antiseptic Treatment of Wounds), Brit. Med. Jour., London, 1871, ii, 225-233; also transl., Jour. de Med., Chir. et Pharmacol., Brux., 1871, liii, 287, 407; 1872, liv, 33-46.

Antiseptic Dressing under Circumstances of Difficulty (see above), Edinb. Med. Jour., 1871, xvii, 144-150.

Demonstration of Antiseptic Surgery before Members of Brit. Med. Assoc., in
    Operating Theatre of the Royal Infirmary, Edinb. Med. Jour., 1875, xxi,
    193, 481.
Principii ed Applicazione del Metodo Antisettico. Indipendente, Torino, 1875,
    xxvi, 438-443.
On Recent Improvements in the Details of Antiseptic Surgery, Lancet, London,
    1875, i, 365, 401, 434, 468, 603, 717, 787.
Antiseptic Surgery, Trans. Internat. Med. Cong., Phila., 1876, 535-544.
The Antiseptic Method of Dressing Open Wounds, Med. Rec., New York, 1876,
    ii, 695.
Sur la Méthode Antiseptique, Bull. et mém. Soc. de chir de Par., 1878, iv, 421-426.
Clinical Lecture on a Case of Excision of the Knee-joint and on Horse-hair as a
    Drain for Wounds, etc., Lancet, London, 1878, i, 5-9.
Ueber antiseptische Woundbehandlung, Allg. Wien. med. Ztg., 1879, xxiv, 395.
A Demonstration in Antiseptic Surgery, Dublin Jour. Med. Soc., 1879, 3 s., lxviii,
    97-114.
Remarks on Dressing, Med. Times and Gaz., London, 1879, ii, 502.

Circulation of the Blood

WILLIAM HARVEY.
From Portrait in Royal College of Physicians, London.

WILLIAM HARVEY
1578–1657

William Harvey was born April 2, 1578. In 1597, being nineteen years of age, he studied medicine at Padua, whence he returned to settle in London. In 1604 he was admitted a candidate of the College of Physicians; in 1607 Fellow, and in 1616 Lecturer of Anatomy and Surgery. In these lectures in 1616 he began to expound and demonstrate his theory of circulation. He was severely cirticized until 1628, when the views set forth in these lectures were published in Latin as a treatise. He selected Frankfort from which to publish this book: various reasons have been assigned for this selection, the best probably being the unfavorable reception his theory met with in England and the superiority of the German bookmaker. Many editions from all parts of the world soon appeared, as may be seen by reference to the list at the end of this article. The Moreton facsimile of the 1628 edition published in 1894, and the Sydenham Society collection of publications, are the most interesting as well as the most complete. The 1628 edition was followed by a profound revolution in medical teaching and thinking. In spite of adverse criticism many laid claim to priority in the discovery. In 1632 Charles I extended royal favor to him by appointing him Physician to His Majesty. In 1645 on account of Harvey's devotion to the king, with whom he shared the dangers of the battle of Edgehill, he was appointed Warden of Merton College, Oxford. When in the following year Oxford was surrendered to the Parliament, Harvey resigned his position as Warden of Merton. In 1654 he was chosen President of the College of Physicians; he was at this date in his seventy-sixth year and so infirm that he was unable to fulfil the duties of this last honor. He died June 3, 1657.

So thorough are the many biographies of Harvey that only the briefest outline of his life is here given. His motives for making the investigations and the way in which he arrived at his conclusions are set forth clearly in the Introduction and Chapter I given below.

EXERCITATIO,
ANATOMICA DE
MOTV CORDIS ET SAN-
GVINIS IN ANIMALI-
BVS,

GVILIELMI HARVEI ANGLI,
Medici Regii, & Professoris Anatomia in Col-
legio Medicorum Londinensi.

FRANCOFVRTI,
Sumptibus GVILIELMI FITZERI.
ANNO M. DC. XXVIII.

1628

AN ANATOMICAL DISQUISITION ON THE MOTION OF THE HEART AND BLOOD IN ANIMALS

By WILLIAM HARVEY, M.D.

WILLIS'S TRANSLATION

REVISED AND EDITED BY ALEX. BOWIE, M.D., C.M.

DEDICATION

I have already and repeatedly presented you, my learned friends,
with my new views of the motion and function of the heart, in my
anatomical lectures; but having now for more than nine years
confirmed these views by multiplied demonstrations in your presence, illustrated them by arguments, and freed them from the
objections of the most learned and skilful anatomists, I at length
yield to the requests, I might say entreaties, of many, and here
present them for general consideration in this treatise.

Were not the work indeed presented through you, my learned
friends, I should scarce hope that it could come out scatheless and
complete; for you have in general been the faithful witnesses of
almost all the instances from which I have either collected the
truth or confuted error. You have seen my dissections, and at
my demonstrations of all that I maintain to be objects of sense,
you have been accustomed to stand by and bear me out with your
testimony. And as this book alone declares the blood to course
and revolve by a new route, very different from the ancient and
beaten pathway trodden for so many ages, and illustrated by such
a host of learned and distinguished men, I was greatly afraid lest
I might be charged with presumption did I lay my work before
the public at home, or send it beyond seas for impression, unless I
had first proposed the subject to you, had confirmed its conclusions
by ocular demonstrations in your presence, had replied to your
doubts and objections, and secured the assent and support of our

distinguished President. For I was most intimately persuaded, that if I could make good my proposition before you and our College, illustrious by its numerous body of learned individuals, I had less to fear from others. I even ventured to hope that I should have the comfort of finding all that you had granted me in your sheer love of truth, conceded by others who were philosophers like yourselves. True philosophers, who are only eager for truth and knowledge, never regard themselves as already so thoroughly informed, but that they welcome further information from whomsoever and from wheresoever it may come; nor are they so narrowminded as to imagine any of the arts or sciences transmitted to us by the ancients, in such a state of forwardness or completeness, that nothing is left for the ingenuity and industry of others. On the contrary, very many maintain that all we know is still infinitely less than all that still remains unknown; nor do philosophers pin their faith to others' precepts in such wise that they lose their liberty, and cease to give credence to the conclusions of their proper senses. Neither do they swear such fealty to their mistress Antiquity, that they openly, and in sight of all, deny and desert their friend Truth. But even as they see that the credulous and vain are disposed at the first blush to accept and believe everything that is proposed to them, so do they observe that the dull and unintellectual are indisposed to see what lies before their eyes, and even deny the light of the noonday sun. They teach us in our course of philosophy to sedulously avoid the fables of the poets and the fancies of the vulgar, as the false conclusions of the sceptics. And then the studious and good and true, never suffer their minds to be warped by the passions of hatred and envy, which unfit men duly to weigh the arguments that are advanced in behalf of truth, or to appreciate the proposition that is even fairly demonstrated. Neither do they think it unworthy of them to change their opinion if truth and undoubted demonstration require them to do so. They do not esteem it discreditable to desert error, though sanctioned by the highest antiquity, for they know full well that to err, to be deceived, is human; that many things are discovered by accident and that many may be learned indifferently from any quarter, by an old man from a youth, by a person of understanding from one of inferior capacity.

My dear colleagues, I had no purpose to swell this treatise into a large volume by quoting the names and writings of anatomists, or to make a parade of the strength of my memory, the extent of my reading, and the amount of my pains; because I profess both to learn and to teach anatomy, not from books but from dissections; not from the positions of philosophers but from the fabric of nature; and then because I do not think it right or proper to strive to take from the ancients any honor that is their due, nor yet to dispute with the moderns, and enter into controversy with those who have excelled in anatomy and been my teachers. I would not charge with wilful falsehood any one who was sincerely anxious for truth, nor lay it to any one's door as a crime that he had fallen into error. I avow myself the partisan of truth alone; and I can indeed say that I have used all my endeavours, bestowed all my pains on an attempt to produce something that should be agreeable to the good, profitable to the learned, and useful to letters.

Farewell, most worthy Doctors,

And think kindly of your Anatomist.

WILLIAM HARVEY

AN ANATOMICAL DISQUISITION ON THE MOTION OF THE HEART AND BLOOD IN ANIMALS

INTRODUCTION

As we are about to discuss the motion, action, and use of the heart and arteries, it is imperative on us first to state what has been thought of these things by others in their writings, and what has been held by the vulgar and by tradition, in order that what is true may be confirmed, and what is false set right by dissection, multiplied experience, and accurate observation.

Almost all anatomists, physicians, and philosophers up to the present time have supposed, with Galen, that the object of the pulse was the same as that of respiration, and only differed in one particular, this being conceived to depend on the animal, the respiration on the vital faculty; the two, in all other respects, whether with reference to purpose or to motion, comporting themselves alike. Whence it is affirmed, as by Hieronymus Fabricius of Aquapendente, in his book on "Respiration," which has lately appeared, that as the pulsation of the heart and arteries does not suffice for the ventilation and refrigeration of the blood, therefore were the lungs fashioned to surround the heart. From this it appears that whatever has hitherto been said upon the systole and diastole, or on the motion of the heart and arteries, has been said with especial reference to the lungs.

But as the structure and movements of the heart differ from those of the lung, and the motions of the arteries from those of the chest, so it seems likely that other ends and offices will thence arise, and that the pulsations and uses of the heart, likewise of the arteries, will differ in many respects from the heavings and uses of the chest

33

and lungs. For did the arterial pulse and the respiration serve
the same ends; did the arteries in their diastole take air into their
cavities, as commonly stated, and in their systole emit fuliginous
vapours by the same pores of the flesh and skin; and further,
did they, in the time intermediate between the diastole and the
systole, contain air, and at all times either air or spirits, or fuliginous vapours, what should then be said to Galen, who wrote a
book on purpose to show that by nature the arteries contained
blood, and nothing but blood, and consequently neither spirits
nor air, as may readily be gathered from the experiments and reasonings contained in the same book? Now, if the arteries are
filled in the diastole with air then taken into them (a larger quantity
of air penetrating when the pulse is large and full), it must come
to pass that if you plunge into a bath of water or of oil when the
pulse is strong and full, it ought forthwith to become either smaller
or much slower, since the circumambient bath will render it either
difficult or impossible for the air to penetrate. In like manner,
as all the arteries, those that are deep-seated as well as those that
are superficial, are dilated at the same instant and with the
same rapidity, how is it possible that air should penetrate to the
deeper parts as freely and quickly through the skin, flesh, and other
structures, as through the cuticle alone? And how should the
arteries of the fœtus draw air into their cavities through the abdomen of the mother and the body of the womb? And how should
seals, whales, dolphins, and other cetaceans, and fishes of every
description, living in the depths of the sea, take in and emit air
by the diastole and systole of their arteries through the infinite
mass of water? For to say that they absorb the air that is present
in the water, and emit their fumes into this medium, were to utter
something like a figment. And if the arteries in their systole expel
fuliginous vapours from their cavities through the pores of the
flesh and skin, why not the spirits, which are said to be contained
in those vessels, at the same time, since spirits are much more
subtile than fuliginous vapours or smoke? And if the arteries
take in and cast out air in the systole and diastole, like the lungs
in the process of respiration, why do they not do the same thing

when a wound is made in one of them, as in the operation of arteriotomy? When the windpipe is divided, it is sufficiently obvious that the air enters and returns through the wound by two opposite movements; but when an artery is divided, it is equally manifest that blood escapes in one continuous stream, and that no air either enters or issues. If the pulsations of the arteries fan and refrigerate the several parts of the body as the lungs do the heart, how comes it, as is commonly said, that the arteries carry the vital blood into the different parts, abundantly charged with vital spirits, which cherish the heat of these parts, sustain them when asleep, and recruit them when exhausted? How should it happen that, if you tie the arteries, immediately the parts not only become torpid, and frigid, and look pale, but at length cease even to be nourished? This, according to Galen, is because they are deprived of the heat which flowed through all parts from the heart, as its source; whence it would appear that the arteries rather carry warmth to the parts than serve for any fanning or refrigeration. Besides, how can their diastole draw spirits from the heart to warm the body and its parts, and means of cooling them from without? Still further, although some affirm that the lungs, arteries, and heart have all the same offices, they yet maintain that the heart is the workshop of the spirits, and that the arteries contain and transmit them; denying, however, in opposition to the opinion of Columbus, that the lungs can either make or contain spirits. They then assert, with Galen, against Erasistratus, that it is the blood, not spirits, which is contained in the arteries.

These opinions are seen to be so incongruous and mutually subversive, that every one of them is justly brought under suspicion. That it is blood and blood alone which is contained in the arteries is made manifest by the experiment of Galen, by arteriotomy, and by wounds; for from a single divided artery, as Galen himself affirms in more than one place, the whole of the blood may be withdrawn in the course of half an hour or less. The experiment of Galen alluded to is this: "If you include a portion of an artery between two ligatures, and slit it open lengthwise you will find nothing but blood"; and thus he proves that the arteries contain only blood. And we too may be permitted to proceed by a like train of reasoning: if we find the same blood in the arteries as in the veins, after having tied them in the same way, as I have myself repeatedly ascertained, both in the dead body and in living animals, we may fairly conclude that the arteries contain the same blood as the veins, and nothing but the same blood. Some, whilst they attempt to lessen the difficulty, affirm that the blood is spirituous and arterous, and virtually concede that the office of the arteries is to carry blood from the heart into the whole of the body, and that they are therefore filled with blood; for spirituous blood is not the less blood on that account. And no one denies the blood as such, even the portion of it which flows in the veins, is imbued with spirits. But if that portion of it which is contained in the arteries be richer in spirits, it is still to be believed that these spirits are inseparable from the blood, like those in the veins; that the blood and spirits constitute one body (like whey and butter in milk, or heat in hot water), with which the arteries are charged, and for the distribution of which from the heart they are provided. This body is nothing else than blood. But if this blood be said to be drawn from the heart into the arteries by the diastole of these vessels, it is then assumed that the arteries by their distension are filled with blood, and not with the surrounding air, as heretofore; for if they be said also to become filled with air from the ambient atmosphere, how and when, I ask, can they receive blood from the heart? If it be answered: during the systole, I take it to be impossible: the arteries would then have to fill while they contracted, to fill, and yet not become distended. But if it be said: during diastole, they would then, and for two opposite purposes, be receiving both blood and air, and heat and cold, which is improbable. Further when it is affirmed that the diastole of the heart and arteries is simultaneous, and the systole of the two is also concurrent, there is another incongruity. For how can two bodies mutually connected, which are simultaneously distended, attract or draw anything from one another? or being simultaneously contracted, receive anything from each other? And then it seems impossible that one body can thus attract another

body into itself, so as to become distended, seeing that to be distended is to be passive, unless, in the manner of a sponge, which
has been previously compressed by an external force, it is returning
to its natural state.   But it is difficult to conceive that there can be
anything of this kind in the arteries.   The arteries dilate, because
they are filled like bladders or leathern bottles; they are not filled
because they expand like bellows.   This I think easy of demonstration, and indeed conceive that I have already proved it.   Nevertheless, in that book of Galen headed "Quod Sanguis continetur
in Arteriis," he quotes an experiment to prove the contrary.   An
artery having been exposed, is opened longitudinally, and a reed
or other pervious tube is inserted into the vessel through the opening, by which the blood is prevented from being lost, and the wound
is closed.   "So long," he says, "as things are thus arranged, the
whole artery will pulsate; but if you now throw a ligature about
the vessel and tightly compress its wall over the tube, you will
no longer see the artery beating beyond the ligature."   I have
never performed this experiment of Galen's nor do I think that it
could very well be performed in the living body, on account of
the profuse flow of blood that would take place from the vessel
that was operated on; neither would the tube effectually close the
wound in the vessel without a ligature; and I cannot doubt but
that the blood would be found to flow out between the tube and the
vessel.   Still Galen appears by this experiment to prove both
that the pulsative property extends from the heart by the walls
of the arteries, and that the arteries, whilst they dilate, are filled
by that pulsific force, because they expand like bellows, and do
not dilate as if they are filled like skins.   But the contrary is obvious in arteriotomy and in wounds; for the blood spurting from
the arteries escapes with force, now farther, now not so far, alternately, or in jets; and the jet always takes place with the diastole
of the artery, never with the systole.   By which it clearly appears
that the artery is dilated with the impulse of the blood; for of
itself it would not throw the blood to such a distance and whilst
it was dilating; it ought rather to draw air into its cavity through
the wound, were those things true that are commonly stated con-

cerning the uses of the arteries.   Do not let the thickness of the
arterial tunics impose upon us, and lead us to conclude that the
pulsative property proceeds along them from the heart.   For in
several animals the arteries do not apparently differ from the
veins; and in extreme parts of the body where the arteries are
minutely subdivided, as in the brain, the hand, etc., no one could
distinguish the arteries from the veins by the dissimilar characters
of their coats: the tunics of both are identical.   And then, in the
aneurism proceeding from a wounded or eroded artery, the pulsation is precisely the same as in the other arteries, and yet it has no
proper arterial covering.   To this the learned Riolanus testifies
along with me, in his Seventh Book.

Nor let any one imagine that the uses of the pulse and the respiration are the same, because, under the influences of the same causes,
such as running, anger, the warm bath, or any other heating
thing, as Galen says, they become more frequent and forcible
together.   For not only is experience in opposition to this idea,
though Galen endeavors to explain it away, when we see that with
excessive repletion the pulse beats more forcibly, whilst the
respiration is diminished in amount; but in young persons the
pulse is quick, whilst respiration is slow.   So it is also in alarm,
and amidst care, and under anxiety of mind; sometimes, too, in
fevers, the pulse is rapid, but the respiration is slower than usual.

These and other objections of the same kind may be urged
against the opinions mentioned.   Nor are the views that are entertained of the offices and pulse of the heart, perhaps, less bound up
with great and most inextricable difficulties.   The heart, it is vulgarly said, is the fountain and workshop of the vital spirits, the
centre from which life is dispensed to the several parts of the
body.   Yet it is denied that the right ventricle makes spirits, which
is rather held to supply nourishment to the lungs.   For these
reasons it is maintained that fishes are without any right ventricle
(and indeed every animal wants a right ventricle which is un-
furnished with lungs), and that the right ventricle is present
solely for the sake of the lungs.

1. Why, I ask, when we see that the structure of both ventricles

is almost identical, there being the same apparatus of fibres, and braces, and valves, and vessels, and auricles, and both in the same way in our dissections are found to be filled up with blood similarly black in color, and coagulated—why, I say, should their uses be imagined to be different, when the action, motion, and pulse of both are the same? If the three tricuspid valves placed at the entrance into the right ventricle prove obstacles to the reflux of the blood into the vena cava, and if the three semilunar valves which are situated at the commencement of the pulmonary artery be there, that they may prevent the return of the blood into the ventricle; why, when we find similar structures in connexion with the left ventricle, should we deny that they are there for the same end, of preventing here the egress, there the regurgitation, of the blood?

2. And, when we have these structures, in points of size, form, and situation, almost in every respect the same in the left as in the right ventricle, why should it be said that things are arranged in the former for the egress and regress of spirits, and in the latter or right ventricle, for the blood? The same arrangement cannot be held fitted to favor or impede the motion of the blood and of spirits indifferently.

3. And when we observe that the passages and vessels are severally in relation to one another in point of size, viz., the pulmonary artery to the pulmonary veins; why should the one be destined to a private purpose, that of furnishing the lungs, the other to a public function?

4. And as Realdus Columbus says, is it probable that such a quantity of blood should be required for the nutrition of the lungs; the vessel that leads to them, the vena arteriosa or pulmonary artery being of greater capacity than both the iliac veins?

5. And I ask, as the lungs are so close at hand, and in continual motion, and the vessel that supplies them is of such dimensions, what is the use or meaning of this pulse of the right ventricle? and why was nature reduced to the necessity of adding another ventricle for the sole purpose of nourishing the lungs?

When it is said that the left ventricle draws materials for the

formation of spirits, air and blood, from the lungs and right
sinuses of the heart, and in like manner sends spirituous blood
into the aorta, drawing fuliginous vapours from there, and sending them by the pulmonary vein into the lungs, whence spirits
are at the same time obtained for transmission into the aorta, I
ask how, and by what means is the separation effected? And how
comes it that spirits and fuliginuous vapors can pass hither and
thither without admixture or confusion? If the mitral cuspidate
valves do not prevent the egress of fuliginous vapours to the
lungs, how should they oppose the escape of air? And how should
the semilunars hinder the regress of spirits from the aorta upon
each supervening diastole of the heart? Above all, how can they
say that the spirituous blood is sent from the pulmonary veins by
the left ventricle into the lungs without any obstacle to its passage
from the mitral valves, when they have previously asserted that
the air entered by the same vessel from the lungs into the left
ventricle, and have brought forward these same mitral valves as
obstacles to its retrogression? Good God! how should the mitral
valves prevent the regurgitation of air and not of blood?

Moreover, when they appoint the pulmonary artery, a vessel of
great size, with the coverings of an artery, to none but a kind of
private and single purpose, that, namely, of nourishing the lungs,
why should the pulmonary vein, which is scarcely so large, which
has the coats of a vein, and is soft and lax, be presumed to be made
for many—three or four different—uses? For they will have it that
air passes through this vessel from the lungs into the left ventricle;
that fuliginous vapours escape by it from the heart into the lungs;
and that a portion of the spirituous blood is distributed to the
lungs for their refreshment.

If they will have it that fumes and air—fumes flowing from, air
proceeding towards the heart—are transmitted by the same
conduit, I reply, that nature is not wont to construct but one
vessel, to contrive but one way for such contrary motions and
purposes, nor is anything of the kind seen elsewhere.

If fumes or fuliginous vapors and air permeate this vessel,
as they do the pulmonary bronchia, wherefore do we find neither

air nor fuliginous vapours when we divide the pulmonary vein?
Why do we always find this vessel full of sluggish blood, never
of air, whilst in the lungs we find abundance of air remaining?

If any one will perform Galen's experiment of dividing the
trachea of a living dog, forcibly distending the lungs with a pair
of bellows, and then tying the trachea securely, he will find, when
he has laid open the thorax, abundance of air in the lungs, even to
their extreme investing tunic, but none in either the pulmonary
veins or the left ventricle of the heart. But did the heart either
attract air from the lungs, or did the lungs transmit any air to the
heart, in the living dog, much more ought this to be the case in the
experiment just referred to. Who, indeed, doubts that, did he
inflate the lungs of a subject in the dissecting-room, he would
instantly see the air making its way by this route, were there actually any such passage for it? But this office of the pulmonary
veins, namely, the transference of air from the lungs to the heart,
is held of such importance, that Hieronymus Fabricius of Aquapendente, contends that the lungs were made for the sake of this
vessel, and that it constitutes the principal element in their structure.

But I should like to be informed why, if the pulmonary vein were
destined for the conveyance of air, it has the structure of a blood-
vessel here. Nature had rather need of annular tubes, such as
those of the bronchi, in order that they might always remain open,
and not be liable to collapse; and that they might continue entirely
free from blood, lest the liquid should interfere with the passage
of the air, as it so obviously does when the lungs labour from
being either greatly oppressed or loaded in a less degree with
phlegm, as they are when the breathing is performed with a sibilous or rattling noise.

Still less is that opinion to be tolerated which, as a two-fold
material, one aerial, one sanguineous, is required for the composition
of vital spirits, supposes the blood to ooze through the septum of the
heart from the right to the left ventricle by certain hidden porosities, and the air to be attracted from the lungs through the great
vessel, the pulmonary vein; and which, consequently, will have

it, that there are numerous porosities in the septum of the heart adapted for the transmission of the blood. But by Hercules! no such pores can be demonstrated, nor in fact do any such exist. For the septum of the heart is of a denser and more compact structure than any portion of the body, except the bones and sinews. But even supposing that there were foramina or pores in this situation, how could one of the ventricles extract anything from the other—the left, e. g., obtain blood from the right, when we see that both ventricles contract and dilate simultaneously? Why should we not rather believe that the right took spirits from the left, than that the left obtained blood from the right ventricle through these foramina? But it is certainly mysterious and incongruous that blood should be supposed to be most commodiously drawn through a set of obscure or invisible ducts, and air through perfectly open passages, at one and the same moment. And why, I ask, is recourse had to secret and invisible porosities, to uncertain and obscure channels, to explain the passage of the blood into the left ventricle, when there is so open a way through the pulmonary veins? I own it has always appeared extraordinary to me that they should have chosen to make, or rather to imagine, a way through the thick, hard, dense, and most compact septum of the heart, rather than take that by the open pulmonary vein, or even through the lax, soft and spongy substance of the lungs at large. Besides, if the blood could permeate the substance of the septum, or could be imbibed from the ventricles, what use were there for the coronary artery and vein, branches of which proceed to the septum itself, to supply it with nourishment? And what is especially worthy of notice is this: if in the fœtus, where everything is more lax and soft, nature saw herself reduced to the necessity of bringing the blood from the right to the left side of the heart by the foramen ovale, from the vena cava through the pulmonary vein, how should it be likely that in the adult she should pass it so commodiously, and without an effort through the septum of the ventricles which has now become denser by age?

Andreas Laurentius,* resting on the authority of Galen† and

---

* Lib. ix, cap. xi, quest. 12.   † De Locis Affectis. lib. vi, cap. 7.

the experience of Hollerius, asserts and proves that the serum and pus in empyema, absorbed from the cavities of the chest into the pulmonary vein may be expelled and got rid of with the urine and fæces through the left ventricle of the heart and arteries. He quotes the case of a certain person affected with melancholia, and who suffered from repeated fainting fits, who was relieved from the paroxysms on passing a quantity of turbid fetid and acrid urine. But he died at last, worn out by disease; and when the body came to be opened after death, no fluid like that he had micturated was discovered either in the bladder or the kidneys; but in the left ventricle of the heart and cavity of the thorax plenty of it was met with. And then Laurentius boasts that he had predicted the cause of the symptoms. For my own part, however, I cannot but wonder, since he had devined and predicted that heterogeneous matter could be discharged by the course he indicates, why he could not or would not perceive, and inform us that, in the natural state of things, the blood might be commodiously transferred from the lungs to the left ventricle of the heart by the very same route.

Since, therefore, from the foregoing considerations and many others to the same effect, it is plain that what has heretofore been said concerning the motion and function of the heart and arteries must appear obscure, inconsistent, or even impossible to him who carefully considers the entire subject, it will be proper to look more narrowly into the matter to contemplate the motion of the heart and arteries, not only in man, but in all animals that have hearts; and also, by frequent appeals to vivisection, and much ocular inspection, to investigate and discern the truth.

CHAPTER I

The Author's Motives for Writing

When I first gave my mind to vivisections, as a means of discovering the motions and uses of the heart, and sought to discover these from actual inspection, and not from the writings of others, I found the task so truly arduous, so full of difficulties, that I was almost tempted to think, with Fracastorius, that the motion of the heart was only to be comprehended by God. For I could neither rightly perceive at first when the systole and when the diastole took place, nor when and where dilatation and contraction occurred, by reason of the rapidity of the motion, which in many animals is accomplished in the twinkling of an eye, coming and going like a flash of lightning; so that the systole presented itself to me now from this point, now from that; the diastole the same; and then everything was reversed, the motions occurring, as it seemed, variously and confusedly together. My mind was therefore greatly unsettled nor did I know what I should myself conclude, nor what believe from others. I was not surprised that Andreas Laurentius should have written that the motion of the heart was as perplexing as the flux and reflux of Euripus had appeared to Aristotle.

At length, by using greater and daily diligence and investigation, making frequent inspection of many and various animals, and collating numerous observations, I thought that I had attained to the truth, that I should extricate myself and escape from this labyrinth, and that I had discovered what I so much desired, both the motion and the use of the heart and arteries. From that time I have not hesitated to expose my views upon these subjects, not only in private to my friends, but also in public, in my anatomical lectures, after the manner of the Academy of old.

These views as usual, pleased some more, others less; some chid and calumniated me, and laid it to me as a crime that I had dared to depart from the precepts and opinions of all anatomists; others desired further explanations of the novelties, which they said were both worthy of consideration, and might perchance be found of signal use. At length, yielding to the requests of my friends, that all might be made participators in my labors, and partly moved by the envy of others, who, receiving my views with uncandid minds and understanding them indifferently, have essayed to traduce me publicly, I have moved to commit these things to the press, in order that all may be enabled to form an opinion both of me and my labours.   This step I take all the more willingly, seeing that Hieronymus Fabricius of Aquapendente, although he has accurately and learnedly delineated almost every one of the several parts of animals in a special work, has left the heart alone untouched.   Finally, if any use or benefit to this department of the republic of letters should accrue from my labours, it will, perhaps, be allowed that I have not lived idly, and as the old man in the comedy says:

> For never yet hath any one attained
> To such perfection, but that time, and place,
> And use, have brought addition to his knowledge;
> Or made correction, or admonished him,
> That he was ignorant of much which he
> Had thought he knew; or led him to reject
> What he had once esteemed of highest price.

So will it, perchance, be found with reference to the heart at this time; or others, at least, starting hence, with the way pointed out to them, advancing under the guidance of a happier genius, may make occasion to proceed more fortunately, and to inquire more accurately.

CHAPTER II

On the Motions of the Heart as Seen in the Dissection of Living Animals

In the first place, then, when the chest of a living animal is laid open and the capsule that immediately surrounds the heart is slit up or removed, the organ is seen now to move, now to be at rest; there is a time when it moves, and a time when it is motionless.

These things are more obvious in the colder animals, such as toads, frogs, serpents, small fishes, crabs, shrimps, snails, and shell-fish. They also become more distinct in warm-blooded animals, such as the dog and hog, if they be attentively noted when the heart begins to flag, to move more slowly, and, as it were, to die: the movements then become slower and rarer, the pauses longer, by which it is made much more easy to perceive and unravel what the motions really are, and how they are performed. In the pause, as in death, the heart is soft, flaccid, exhausted, lying, as it were, at rest.

In the motion, and interval in which this is accomplished, three principal circumstances are to be noted:

1. That the heart is erected, and rises upwards to a point, so that at this time it strikes against the breast and the pulse is felt externally.

2. That it is everywhere contracted, but more especially towards the sides so that it looks narrower, relatively longer, more drawn together. The heart of an eel taken out of the body of the animal and placed upon the table or the hand, shows these particulars; but the same things are manifest in the hearts of all small fishes and of those colder animals where the organ is more conical or elongated.

3. The heart being grasped in the hand, is felt to become harder during its action. Now this hardness proceeds from tension, precisely as when the forearm is grasped, its tendons are perceived to become tense and resilient when the fingers are moved.

4. It may further be observed in fishes, and the colder blooded animals, such as frogs, serpents, etc., that the heart, when it moves, becomes of a paler color, when quiescent of a deeper blood-red colour.

From these particulars it appears evident to me that the motion of the heart consists in a certain universal tension—both contraction in the line of its fibres, and constriction in every sense. It becomes erect, hard, and of diminished size during its action; the motion is plainly of the same nature as that of the muscles when they contract in the line of their sinews and fibres; for the muscles, when in action, acquire vigor and tenseness, and from soft become hard, prominent, and thickened: and in the same manner the heart.

We are therefore authorized to conclude that the heart, at the moment of its action, is at once constricted on all sides, rendered thicker in its parietes and smaller in its ventricles, and so made apt to project or expel its charge of blood. This, indeed, is made sufficiently manifest by the preceding fourth observation in which we have seen that the heart, by squeezing out the blood that it contains, becomes paler, and then when it sinks into repose and the ventricle is filled anew with blood, that the deeper crimson colour returns. But no one need remain in doubt of the fact, for if the ventricle be pierced the blood will be seen to be forcibly projected outwards upon each motion or pulsation when the heart is tense.

These things, therefore, happen together or at the same instant: the tension of the heart, the pulse of its apex, which is felt externally by its striking against the chest, the thickening of its parietes, and the forcible expulsion of the blood it contains by the constriction of its ventricles.

Hence the very opposite of the opinions commonly received appears to be true; inasmuch as it is generally believed that when the heart strikes the breast and the pulse is felt without, the heart is dilated in its ventricles and is filled with blood; but the contrary of this is the fact, and the heart, when it contracts (and the impulse of the apex is conveyed through the chest wall), is emptied. Whence the motion which is generally regarded as the diastole of the heart, is in truth its systole. And in like manner the intrinsic motion of the heart is not the diastole but the systole; neither is it in the diastole that the heart grows firm and tense, but in the systole, for then only, when tense, is it moved and made vigorous.

Neither is it by any means to be allowed that the heart only moves in the lines of its straight fibres, although the great Vesalius giving this notion countenance, quotes a bundle of osiers bound in a pyramidal heap in illustration; meaning, that as the apex is approached to the base, so are the sides made to bulge out in the fashion of arches, the cavities to dilate, the ventricles to acquire the form of a cupping-glass and so to suck in the blood. But the true effect of every one of its fibres is to constringe the heart at the same time they render it tense; and this rather with the effect of thickening and amplifying the walls and substance of the organ than enlarging its ventricles. And, again, as the fibres run from the apex to the base, and draw the apex towards the base, they do not tend to make the walls of the heart bulge out in circles, but rather the contrary; inasmuch as every fibre that is circularly disposed, tends to become straight when it contracts; and is distended laterally and thickened, as in the case of muscular fibres in general, when they contract, that is, when they are shortened longitudinally, as we see them in the bellies of the muscles of the body at large. To all this let it be added, that not only are the ventricles contracted in virtue of the direction and condensation of their walls, but farther, that those fibres, or bands, styled nerves by Aristotle, which are so conspicuous in the ventricles of the larger animals, and contain all the straight fibres (the parietes of the heart containing only circular ones), when they contract simultaneously by an admirable adjustment all the internal surfaces are drawn together as if with cords, and so is the charge of blood expelled with force.

Neither is it true, as vulgarly believed, that the heart by any dilatation or motion of its own, has the power of drawing the blood into the ventricles; for when it acts and becomes tense, the blood is expelled; when it relaxes and sinks together it receives the blood in the manner and wise which will by-and-by be explained.

CHAPTER III

OF THE MOTIONS OF THE ARTERIES, AS SEEN IN THE DISSECTION OF LIVING ANIMALS

In connexion with the motions of the heart these things are further to be observed having reference to the motions and pulses of the arteries.

1. At the moment the heart contracts, and when the breast is struck, when in short the organ is in its state of systole, the arteries are dilated, yield a pulse, and are in the state of diastole. In like manner, when the right ventricle contracts and propels its charge of blood, the pulmonary artery is distended at the same time with the other arteries of the body.

2. When the left ventricle ceases to act, to contract, to pulsate, the pulse in the arteries also ceases; further, when this ventricle contracts languidly, the pulse in the arteries is scarcely perceptible. In like manner, the pulse in the right ventricle failing, the pulse in the pulmonary artery ceases also.

3. Further, when an artery is divided or punctured, the blood is seen to be forcibly propelled from the wound the moment the left ventricle contracts; and, again, when the pulmonary artery is wounded, the blood will be seen spouting forth with violence at the instant when the right ventricle contracts.

So also in fishes, if the vessel which leads from the heart to the gills be divided, at the moment when the heart becomes tense and contracted, at the same moment does the blood flow with force from the divided vessel.

In the same way, when we see the blood in arteriotomy projected now to a greater, now to a less distance, and that the greater jet corresponds to the diastole of the artery and to the time when the heart contracts and strikes the ribs, and is in its state of systole, we understand that the blood is expelled by the same movement.

From these facts it is manifest, in opposition to commonly received opinions, that the diastole of the arteries corresponds with the time of the heart's systole; and that the arteries are filled and distended by the blood forced into them by the contraction of the ventricles; the arteries, therefore, are distended, because they are filled like sacs or bladders, and are not filled because they expand like bellows. It is in virtue of one and the same cause, therefore, that all the arteries of the body pulsate, viz., the contraction of the left ventricle; in the same way as the pulmonary artery pulsates by the contraction of the right ventricle.

Finally, that the pulses of the arteries are due to the impulses of the blood from the left ventricle, may be illustrated by blowing into a glove, when the whole of the fingers will be found to become distended at one and the same time, and in their tension to bear some resemblance to the pulse. For in the ratio of the tension is the pulse of the heart, fuller, stronger, and more frequent as that acts more vigorously, still preserving the rhythm and volume, and order of the heart's contractions. Nor is it to be expected that because of the motion of the blood, the time at which the contraction of the heart takes place, and that at which the pulse in an artery (especially a distant one) is felt, shall be otherwise than simultaneous: it is here the same as in blowing up a glove or bladder; for in a plenum (as in a drum, a long piece of timber, etc.) the stroke and the motion occur at both extremities at the same time. Aristotle,*too,has said, "the blood of all animals palpitates within their veins (meaning the arteries), and by the pulse is sent everywhere simultaneously." And further,† "thus do all the veins pulsate together and by successive strokes, because they all depend upon the heart; and, as it is always in motion, so are they likewise always moving together, but by successive movements." It is well to observe with Galen, in this place, that the old philosophers called the arteries veins.

I happened upon one occasion to have a particular case under my care, which plainly satisfied me of this truth: A certain person was affected with a large pulsating tumour on the right side of the neck, called an aneurism, just at that part where the artery descends into the axilla, produced by an erosion of the artery itself, and daily increasing in size; this tumour was visibly distended as it received the charge of blood brought to it by the artery, with each stroke of the heart; the connexion of parts was obvious when the body of the patient came to be opened after his death. The pulse in the corresponding arm was small, in consequence of the greater portion of the blood being diverted into the tumour and so intercepted.

Whence it appears that whenever the motion of the blood through the arteries is impeded, whether it be by compression or infarction, or interception, there do the remote divisions of the arteries beat less forcibly, seeing that the pulse of the arteries is nothing more than the impulse or shock of the blood in these vessels.

CHAPTER IV

OF THE MOTION OF THE HEART AND ITS AURICLES, AS SEEN IN THE BODIES OF LIVING ANIMALS

Besides the motions already spoken of, we have still to consider those that appertain to the auricles.

* De Anim., iii, cap. 9.   † De Respir., cap. 20.

Caspar Bauhin and John Riolan,* most learned men and skilful anatomists, inform us that from their observations, that if we carefully watch the movements of the heart in the vivisection of an animal, we shall perceive four motions distinct in time and in place, two of which are proper to the auricles, two to the ventricles. With all deference to such authority I say that there are four motions distinct in point of place, but not of time; for the two auricles move together, and so also do the two ventricles, in such wise that though the places be four, the times are only two. And this occurs in the following manner:

There are, as it were, two motions going on together: one of the auricles, another of the ventricles; these by no means taking place simultaneously, but the motion of the auricles preceding that of the heart following; the motion appearing to begin from the auricles and to extend to the ventricles. When all things are becoming languid, and the heart is dying, as also in fishes and the colder blooded animals, there is a short pause between these two motions, so that the heart aroused, as it were, appears to respond to the motion, now more quickly, now more tardily; and at length, when near to death, it ceases to respond by its proper motion, but seems, as it were, to nod the head, and is so slightly moved that it appears rather to give signs of motion to the pulsating auricles than actually to move. The heart, therefore, ceases to pulsate sooner than the auricles, so that the auricles have been said to outlive it, the left ventricle ceasing to pulsate first of all; then its auricle, next the right ventricle; and, finally, all the other parts being at rest and dead, as Galen long since observed, the right auricle still continues to beat; life, therefore, appears to linger longest in the right auricle. Whilst the heart is gradually dying, it is sometimes seen to reply, after two or three contractions of the auricles, roused as it were to action, and making a single pulsation, slowly, unwillingly, and with an effort.

But this especially is to be noted, that after the heart has ceased to beat, the auricles however still contracting, a finger placed upon the ventricles perceives the several pulsations of the auricles, pre-

* Bauhin, lib. ii, cap. 21.   Riolan, lib. viii, cap. 1.

cisely in the same way and for the same reason, as we have said, that the pulses of the ventricles are felt in the arteries, to wit, the distension produced by the jet of blood. And if at this time, the auricles alone pulsating, the point of the heart be cut off with a pair of scissors, you will perceive the blood flowing out upon each contraction of the auricles. Whence it is manifest that the blood enters the ventricles, not by any attraction or dilatation of the heart, but by being thrown into them by the pulses of the auricles.

And here I would observe, that whenever I speak of pulsations as occurring in the auricles or ventricles, I mean contractions: first the auricles contract, and then and subsequently the heart itself contracts. When the auricles contract they are seen to become whiter, especially where they contain but little blood; but they are filled as magazines or reservoirs of the blood, which is tending spontaneously and, by its motion in the veins, under pressure towards the centre; the whiteness indicated is most conspicuous towards the extremities or edges of the auricles at the time of their contractions.

In fishes and frogs, and other animals which have hearts with but a single ventricle, and for an auricle have a kind of bladder much distended with blood, at the base of the organ, you may very plainly perceive this bladder contracting first, and the contraction of the heart or ventricle following afterwards.

But I think it right to describe what I have observed of an opposite character: the heart of an eel, of several fishes, and even of some (of the higher) animals taken out of the body, pulsates without auricles; nay, if it be cut in pieces the several parts may still be seen contracting and relaxing; so that in these creatures the body of the heart may be seen pulsating and palpitating, after the cessation of all motion in the auricle. But is not this perchance peculiar to animals more tenacious of life, whose radical moisture is more glutinous, or fat and sluggish, and less readily soluble? The same faculty indeed appears in the flesh of eels, which even when skinned and embowelled, and cut into pieces, are still seen to move.

Experimenting with a pigeon upon one occasion, after the heart had wholly ceased to pulsate, and the auricles too had become motionless, I kept my finger wetted with saliva and warm for a short time upon the heart, and observed that under the influence of this fomentation it recovered new strength and life, so that both ventricles and auricles pulsated, contracting and relaxing alternately, recalled as it were from death to life.

Besides this, however, I have occasionally observed, after the heart and even its right auricle had ceased pulsating,—when it was in articulo mortis in short,—that an obscure motion, an undulation or palpitation, remained in the blood itself, which was contained in the right auricle, this being apparent so long as it was imbued with heat and spirit. And, indeed, a circumstance of the same kind is extremely manifest in the course of the generation of animals, as may be seen in the course of the first seven days of the incubation of the chick: A drop of blood makes its appearance which palpitates, as Aristotle had already observed; from this, when the growth is further advanced and the chick is fashioned, the auricles of the heart are formed, which pulsating henceforth give constant signs of life. When at length, and after the lapse of a few days, the outline of the body begins to be distinguished, then is the ventricular part of the heart also produced; but it continues for a time white and apparently bloodless, like the rest of the animal; neither does it pulsate or give signs of motion. I have seen a similar condition of the heart in the human fœtus about the beginning of the third month, the heart then being whitish and bloodless, although its auricles contained a considerable quantity of purple blood. In the same way in the egg, when the chick was formed and had increased in size, the heart too increased and acquired ventricles, which then began to receive and to transmit blood.

And this leads me to remark that he who inquires very particularly into this matter will not conclude that the heart, as a whole, is the primum vivens, ultimum moriens,—the first part to live, the last to die,—but rather its auricles, or the part which corresponds to the auricles in serpents, fishes, etc., which both lives before the heart and dies after it.

Nay, has not the blood itself or spirit an obscure palpitation inherent in it, which it has even appeared to me to retain after death ? and it seems very questionable whether or not we are to say that life begins with the palpitation or beating of the heart. The seminal fluid of all animals—the prolific spirit, as Aristotle observed, leaves their body with a bound and like a living thing; and nature in death, as Aristotle* further remarks, retracing her steps, reverts to where she had set out, and returns at the end of her course to the goal whence she had started. As animal generation proceeds from that which is not animal, entity from nonentity, so, by a retrograde course, entity, by corruption, is resolved into nonentity, whence that in animals, which was last created, fails first; and that which was first, fails last.

I have also observed that almost all animals have truly a heart, not the larger creatures only, and those that have red blood, but the smaller, and pale-blooded ones also, such as slugs, snails, scallops, shrimps, crabs, crayfish, and many others; nay, even in wasps, hornets, and flies, I have, with the aid of a magnifying glass, and at the upper part of what is called the tail, both seen the heart pulsating myself, and shown it to many others.

But in the pale-blooded tribes the heart pulsates sluggishly and deliberately, contracting slowly as in animals that are moribund, a fact that may readily be seen in the snail, whose heart will be found at the bottom of that orifice in the right side of the body which is seen to be opened and shut in the course of respiration, and whence saliva is discharged, the incision being made in the upper aspect of the body, near the part which corresponds to the liver.

This, however, is to be observed: that in winter and the colder season, exsanguine animals, such as the snail, show no pulsation; they seem rather to live after the manner of vegetables, or of those other productions which are therefore designated plant-animals.

It is also to be noted that all animals which have a heart have also auricles, or something analogous to auricles; and, further, that whenever the heart has a double ventricle, there are always two auricles present, but not otherwise. If you turn to the production

* De Motu Animal., cap. 8.

of the chick in ovo, however, you will find at first no more a vesicle or auricle, or pulsating drop of blood; it is only by and by, when the development has made some progress, that the heart is fashioned; even so in certain animals not destined to attain to the highest perfection in their organization, such as bees, wasps, snails, shrimps, crayfish, etc., we only find a certain pulsating vesicle, like a sort of red or white palpitating point, as the beginning or principle of their life.

We have a small shrimp in these countries, which is taken in the Thames and in the sea, the whole of whose body is transparent; this creature, placed in a little water, has frequently afforded myself and particular friends an opportunity of observing the motions of the heart with the greatest distinctness, the external parts of the body presenting no obstacle to our view, but the heart being perceived as though it had been seen through a window.

I have also observed the first rudiments of the chick in the course of the fourth or fifth day of the incubation, in the guise of a little cloud, the shell having been removed and the egg immersed in clear tepid water. In the midst of the cloudlet in question there was a bloody point so small that it disappeared during the contraction and escaped the sight, but in the relaxation it reappeared again, red and like the point of a pin; so that betwixt the visible and invisible, betwixt being and not being, as it were, it gave by its pulses a kind of representation of the commencement of life.

CHAPTER V

OF THE MOTION, ACTION AND OFFICE OF THE HEART

From these and other observations of a similar nature, I am persuaded it will be found that the motion of the heart is as follows:

First of all, the auricle contracts, and in the course of its contraction forces the blood (which it contains in ample quantity as the head of the veins, the store-house and cistern of the blood)

into the ventricle, which, being filled, the heart raises itself straight-
way, makes all its fibres tense, contracts the ventricles, and performs
a beat, by which beat it immediately sends the blood supplied to it
by the auricle into the arteries.   The right ventricle sends its charge
into the lungs by the vessel which is called vena arteriosa, but which
in structure and function, and all other respects, is an artery.   The
left ventricle sends its charge into the aorta, and through this by
the arteries to the body at large.

These two motions, one of the ventricles, the other of the auricles,
take place consecutively, but in such a manner that there is a kind of
harmony or rhythm preserved between them, the two concurring
in such wise that but one motion is apparent, especially in the
warmer blooded animals, in which the movements in question are
rapid.   Nor is this for any other reason than it is in a piece of
machinery, in which, though one wheel gives motion to another,
yet all the wheels seem to move simultaneously; or in that mechanical contrivance which is adapted to firearms, where, the trigger being touched, down comes the flint, strikes against the steel, elicits a
spark, which falling among the powder, ignites it, when the flame
extends, enters the barrel, causes the explosion, propels the ball,
and the mark is attained—all of which incidents, by reason of the
celerity with which they happen, seem to take place in the twinkling
of an eye.   So also in deglutition: by the elevation of the root of
the tongue, and the compression of the mouth, the food or drink is
pushed into the fauces, when the larynx is closed by its muscles and
by the epiglottis.   The pharynx is then raised and opened by its
muscles in the same way as a sac that is to be filled is lifted up and
its mouth dilated.   Upon the mouthful being received, it is forced
downwards by the transverse muscles, and then carried farther by
the longitudinal ones.   Yet all these motions, though executed by
different and distinct organs, are performed harmoniously, and in
such order that they seem to constitute but a single motion and act,
which we call deglutition.

Even so does it come to pass with the motions and action of the
heart, which constitute a kind of deglutition, a transfusion of the
blood from the veins to the arteries.   And if anyone, bearing these

things in mind, will carefully watch the motions of the heart in the body of a living animal, he will perceive not only all the particulars I have mentioned, viz., the heart becoming erect, and making one continuous motion with its auricles; but farther, a certain obscure undulation and lateral inclination in the direction of the axis of the right ventricle, as if twisting itself slightly in performing its work. And indeed everyone may see, when a horse drinks, that the water is drawn in and transmitted to the stomach at each movement of the throat, which movement produces a sound and yields a pulse both to the ear and the touch; in the same way it is with each motion of the heart, when there is the delivery of a quantity of blood from the veins to the arteries a pulse takes place, and can be heard within the chest.

The motion of the heart, then, is entirely of this description, and the one action of the heart is the transmission of the blood and its distribution, by means of the arteries, to the very extremities of the body; so that the pulse which we feel in the arteries is nothing more than the impulse of the blood derived from the heart.

Whether or not the heart, besides propelling the blood, giving it motion locally, and distributing it to the body, adds anything else to it—heat, spirit, perfection,—must be inquired into by-and-by, and decided upon other grounds. So much may suffice at this time, when it is shown that by the action of the heart the blood is transfused through the ventricles from the veins to the arteries, and distributed by them to all parts of the body.

The above, indeed, is admitted by all, both from the structure of the heart and the arrangement and action of its valves. But still they are like persons purblind or groping about in the dark, for they give utterance to various, contradictory, and incoherent sentiments, delivering many things upon conjecture, as we have already shown.

The grand cause of doubt and error in this subject appears to me to have been the intimate connexion between the heart and the lungs. When men saw both the pulmonary artery and the pulmonary veins losing themselves in the lungs, of course it became a puzzle to them to know how or by what means the right ventricle should distribute the blood to the body, or the left draw it from the venæ cavæ. This fact is borne witness to by Galen, whose words, when writing against Erasistratus in regard to the origin and use of the veins and the coction of the blood, are the following*: "You will reply," he says, "that the effect is so; that the blood is prepared in the liver, and is thence transferred to the heart to receive its proper form and last perfection; a statement which does not appear devoid of reason; for no great and perfect work is ever accomplished at a single effort, or receives its final polish from one instrument. But if this be actually so, then show us another vessel which draws the absolutely perfect blood from the heart, and distributes it as the arteries do the spirits over the whole body." Here then is a reasonable opinion not allowed, because, forsooth, besides not seeing the true means of transit, he could not discover the vessel which should transmit the blood from the heart to the body at large!

But had anyone been there in behalf of Erasistratus, and of that opinion which we now espouse, and which Galen himself acknowledges in other respects consonant with reason, to have pointed to the aorta as the vessel which distributes the blood from the heart to the rest of the body, I wonder what would have been the answer of that most ingenious and learned man? Had he said that the artery transmits spirits and not blood, he would indeed sufficiently have answered Erasistratus, who imagined that the arteries contained nothing but spirits; but then he would have contradicted himself, and given a foul denial to that for which he had keenly contended in his writings against this very Erasistratus, to wit, that blood in substance is contained in the arteries, and not spirits; a fact which he demonstrated not only by many powerful arguments, but by experiments.

But if the divine Galen will here allow, as in other places he does, "that all the arteries of the body arise from the great artery, and that this takes its origin from the heart; that all these vessels naturally contain and carry blood; that the three semilunar valves situated at the orifice of the aorta prevent the return of the blood into the heart, and that nature never connected them with this, the most noble viscus of the body, unless for some most important end";

* De Placitis Hippocratis et Platonis, vi.

if, I say, this father of physicians concedes all these things,—
and I quote his own words,—I do not see how he can deny that the
great artery is the very vessel to carry the blood, when it has attained its highest term of perfection, from the heart for distribution
to all parts of the body.   Or would he perchance still hesitate, like
all who have come after him, even to the present hour, because he
did not perceive the route by which the blood was transferred from
the veins to the arteries, in consequence, as I have already said, of
the intimate connexion between the heart and the lungs ?   And that
this difficulty puzzled anatomists not a little, when in their dissections they found the pulmonary artery and left ventricle full of
thick, black, and clotted blood, plainly appears, when they felt
themselves compelled to affirm that the blood made its way from the
right to the left ventricle by transuding through the septum of the
heart.   But this fancy I have already refuted.   A new pathway
for the blood must therefore be prepared and thrown open, and
being once exposed, no further difficulty will, I believe, be experienced by anyone in admitting what I have already proposed in
regard to the pulse of the heart and arteries, viz., the passage of the
blood from the veins to the arteries, and its distribution to the whole
of the body by means of these vessels.

CHAPTER VI

Of the Course by which the Blood is Carried from the Vena Cava into the Arteries, or from the Right into the Left Ventricle of the Heart.

Since the intimate connexion of the heart with the lungs, which
is apparent in the human subject, has been the probable cause of the
errors that have been committed on this point, they plainly do amiss
who, pretending to speak of the parts of animals generally, as anatomists for the most part do, confine their researches to the human
body alone, and that when it is dead.   They obviously do not act

otherwise than he who, having studied the forms of a single commonwealth, should set about the composition of a general system of polity; or who, having taken cognizance of the nature of a single field, should imagine that he had mastered the science of agriculture; or who, upon the ground of one particular proposition, should proceed to draw general conclusions.

Had anatomists only been as conversant with the dissection of the lower animals as they are with that of the human body, the matters that have hitherto kept them in a perplexity of doubt would, in my opinion, have met them freed from every kind of difficulty.

And first, in fishes, in which the heart consists of but a single ventricle, being devoid of lungs, the thing is sufficiently manifest. Here the sac, which is situated at the base of the heart, and is the part analogous to the auricle in man, plainly forces the blood into the heart, and the heart, in its turn, conspicuously transmits it by a pipe or artery, or vessel analogous to an artery; these are facts which are confirmed by simple ocular inspection, as well as by a division of the vessel, when the blood is seen to be projected by each pulsation of the heart.

The same thing is also not difficult of demonstration in those animals that have, as it were, no more than a single ventricle to the heart, such as toads, frogs, serpents, and lizards, which have lungs in a certain sense, as they have a voice. I have many observations by me on the admirable structure of the lungs of these animals, and matters appertaining, which, however, I cannot introduce in this place. Their anatomy plainly shows us that the blood is transferred in them from the veins to the arteries in the same manner as in higher animals, viz., by the action of the heart; the way, in fact, is patent, open, manifest; there is no difficulty, no room for doubt about it; for in them the matter stands precisely as it would in man were the septum of his heart perforated or removed, or one ventricle made out of two; and this being the case, I imagine that no one will doubt as to the way by which the blood may pass from the veins into the arteries.

But as there are actually more animals which have no lungs than there are furnished with them, and in like manner a greater number which have only one ventricle than there are with two, it is open to us to conclude, judging from the mass or multitude of living creatures, that for the major part, and generally, there is an open way by which the blood is transmitted from the veins through the sinuses or cavities of the heart into the arteries.

I have, however, cogitating with myself, seen further, that the same thing obtained most obviously in the embryos of those animals that have lungs; for in the fœtus the four vessels belonging to the heart, viz., the vena cava, the pulmonary artery, the pulmonary vein, and the great artery or aorta, are all connected otherwise than in the adult, a fact sufficiently known to every anatomist. The first contact and union of the vena cava with the pulmonary veins, which occurs before the cava opens properly into the right ventricle of the heart, or gives off the coronary vein, a little above its escape from the liver, is by a lateral anastomosis; this is an ample foramen, of an oval form, communicating between the cava and the pulmonary vein, so that the blood is free to flow in the greatest abundance by that foramen from the vena cava into the pulmonary vein, and left auricle, and from thence into the left ventricle. Farther, in this foramen ovale, from that part which regards the pulmonary vein, there is a thin tough membrane, larger than the opening, extended like an operculum or cover; this membrane in the adult blocking up the foramen, and adhering on all sides, finally closes it up, and almost obliterates every trace of it. In the fœtus, however, this membrane is so contrived that falling loosely upon itself, it permits a ready access to the lungs and heart, yielding a passage to the blood which is streaming from the cava, and hindering the tide at the same time from flowing back into that vein. All things, in short, permit us to believe that in the embryo the blood must constantly pass by this foramen from the vena cava into the pulmonary vein, and from thence into the left auricle of the heart; and having once entered there, it can never regurgitate.

Another union is that by the pulmonary artery, and is effected when that vessel divides into two branches after its escape from the right ventricle of the heart. It is as if to the two trunks already mentioned a third were superadded, a kind of arterial canal, carried obliquely from the pulmonary artery, to perforate and terminate in the great artery or aorta. So that in the dissection of the embryo, as it were, two aortas, or two roots of the great artery, appear springing from the heart. This canal shrinks gradually after birth, and after a time becomes withered, and finally almost removed, like the umbilical vessels.

The arterial canal contains no membrane or valve to direct or impede the flow of blood in this or in that direction: for at the root of the pulmonary artery, of which the arterial canal is the continuation in the fœtus, there are three semilunar valves, which open from within outwards, and oppose no obstacle to the blood flowing in this direction or from the right ventricle into the pulmonary artery and aorta; but they prevent all regurgitation from the aorta or pulmonic vessels back upon the right ventricle; closing with perfect accuracy, they oppose an effectual obstacle to everything of the kind in the embryo. So that there is also reason to believe that when the heart contracts, the blood is regularly propelled by the canal or passage indicated from the right ventricle into the aorta.

What is commonly said in regard to these two great communications, to wit, that they exist for the nutrition of the lungs, is both improbable and inconsistent; seeing that in the adult they are closed up, abolished, and consolidated, although the lungs, by reason of their heat and motion, must then be presumed to require a larger supply of nourishment. The same may be said in regard to the assertion that the heart in the embryo does not pulsate, that it neither acts nor moves, so that nature was forced to make these communications for the nutrition of the lungs. This is plainly false; for simple inspection of the incubated egg, and of embryos just taken out of the uterus, shows that the heart moves in them precisely as in adults, and that nature feels no such necessity. I have myself repeatedly seen these motions, and Aristotle is likewise witness of their reality. "The pulse," he observes, "inheres in the very constitution of the heart, and appears from the beginning as is learned both from the dissection of living animals and the formation of the chick in the egg."* But we further observe that the pas-

* Lib. de Spiritu, cap. v.

sages in question are not only pervious up to the period of birth in man, as well as in other animals, as anatomists in general have described them, but for several months subsequently, in some indeed for several years, not to say for the whole course of life; as, for example, in the goose, snipe, and various birds and many of the smaller animals. And this circumstance it was, perhaps, that imposed upon Botallus, who thought he had discovered a new passage for the blood from the vena cava into the left ventricle of the heart; and I own that when I met with the same arrangement in one of the larger members of the mouse family, in the adult state, I was myself at first led to something of a like conclusion.

From this it will be understood that in the human embryo, and in the embryos of animals in which the communications are not closed, the same thing happens, namely, that the heart by its motion propels the blood by obvious and open passages from the vena cava into the aorta through the cavities of both the ventricles, the right one receiving the blood from the auricle, and propelling it by the pulmonary artery and its continuation, named the ductus arteriosus, into the aorta; the left, in like manner, charged by the contraction of its auricle, which has received its supply through the foramen ovale from the vena cava, contracting, and projecting the blood through the root of the aorta into the trunk of that vessel.

In embryos, consequently, whilst the lungs are yet in a state of inaction, performing no function, subject to no motion any more than if they had not been present, nature uses the two ventricles of the heart as if they formed but one, for the transmission of the blood. The condition of the embryos of those animals which have lungs, whilst these organs are yet in abeyance and not employed, is the same as that of those animals which have no lungs.

So it clearly appears in the case of the fœtus that the heart by its action transfers the blood from the vena cava into the aorta, and that by a route as obvious and open, as if in the adult the two ventricles were made to communicate by the removal of their septum. We therefore find that in the greater number of animals—in all, indeed, at a certain period of their existence—the channels for the transmission of the blood through the heart are conspicuous. But we have to inquire why in some creatures—those, namely, that have warm blood, and that have attained to the adult age, man among the number—we should not conclude that the same thing is accomplished through the substance of the lungs, which in the embryo, and at a time when the function of these organs is in abeyance, nature effects by the direct passages described, and which, indeed, she seems compelled to adopt through want of a passage by the lungs; or why it should be better (for nature always does that which is best) that she should close up the various open routes which she had formerly made use of in the embryo and fœtus, and still uses in all other animals. Not only does she thereby open up no new apparent channels for the passage of the blood, but she even shuts up those which formerly existed.

And now the discussion is brought to this point, that they who inquire into the ways by which the blood reaches the left ventricle of the heart and pulmonary veins from the vena cava, will pursue the wisest course if they seek by dissection to discover the causes why in the larger and more perfect animals of mature age nature has rather chosen to make the blood percolate the parenchyma of the lungs, than, as in other instances, chosen a direct and obvious course —for I assume that no other path or mode of transit can be entertained. It must be because the larger and more perfect animals are warmer, and when adult their heat greater—ignited, as I might say, and requiring to be damped or mitigated, that the blood is sent through the lungs, in order that it may be tempered by the air that is inspired, and prevented from boiling up, and so becoming extinguished, or something else of the sort. But to determine these matters, and explain them satisfactorily, were to enter on a speculation in regard to the office of the lungs and the ends for which they exist. Upon such a subject, as well as upon what pertains to respiration, to the necessity and use of the air, etc., as also to the variety and diversity of organs that exist in the bodies of animals in connexion with these matters, although I have made a vast number of observations, I shall not speak till I can more conveniently set them forth in a treatise apart, lest I should be held as wandering too wide of my present purpose, which is the use and motion of the heart, and be charged with speaking of things beside the question, and rather complicating and quitting than illustrating it. And now returning to my immediate subject, I go on with what yet remains for demonstration, viz., that in the more perfect and warmer adult animals, and man, the blood passes from the right ventricle of the heart by the pulmonary artery, into the lungs, and thence by the pulmonary veins into the left auricle, and from there into the left ventricle of the heart. And, first, I shall show that this may be so, and then I shall prove that it is so in fact.

CHAPTER VII

THE BLOOD PASSES THROUGH THE SUBSTANCE OF THE LUNGS FROM THE RIGHT VENTRICLE OF THE HEART INTO THE PUL- MONARY VEINS AND LEFT VENTRICLE

That this is possible, and that there is nothing to prevent it from being so, appears when we reflect on the way in which water permeating the earth produces springs and rivulets, or when we speculate on the means by which the sweat passes through the skin, or the urine through the substance of the kidneys. It is well known that persons who use the Spa waters or those of La Ma- donna, in the territories of Padua, or others of an acidulous or vitrio- lated nature, or who simply swallow drinks by the gallon, pass all off again within an hour or two by the bladder. Such a quantity of liquid must take some short time in the concoction: it must pass through the liver (it is allowed by all that the juices of the food we consume pass twice through this organ in the course of the day); it must flow through the veins, through the tissues of the kidneys, and through the ureters into the bladder.

To those, therefore, whom I hear denying that the blood, aye, the whole mass of the blood, may pass through the substance of the lungs, even as the nutritive juices percolate the liver, asserting such a proposition to be impossible, and by no means to be entertained as credible, I reply, with the poet, that they are of that race of men who, when they will, assent full readily, and when they will not, by no manner of means; who, when their assent is wanted, fear, and when it is not, fear not to give it.

The substance of the liver is extremely dense, so is that of the kidney; the lungs, however, are of a much looser texture, and if compared with the kidneys are absolutely spongy. In the liver there is no forcing, no impelling power; in the lungs the blood is forced on by the pulse of the right ventricle, the necessary effect of whose impulse is the distension of the vessels and the pores of the lungs. And then the lungs, in respiration, are perpetually rising and falling: motions, the effect of which must needs be to open and shut the pores and vessels, precisely as in the case of a sponge, and of parts having a spongy structure, when they are alternately compressed and again are suffered to expand. The liver, on the contrary, remains at rest, and is never seen to be dilated or constricted. Lastly, if no one denies the possibility in man, oxen, and the larger animals generally, of the whole of the ingested juices passing through the liver, in order to reach the vena cava, for this reason, that if nourishment is to go on, these juices must needs get into the veins, and there is no other way but the one indicated, why should not the same arguments be held of avail for the passage of the blood in adults through the lungs? Why not maintain, with Columbus, that skilful and learned anatomist, that it must be so from the capacity and structure of the pulmonary vessels, and from the fact of the pulmonary veins and ventricle corresponding with them, being always found to contain blood, which must needs have come from the veins, and by no other passage save through the lungs? Columbus, and we also, from what precedes, from dissections and other arguments, conceive the thing to be clear. But as there are some who admit nothing unless upon authority, let them learn that the truth I am contending for can be confirmed from Galen's own words, namely, that not only may the blood be transmitted from the pulmonary artery into the pulmonary veins, then into the left ventricle of the heart, and from thence into the arteries of the body, but that this is effected by the ceaseless pulsation of the heart and the motion of the lungs in breathing.

There are, as everyone knows, three sigmoid or semilunar valves situated at the orifice of the pulmonary artery, which effectually prevent the blood sent into the vessel from returning into the cavity of the heart. Now Galen, explaining the use of these valves, and the necessity for them, employs the following language:* "There is everywhere a mutual anastomosis and inosculation of the arteries with the veins, and they severally transmit both blood and spirit, by certain invisible and undoubtedly very narrow passages. Now if the mouth of the pulmonary artery had stood in like manner continually open, and nature had found no contrivance for closing it when requisite, and opening it again, it would have been impossible that the blood could ever have passed by the invisible and delicate mouths, during the contractions of the thorax, into the arteries; for all things are not alike readily attracted or repelled; but that which is light is more readily drawn in, the instrument being dilated, and forced out again when it is contracted, than that which is heavy; and in like manner is anything drawn more rapidly along an ample conduit, and again driven forth, than it is through a narrow tube. But when the thorax is contracted the pulmonary veins, which are in the lungs, being driven inwardly, and powerfully compressed on every side, immediately force out some of the spirit they contain, and at the same time assume a certain portion of blood by those subtile mouths, a thing that could never come to pass were the blood at liberty to flow back into the heart through the great orifice of the pulmonary artery. But its return through this great opening being prevented, when it is compressed on every side, a certain portion of it distils into the pulmonary veins by the minute orifices mentioned." And shortly afterwards, in the next chapter, he says: "The more the thorax contracts, the more it strives to force out the blood, the more exactly do these membranes (viz., the semilunar valves) close up the mouth of the vessel, and suffer nothing to regurgitate." The same fact he has also alluded to in a preceding part of the tenth chapter: "Were there no valves, a

* De Usu partium, lib. vi, cap. 10.

three-fold inconvenience would result, so that the blood would then perform this lengthened course in vain; it would flow inwards during the diastoles of the lungs and fill all their arteries; but in the systoles, in the manner of the tide, it would ever and anon, like the Euripus, flow backwards and forwards by the same way, with a reciprocating motion, which would nowise suit the blood. This, however, may seem a matter of little moment; but if it meantime appear that the function of respiration suffer, then I think it would be looked upon as no trifle, etc." Shortly afterwards he says: "And then a third inconvenience, by no means to be thought lightly of, would follow, were the blood moved backwards during the expirations, had not our Maker instituted those supplementary membranes." In the eleventh chapter he concludes: "That they (the valves) have all a common use, and that it is to prevent regurgitation or backward motion; each, however, having a proper function, the one set drawing matters from the heart, and preventing their return, the other drawing matters into the heart, and preventing their escape from it. For nature never intended to distress the heart with needless labour, neither to bring aught into the organ which it had been better to have kept away, nor to take from it again aught which it was requisite should be brought. Since, then, there are four orifices in all, two in either ventricle, one of these induces, the other educes." And again he says: "Farther, since there is one vessel, which consists of a simple covering implanted in the heart, and another which is double, extending from it (Galen is here speaking of the right side of the heart, but I extend his observations to the left side also), a kind of reservoir had to be provided, to which both belonging, the blood should be drawn in by one, and sent out by the other."

Galen adduces this argument for the transit of the blood by the right ventricle from the vena cava into the lungs; but we can use it with still greater propriety, merely changing the terms, for the passage of the blood from the veins through the heart into the arteries. From Galen, however, that great man, that father of physicians, it clearly appears that the blood passes through the lungs from the pulmonary artery into the minute branches of the pulmonary veins, urged to this both by the pulses of the heart and by the motions of the lungs and thorax; that the heart, moreover, is incessantly receiving and expelling the blood by and from its ventricles, as from a magazine or cistern, and for this end it is furnished with four sets of valves, two serving for the induction and two for the eduction of the blood, lest, like the Euripus, it should be incommodiously sent hither and thither, or flow back into the cavity which it should have quitted, or quit the part where its presence was required, and so the heart might be oppressed with labour in vain, and the office of the lungs be interfered with.* Finally, our position that the blood is continually permeating from the right to the left ventricle, from the vena cava into the aorta, through the porosities of the lungs, plainly appears from this, that since the blood is incessantly sent from the right ventricle into the lungs by the pulmonary artery, and in like manner is incessantly drawn from the lungs into the left ventricle, as appears from what precedes and the position of the valves, it cannot do otherwise than pass through continuously. And then, as the blood is incessantly flowing into the right ventricle of the heart, and is continually passed out from the left, as appears in like manner, and as is obvious, both to sense and reason, it is impossible that the blood can do otherwise than pass continually from the vena cava into the aorta.

Dissection consequently shows distinctly what takes place in the majority of animals, and indeed in all, up to the period of their maturity; and that the same thing occurs in adults is equally certain, both from Galen's words, and what has already been said, only that in the former the transit is effected by open and obvious passages, in the latter by the hidden porosities of the lungs and the minute inosculations of vessels. It therefore appears that, although one ventricle of the heart, the left to wit, would suffice for the distribution of the blood over the body, and its eduction from the vena cava, as indeed is done in those creatures that have no lungs, nature, nevertheless, when she ordained that the same blood should also percolate the lungs, saw herself obliged to add the right ven-

* See the Commentary of the learned Hofmann upon the Sixth Book of Galen, "De Usu partium," a work which I first saw after I had written what precedes.

tricle, the pulse of which should force the blood from the vena cava through the lungs into the cavity of the left ventricle. In this way, it may be said, that the right ventricle is made for the sake of the lungs, and for the transmission of the blood through them, not for their nutrition; for it were unreasonable to suppose that the lungs should require so much more copious a supply of nutriment, and that of so much purer and more spirituous a nature as coming immediately from the ventricle of the heart, that either the brain, with its peculiarly pure substance, or the eyes, with their lustrous and truly admirable structure, or the flesh of the heart itself, which is more suitably nourished by the coronary artery.

CHAPTER VIII

Of the Quantity of Blood Passing Through the Heart from the Veins to the Arteries; and of the Circular Motion of the Blood

Thus far I have spoken of the passage of the blood from the veins into the arteries, and of the manner in which it is transmitted and distributed by the action of the heart; points to which some, moved either by the authority of Galen or Columbus, or the reasonings of others, will give in their adhesion. But what remains to be said upon the quantity and source of the blood which thus passes is of a character so novel and unheard-of that I not only fear injury to myself from the envy of a few, but I tremble lest I have mankind at large for my enemies, so much doth wont and custom become a second nature. Doctrine once sown strikes deep its root, and respect for antiquity influences all men. Still the die is cast, and my trust is in my love of truth and the candour of cultivated minds. And sooth to say, when I surveyed my mass of evidence, whether derived from vivisections, and my various reflections on them, or from the study of the ventricles of the heart and the vessels that enter into and issue from them, the symmetry and size of these conduits,—for nature doing nothing in vain, would never have given them so large a relative size without a purpose,—or from observing the arrangement and intimate structure of the valves in particular, and of the other parts of the heart in general, with many things besides, I frequently and seriously bethought me, and long revolved in my mind, what might be the quantity of blood which was transmitted, in how short a time its passage might be effected, and the like. But not finding it possible that this could be supplied by the juices of the ingested aliment without the veins on the one hand becoming drained, and the arteries on the other getting ruptured through the excessive charge of blood, unless the blood should somehow find its way from the arteries into the veins, and so return to the right side of the heart, I began to think whether there might not be a A MOTION, AS IT WERE, IN A CIRCLE. Now, this I afterwards found to be true; and I finally saw that the blood, forced by the action of the left ventricle into the arteries, was distributed to the body at large, and its several parts, in the same manner as it is sent through the lungs, impelled by the right ventricle into the pulmonary artery, and that it then passed through the veins and along the vena cava, and so round to the left ventricle in the manner already indicated. This motion we may be allowed to call circular, in the same way as Aristotle says that the air and the rain emulate the circular motion of the superior bodies; for the moist earth, warmed by the sun, evaporates; the vapours drawn upwards are condensed, and descending in the form of rain, moisten the earth again. By this arrangement are generations of living things produced; and in like manner are tempests and meteors engendered by the circular motion, and by the approach and recession of the sun.

And similarly does it come to pass in the body, through the motion of the blood, that the various parts are nourished, cherished, quickened by the warmer, more perfect, vaporous, spirituous, and, as I may say, alimentive blood; which, on the other hand, owing to its contact with these parts, becomes cooled, coagulated, and, so to speak, effete. It then returns to its sovereign, the heart, as if to its source, or to the inmost home of the body, there to recover its state of excellence or perfection.   Here it renews its fluidity, natural heat, and becomes powerful, fervid, a kind of treasury of life, and impregnated with spirits, it might be said with balsam.   Thence it is again dispersed.   All this depends on the motion and action of the heart.

The heart, consequently, is the beginning of life; the sun of the microcosm, even as the sun in his turn might well be designated the heart of the world; for it is the heart by whose virtue and pulse the blood is moved, perfected, and made nutrient, and is preserved from corruption and coagulation; it is the household divinity which, discharging its function, nourishes, cherishes, quickens the whole body, and is indeed the foundation of life, the source of all action· But of these things we shall speak more opportunely when we come to speculate upon the final cause of this motion of the heart.

As the blood-vessels, therefore, are the canals and agents that transport the blood, they are of two kinds, the cava and the aorta; and this not by reason of there being two sides of the body, as Aristotle has it, but because of the difference of office, not, as is commonly said, in consequence of any diversity of structure, for in many animals, as I have said, the vein does not differ from the artery in the thickness of its walls, but solely in virtue of their distinct functions and uses.   A vein and an artery, both styled veins by the ancients, and that not without reason, as Galen has remarked, for the artery is the vessel which carries the blood from the heart to the body at large, the vein of the present day bringing it back from the general system to the heart; the former is the conduit from, the latter the channel to, the heart; the latter contains the cruder, effete blood, rendered unfit for nutrition; the former transmits the digested, perfect, peculiarly nutritive fluid.

CHAPTER IX

That there is a Circulation of the Blood is Confirmed from the First Proposition

But lest anyone should say that we give them words only, and make mere specious assertions without any foundation, and desire to innovate without sufficient cause, three points present themselves for confirmation, which, being stated, I conceive that the truth I contend for will follow necessarily, and appear as a thing obvious to all. First, the blood is incessantly transmitted by the action of the heart from the vena cava to the arteries in such quantity that it cannot be supplied from the ingesta, and in such a manner that the whole must very quickly pass through the organ; second, the blood under the influence of the arterial pulse enters and is impelled in a continuous, equable, and incessant stream through every part and member of the body, in much larger quantity than were sufficient for nutrition, or than the whole mass of fluids could supply; third, the veins in like manner return this blood incessantly to the heart from parts and members of the body. These points proved, I conceive it will be manifest that the blood circulates, revolves, propelled and then returning, from the heart to the extremities, from the extremities to the heart, and thus that it performs a kind of circular motion.

Let us assume, either arbitrarily or from experiment, the quantity of blood which the left ventricle of the heart will contain when distended, to be, say, two ounces, three ounces, or one ounce and a half—in the dead body I have found it to hold upwards of two ounces. Let us assume further how much less the heart will hold in the contracted than in the dilated state; and how much blood it will project into the aorta upon each contraction; and all the world allows that with the systole something is always projected, a necessary consequence demonstrated in the third chapter, and obvious from the structure of the valves; and let us suppose as approaching the truth that the fourth, or fifth, or sixth, or even but the eighth part of its charge is thrown into the artery at each contraction; this would give either half an ounce, or three drachms, or one drachm of blood as propelled by the heart at each pulse into the aorta; which quantity, by reason of the valves at the root of the vessel, can by no means return into the ventricle. Now, in the course of half an hour, the heart will have made more than one thousand beats, in some as many as two, three, and even four thousand. Multiplying the number of drachms propelled by the number of pulses, we shall have either one thousand half ounces, or one thousand times three drachms, or a like proportional quantity of blood, according to the amount which we assume as propelled with each stroke of the heart, sent from this organ into the artery—a larger quantity in every case than is contained in the whole body! In the same way, in the sheep or dog, say but a single scruple of blood passes with each stroke of the heart, in one half-hour we should have one thousand scruples, or about three pounds and a half, of blood injected into the aorta; but the body of neither animal contains above four pounds of blood, a fact which I have myself ascertained in the case of the sheep.

Upon this supposition, therefore, assumed merely as a ground for reasoning, we see the whole mass of blood passing through the heart, from the veins to the arteries, and in like manner through the lungs.

But let it be said that this does not take place in half an hour, but in an hour, or even in a day; any way, it is still manifest that more blood passes through the heart in consequence of its action, than can either be supplied by the whole of the ingesta, or than can be contained in the veins at the same moment.

Nor can it be allowed that the heart in contracting sometimes propels and sometimes does not propel, or at most propels but very little, a mere nothing, or an imaginary something: all this, indeed, has already been refuted, and is, besides, contrary both to sense and reason. For if it be a necessary effect of the dilatation of the heart that its ventricles become filled with blood, it is equally so that, contracting, these cavities should expel their contents; and this not in any trifling measure. For neither are the conduits small, nor the contractions few in number, but frequent, and always in some certain proportion, whether it be a third or a sixth, or an eighth, to the total capacity of the ventricles, so that a like proportion of blood must be expelled, and a like proportion received with each stroke of the heart, the capacity of the ventricle contracted always bearing a certain relation to the capacity of the ventricle when dilated. And since, in dilating, the ventricles cannot be supposed to get filled with nothing, or with an imaginary something, so in contracting they never expel nothing or aught imaginary, but always a certain something, viz., blood, in proportion to the amount of the contraction. Whence it is to be concluded that if at one stroke the heart of man, the ox, or the sheep, ejects but a single drachm of blood and there are one thousand strokes in half an hour, in this interval there will have been ten pounds five ounces expelled; if with each stroke two drachms are expelled, the quantity would, of course, amount to twenty pounds and ten ounces; if half an ounce, the quantity would come to forty-one pounds and eight ounces; and were there one ounce, it would be as much as eighty-three pounds and four ounces; the whole of which, in the course of one-half hour, would have been transfused from the veins to the arteries. The actual quantity of blood expelled at each stroke of the heart, and the circumstances under which it is either greater or less than ordinary, I leave for particular determination afterwards, from numerous observations which I have made on the subject.

Meantime this much I know, and would here proclaim to all, that the blood is transfused at one time in larger, at another in smaller, quantity; and that the circuit of the blood is accomplished now more rapidly, now more slowly, according to the temperament, age, etc., of the individual, to external and internal circumstances, to naturals and non-naturals—sleep, rest, food, exercise, affections of the mind, and the like. But, supposing even the smallest quantity of blood to be passed through the heart and the lungs with each pulsation, a vastly greater amount would still be thrown into the arteries and whole body than could by any possibility be supplied by the food consumed. It could be furnished in no other way than by making a circuit and returning.

This truth, indeed, presents itself obviously before us when we consider what happens in the dissection of living animals; the great artery need not be divided, but a very small branch only (as Galen even proves in regard to man), to have the whole of the blood in the body, as well that of the veins as of the arteries, drained away in the course of no long time—some half-hour or less. Butchers are well aware of the fact and can bear witness to it; for, cutting the throat of an ox and so dividing the vessels of the neck, in less than a quarter of an hour they have all the vessels bloodless—the whole mass of blood has escaped. The same thing also occasionally occurs with great rapidity in performing amputations and removing tumors in the human subject.

Nor would this argument lose any of its force, did any one say that in killing animals in the shambles, and performing amputations, the blood escaped in equal, if not perchance in larger quantity by the veins than by the arteries. The contrary of this statement, indeed, is certainly the truth; the veins, in fact, collapsing, and being without any propelling power, and further, because of the impediment of the valves, as I shall show immediately, pour out but very little blood; whilst the arteries spout it forth with force abundantly, impetuously, and as if it were propelled by a syringe. And then the experiment is easily tried of leaving the vein untouched and only dividing the artery in the neck of a sheep or dog, when it will be seen with what force, in what abundance, and how quickly, the whole blood in the body, of the veins as well as of the arteries, is emptied. But the arteries receive blood from the veins in no other way than by transmission through the heart, as we have already seen; so that if the aorta be tied at the base of the heart, and the carotid or any other artery be opened, no one will now be surprised to find it empty, and the veins only replete with blood.

And now the cause is manifest, why in our dissections we usually find so large a quantity of blood in the veins, so little in the arteries; why there is much in the right ventricle, little in the left, which probably led the ancients to believe that the arteries (as their name implies) contained nothing but spirits during the life of an animal. The true cause of the difference is perhaps this, that as there is no passage to the arteries, save through the lungs and heart, when an animal has ceased to breathe and the lungs to move, the blood in the pulmonary artery is prevented from passing into the pulmonary veins, and from thence into the left ventricle of the heart; just as we have already seen the same transit prevented in the embryo, by the want of movement in the lungs and the alternate opening and shutting of their hidden and invisible porosities and apertures.   But the heart not ceasing to act at the same precise moment as the lungs, but surviving them and continuing to pulsate for a time, the left ventricle and arteries go on distributing their blood to the body at large and sending it into the veins; receiving none from the lungs, however, they are soon exhausted, and left, as it were, empty.   But even this fact confirms our views, in no trifling manner, seeing that it can be ascribed to no other than the cause we have just assumed.

Moreover, it appears from this that the more frequently or forcibly the arteries pulsate, the more speedily will the body be exhausted of its blood during hemorrhage.   Hence, also, it happens, that in fainting fits and in states of alarm, when the heart beats more languidly and less forcibly, hemorrhages are diminished and arrested.

Still further, it is from this, that after death, when the heart has ceased to beat, it is impossible, by dividing either the jugular or femoral veins and arteries, by any effort, to force out more than one-half of the whole mass of the blood.   Neither could the butcher ever bleed the carcass effectually did he neglect to cut the throat of the ox which he has knocked on the head and stunned, before the heart had ceased beating.

Finally, we are now in a condition to suspect wherefore it is that no one has yet said anything to the purpose upon the anastomosis of the veins and arteries, either as to where or how it is effected, or for what purpose.   I now enter upon the investigation of the subject.

CHAPTER X

THE FIRST POSITION: OF THE QUANTITY OF BLOOD PASSING FROM
THE VEINS TO THE ARTERIES. AND THAT THERE IS A CIRCUIT
OF THE BLOOD, FREED FROM OBJECTIONS, AND FARTHER
CONFIRMED BY EXPERIMENT

So far our first position is confirmed, whether the thing be referred
to calculation or to experiment and dissection, viz., that the blood is
incessantly poured into the arteries in larger quantities than it can
be supplied by the food; so that the whole passing over in a short
space of time, it is matter of necessity that the blood perform a
circuit, that it return to whence it set out.

But if anyone shall here object that a large quantity may pass
through and yet no necessity be found for a circulation, that all
may come from the meat and drink consumed, and quote as an
illustration the abundant supply of milk in the mammæ—for a cow
will give three, four, and even seven gallons and more in a day, and
a woman two or three pints whilst nursing a child or twins, which
must manifestly be derived from the food consumed; it may be
answered that the heart by computation does as much and more in
the course of an hour or two.

And if not yet convinced, he shall still insist that when an artery
is divided, a preternatural route is, as it were, opened, and that so
the blood escapes in torrents, but that the same thing does not
happen in the healthy and uninjured body when no outlet is made;
and that in arteries filled, or in their natural state, so large a
quantity of blood cannot pass in so short a space of time as to
make any return necessary—to all this it may be answered that,
from the calculation already made, and the reasons assigned, it
appears that by so much as the heart in its dilated state contains,
in addition to its contents in the state of constriction, so much
in a general way must it emit upon each pulsation, and in such
quantity must the blood pass, the body being entire and naturally
constituted.

But in serpents, and several fishes, by tying the veins some way below the heart you will perceive a space between the ligature and the heart speedily to become empty; so that, unless you would deny the evidence of your senses, you must needs admit the return of the blood to the heart.   The same thing will also plainly appear when we come to discuss our second position.

Let us here conclude with a single example, confirming all that has been said, and from which everyone may obtain conviction through the testimony of his own eyes.

If a live snake be laid open, the heart will be seen pulsating quietly, distinctly, for more than an hour, moving like a worm, contracting in its longitudinal dimensions, (for it is of an oblong shape,) and propelling its contents.   It becomes of a paler colour in the systole, of a deeper tint in the diastole; and almost all things else are seen by which I have already said that the truth I contend for is established, only that here everything takes place more slowly, and is more distinct.   This point in particular may be observed more clearly than the noon-day sun: the vena cava enters the heart at its lower part, the artery quits it at the superior part; the vein being now seized either with forceps or between the finger and the thumb, and the course of the blood for some space below the heart interrupted, you will perceive the part that intervenes between the fingers and the heart almost immediately to become empty, the blood being exhausted by the action of the heart; at the same time the heart will become of a much paler colour, even in its state of dilatation, than it was before; it is also smaller than at first, from wanting blood: and then it begins to beat more slowly, so that it seems at length as if it were about to die.   But the impediment to the flow of blood being removed, instantly the colour and the size of the heart are restored.

If, on the contrary, the artery instead of the vein be compressed or tied, you will observe the part between the obstacle and the heart, and the heart itself, to become inordinately distended, to assume a deep purple or even livid colour, and at length to be so much oppressed with blood that you will believe it about to be choked; but the obstacle removed, all things immediately return to their natural state in colour, size, and impulse.

Here then we have evidence of two kinds of death: extinction from deficiency, and suffocation from excess. Examples of both have now been set before you, and you have had opportunity of viewing the truth contended for with your own eyes in the heart.

———

CHAPTER XI

THE SECOND POSITION IS DEMONSTRATED

That this may the more clearly appear to everyone, I have here to cite certain experiments, from which it seems obvious that the blood enters a limb by the arteries, and returns from it by the veins; that the arteries are the vessels carrying the blood from the heart, and the veins the returning channels of the blood to the heart; that in the limbs and extreme parts of the body the blood passes either immediately by anastomosis from the arteries into the veins, or mediately by the porosities of the flesh, or in both ways, as has already been said in speaking of the passage of the blood through the lungs whence it appears manifest that in the circuit the blood moves from that place to this place, and from that point to this one; from the centre to the extremities, to wit; and from the extreme parts back again to the centre. Finally, upon grounds of calculation, with the same elements as before, it will be obvious that the quantity can neither be accounted for by the ingesta, nor yet be held necessary to nutrition.

The same thing will also appear in regard to ligatures, and wherefore they are said to *draw;* though this is neither from the heat, nor the pain, nor the vacuum they occasion, nor indeed from any other cause yet thought of; it will also explain the uses and advantages to be derived from ligatures in medicine, the principle upon which they either suppress or occasion hemorrhage; how they induce sloughing and more extensive mortification in extremities; and how they act in the castration of animals and the removal of warts and fleshy tumours. But it has come to pass, from no one having duly weighed and understood the causes and rationale of these various effects, that though almost all, upon the faith of the old writers, recommend ligatures in the treatment of disease, yet very few comprehend their proper employment, or derive any real assistance from them in effecting cures.

Ligatures are either very tight or of medium tightness. A ligature I designate as tight or perfect when it so constricts an extremity that no vessel can be felt pulsating beyond it. Such a ligature we use in amputations to control the flow of blood; and such also are employed in the castration of animals and the ablation of tumours. In the latter instances, all afflux of nutriment and heat being prevented by the ligature, we see the testes and large fleshy tumours dwindle, die, and finally fall off.

Ligatures of medium tightness I regard as those which compress a limb firmly all round, but short of pain, and in such a way as still suffers a certain degree of pulsation to be felt in the artery beyond them. Such a ligature is in use in blood-letting, an operation in which the fillet applied above the elbow is not drawn so tight but that the arteries at the wrist may still be felt beating under the finger.

Now let anyone make an experiment upon the arm of a man, either using such a fillet as is employed in blood-letting, or grasping the limb lightly with his hand, the best subject for it being one who is lean, and who has large veins, and the best time after exercise, when the body is warm, the pulse is full, and the blood carried in larger quantity to the extremities, for all then is more conspicuous; under such circumstances let a ligature be thrown about the extremity, and drawn as tightly as can be borne, it will first be perceived that beyond the ligature, neither in the wrist nor anywhere else, do the arteries pulsate, at the same time that immediately above the ligature the artery begins to rise higher at each diastole, to throb more violently, and to swell in its vicinity with a kind of tide, as if it strove to break through and overcome the obstacle to its current; the artery here, in short, appears as if it were preternaturally full. The hand under such circumstances retains its natural colour and appearance; in the course of time it begins to fall somewhat in temperature, indeed, but nothing is *drawn* into it.

After the bandage has been kept on for some short time in this way, let it be slackened a little, brought to that state or term of medium tightness which is used in bleeding, and it will be seen that the whole hand and arm will instantly become deeply coloured and distended, and the veins show themselves tumid and knotted; after ten or twelve pulses of the artery, the hand will be perceived excessively distended, injected, gorged with blood, *drawn*, as it is said, by this medium ligature, without pain, or heat, or any horror of a vacuum, or any other cause yet indicated.

If the finger be applied over the artery as it is pulsating by the edge of the fillet, at the moment of slackening it, the blood will be felt to glide through, as it were, underneath the finger; and he, too, upon whose arm the experiment is made, when the ligature is slackened, is distinctly conscious of a sensation of warmth, and of something, viz., a stream of blood suddenly making its way along the course of the vessels and diffusing itself through the hand, which at the same time begins to feel hot, and becomes distended.

As we had noted, in connexion with the tight ligature, that the artery above the bandage was distended and pulsated, not below it, so, in the case of the moderately tight bandage, on the contrary, do we find that the veins below, never above, the fillet, swell, and become dilated, whilst the arteries shrink; and such is the degree of distension of the veins here, that it is only very strong pressure that will force the blood beyond the fillet, and cause any of the veins in the upper part of the arm to rise.

From these facts it is easy for every careful observer to learn that the blood enters an extremity by the arteries; for when they are effectually compressed nothing is *drawn* to the member; the hand preserves its colour; nothing flows into it, neither is it distended; but when the pressure is diminished, as it is with the bleeding fillet, it is manifest that the blood is instantly thrown in with force, for then the hand begins to swell; which is as much as to say, that when the arteries pulsate the blood is flowing through them, as it is when the moderately tight ligature is applied; but where they do not pulsate, as, when a tight ligature is used, they cease from transmitting anything, they are only distended above the part where the ligature is applied.   The veins again being compressed, nothing can flow through them; the certain indication of which is, that below the ligature they are much more tumid than above it, and than they usually appear when there is no bandage upon the arm.

It therefore plainly appears that the ligature prevents the return of the blood through the veins to the parts above it, and maintains those beneath it in a state of permanent distension.   But the arteries, in spite of its pressure, and under the force and impulse of the heart, send on the blood from the internal parts of the body to the parts beyond the ligature.   And herein consists the difference between the tight and the medium ligature, that the former not only prevents the passage of the blood in the veins, but in the arteries also; the latter, however, whilst it does not prevent the force of the pulse from extending beyond it, and so propelling the blood to the extremities of the body, compresses the veins, and greatly or altogether impedes the return of the blood through them.

Seeing, therefore, that the moderately tight ligature renders the veins turgid and distended, and the whole hand full of blood, I ask, whence is this?   Does the blood accumulate below the ligature coming through the veins, or through the arteries, or passing by certain hidden porosities?   Through the veins it cannot come; still less can it come through invisible channels; it must needs, then, arrive by the arteries, in conformity with all that has been already said.   That it cannot flow in by the veins appears plainly enough from the fact that the blood cannot be forced towards the heart unless the ligature be removed; when this is done suddenly all the veins collapse, and disgorge themselves of their contents into the superior parts, the hand at the same time resumes its natural pale colour, the tumefaction and the stagnating blood having disappeared.

Moreover, he whose arm or wrist has thus been bound for some little time with the medium bandage, so that it has not only got swollen and livid but cold, when the fillet is undone is aware of something cold making its way upwards along with the returning blood, and reaching the elbow or the axilla.   And I have myself been inclined to think that this cold blood rising upwards to the heart was the cause of the fainting that often occurs after blood-letting: fainting frequently supervenes even in robust subjects, and mostly at the moment of undoing the fillet, as the vulgar say, from the turning of the blood.

Farther, when we see the veins below the ligature instantly swell up and become gorged, when from extreme tightness it is somewhat relaxed, the arteries meantime continuing unaffected, this is an obvious indication that the blood passes from the arteries into the veins, and not from the veins into the arteries, and that there is either an anastomosis of the two orders of vessels, or porosities in the flesh and solid parts generally that are permeable to the blood. It is farther an indication that the veins have frequent communications with one another, because they all become turgid together, whilst under the medium ligature applied above the elbow; and if any single small vein be pricked with a lancet, they all speedily shrink, and disburthening themselves into this they subside almost simultaneously.

These considerations will enable anyone to understand the nature of the attraction that is exerted by ligatures, and perchance of fluxes generally; how, for example, when the veins are compressed by a bandage of medium tightness applied above the elbow, the blood cannot escape, whilst it still continues to be driven in, by the forcing power of the heart, by which the parts are of necessity filled, gorged with blood. And how should it be otherwise? Heat and pain and a vacuum draw, indeed; but in such wise only that parts are filled, not preternaturally distended or gorged, and not so suddenly and violently overwhelmed with the charge of blood forced in upon them, that the flesh is lacerated and the vessels ruptured. Nothing of the kind as an effect of heat, or pain, or the vacuum force, is either credible or demonstrable.

Besides, the ligature is competent to occasion the afflux in question without either pain, or heat, or a vacuum. Were pain in any way the cause, how should it happen that, with the arm bound above the elbow, the hand and fingers should swell below the bandage, and their veins become distended? The pressure of the bandage certainly prevents the blood from getting there by the veins. And then, wherefore is there neither swelling nor repletion of the veins, nor any sign or symptom of attraction or afflux, above the ligature? But this is the obvious cause of the preternatural attraction and swelling below the bandage, and in the hand and fingers, that the blood is entering abundantly, and with force, but cannot pass out again.

Now is not this the cause of all tumefaction, as indeed Avicenna has it, and of all oppressive redundancy in parts, that the access to them is open, but the egress from them is closed? Whence it comes that they are gorged and tumefied. And may not the same thing happen in local inflammations, where, so long as the swelling is on the increase, and has not reached its extreme term, a full pulse is felt in the part, especially when the disease is of the more acute kind, and the swelling usually takes place most rapidly. But these are matters for after discussion. Or does this, which occurred in my own case, happen from the same cause. Thrown from a carriage upon one occasion, I struck my forehead a blow upon the place where a twig of the artery advances from the temple, and immediately, within the time in which twenty beats could have been made I felt a tumour the size of an egg developed, without either heat or any great pain: the near vicinity of the artery had caused the blood to be effused into the bruised part with unusual force and velocity.

And now, too, we understand why in phlebotomy we apply our ligature above the part that is punctured, not below it; did the flow come from above, not from below, the constriction in this case would not only be of no service, but would prove a positive hindrance; it would have to be applied below the orifice, in order to have the flow more free, did the blood descend by the veins from superior to inferior parts; but as it is elsewhere forced through the extreme arteries into the extreme veins, and the return in these last is opposed by the ligature, so do they fill and swell, and being thus filled and distended, they are made capable of projecting their charge with force, and to a distance, when any one of them is suddenly punctured; but the ligature being slackened, and the returning channels thus left open, the blood forthwith no longer escapes, save by drops; and, as all the world knows, if in performing phlebotomy the bandage be either slackened too much or the limb be bound too tightly, the blood escapes without force, because in the one case the returning channels are not adequately obstructed; in the other the channels of influx, the arteries, are impeded.

CHAPTER XII

That there is a Circulation of the Blood is Shown from the Second Position Demonstrated

If these things be so, another point which I have already referred to, viz., the continual passage of the blood through the heart will also be confirmed. We have seen, that the blood passes from the arteries into the veins, not from the veins into the arteries; we have seen, farther, that almost the whole of the blood may be withdrawn from a puncture made in one of the cutaneous veins of the arm if a bandage properly applied be used; we have seen, still farther, that the blood flows so freely and rapidly that not only is the whole quantity which was contained in the arm beyond the ligature, and before the puncture was made, discharged, but the whole which is contained in the body, both that of the arteries and that of the veins.

Whence we must admit, first, that the blood is sent along with an impulse, and that it is urged with force below the ligature; for it escapes with force, which force it receives from the pulse and power of the heart; for the force and motion of the blood are derived from the heart alone. Second, that the afflux proceeds from the heart, and through the heart by a course from the great veins; for it gets into the parts below the ligature through the arteries, not through the veins; and the arteries nowhere receive blood from the veins, nowhere receive blood save and except from the left ventricle of the heart. Nor could so large a quantity of blood be drawn from one vein (a ligature having been duly applied), nor with such impetuosity, such readiness, such celerity, unless through the medium of the impelling power of the heart.

But if all things be as they are now represented, we shall feel ourselves at liberty to calculate the quantity of the blood, and to reason on its circular motion. Should anyone, for instance, performing phlebotomy, suffer the blood to flow in the manner it usually does, with force and freely, for some half hour or so, no question but that the greatest part of the blood being abstracted, faintings and syncopes would ensue, and that not only would the arteries but the great veins also be nearly emptied of their contents. It is only consonant with reason to conclude that in the course of the half hour hinted at, so much as has escaped has also passed from the great veins through the heart into the aorta. And further, if we calculate how many ounces flow through one arm, or how many pass in twenty or thirty pulsations under the medium ligature, we shall have some grounds for estimating how much passes through the other arm in the same space of time: how much through both lower extremities, how much through the neck on either side, and through all the other arteries and veins of the body, all of which have been supplied with fresh blood, and as this blood must have passed through the lungs and ventricles of the heart, and must have come from the great veins,—we shall perceive that a circulation is absolutely necessary, seeing that the quantities hinted at cannot be supplied immediately from the ingesta, and are vastly more than can be requisite for the mere nutrition of the parts.

It is still further to be observed, that in practising phlebotomy the truths contended for are sometimes confirmed in another way; for having tied up the arm properly, and made the puncture duly, still, if from alarm or any other causes, a state of faintness supervenes, in which the heart always pulsates more languidly, the blood does not flow freely, but distils by drops only. The reason is, that with a somewhat greater than usual resistance offered to the transit of the blood by the bandage, coupled with the weaker action of the heart, and its diminished impelling power, the stream cannot make its way under the ligature; and farther, owing to the weak and languishing state of the heart, the blood is not transferred in such quantity as wont from the veins to the arteries through the sinuses of that organ. So also, and for the same reasons, are the menstrual fluxes of women, and indeed hemorrhages of every kind, controlled. And now, a contrary state of things occurring, the patient getting rid of his fear and recovering his courage, the pulse strength is increased, the arteries begin again to beat with greater force, and to drive the blood even into the part that is bound; so that the blood now springs from the puncture in the vein, and flows in a continuous stream.

CHAPTER XIII

The Third Position is Confirmed: and the Circulation of the Blood is Demonstrated from It

Thus far we have spoken of the quantity of blood passing through the heart and the lungs in the centre of the body, and in like manner from the arteries into the veins in the peripheral parts and the body at large. We have yet to explain, however, in what manner the blood finds its way back to the heart from the extremities by the veins, and how and in what way these are the only vessels that convey the blood from the external to the central parts; which done, I conceive that the three fundamental propositions laid down for the circulation of the blood will be so plain, so well established, so obviously true, that they may claim general credence. Now the remaining position will be made sufficiently clear from the valves which are found in the cavities of the veins themselves, from the uses of these, and from experiments cognizable by the senses.

The celebrated Hieronymus Fabricius of Aquapendente, a most skilful anatomist, and venerable old man, or, as the learned Riolan will have it, Jacobus Silvius, first gave representations of the valves in the veins, which consist of raised or loose portions of the inner membranes of these vessels, of extreme delicacy, and a sigmoid or semilunar shape. They are situated at different distances from one another, and diversely in different individuals; they are connate at the sides of the veins; they are directed upwards towards the trunks of the veins; the two—for there are for the most part two together—regard each other, mutually touch, and are so ready to come into contact by their edges, that if anything attempts to pass from the trunks into the branches of the veins, or from the greater vessels into the less, they completely prevent it; they are farther so arranged, that the horns of those that succeed are opposite the middle of the convexity of those that precede, and so on alternately.

The discoverer of these valves did not rightly understand their use, nor have succeeding anatomists added anything to our knowledge: for their office is by no means explained when we are told that it is to hinder the blood, by its weight, from all flowing into inferior parts; for the edges of the valves in the jugular veins hang downwards, and are so contrived that they prevent the blood from rising upwards; the valves, in a word, do not invariably look upwards, but always toward the trunks of the veins, invariably towards the seat of the heart.   I, and indeed others, have sometimes found valves in the emulgent veins, and in those of the mesentery, the edges of which were directed towards the vena cava and vena portæ.   Let it be added that there are no valves in the arteries, and that dogs, oxen, etc., have invariably valves at the divisions of their crural veins, in the veins that meet towards the top of the os sacrum, and in those branches which come from the haunches, in which no such effect of gravity from the erect position was to be apprehended. Neither are there valves in the jugular veins for the purpose of guarding against apoplexy, as some have said; because in sleep the head is more apt to be influenced by the contents of the carotid arteries.   Neither are the valves present, in order that the blood may be retained in the divarications or smaller trunks and minuter branches, and not be suffered to flow entirely into the more open and capacious channels; for they occur where there are no divarications; although it must be owned that they are most frequent at the points where branches join.   Neither do they exist for the purpose of rendering the current of blood more slow from the centre of the body; for it seems likely that the blood would be disposed to flow with sufficient slowness of its own accord, as it would have to pass from larger into continually smaller vessels, being separated from the mass and fountain head, and attaining from warmer into colder places.

But the valves are solely made and instituted lest the blood should pass from the greater into the lesser veins, and either rupture them or cause them to become varicose; lest, instead of advancing from the extreme to the central parts of the body, the blood should rather proceed along the veins from the centre to the extremities; but the delicate valves, while they readily open in the right direction, entirely prevent all such contrary motion, being so situated and arranged, that if anything escapes, or is less perfectly obstructed by the cornua of the one above, the fluid passing, as it were, by the chinks between the cornua, it is immediately received on the convexity of the one beneath, which is placed transversely with reference to the former, and so is effectually hindered from getting any farther.

And this I have frequently experienced in my dissections of the veins: if I attempted to pass a probe from the trunk of the veins into one of the smaller branches, whatever care I took I found it impossible to introduce it far any way, by reason of the valves; whilst, on the contrary, it was most easy to push it along in the opposite direction, from without inwards, or from the branches towards the trunks and roots. In many places two valves are so placed and fitted, that when raised they come exactly together in the middle of the vein, and are there united by the contact of their margins; and so accurate is the adaptation, that neither by the eye nor by any other means of examination, can the slightest chink along the line of contact be perceived. But if the probe be now introduced from the extreme towards the more central parts, the valves, like the floodgates of a river, give way, and are most readily pushed aside. The effect of this arrangement plainly is to prevent all motion of the blood from the heart and vena cava, whether it be upwards towards the head, or downwards towards the feet, or to either side towards the arms, not a drop can pass; all motion of the blood, beginning in the larger and tending towards the smaller veins, is opposed and resisted by them; whilst the motion that proceeds from the lesser to end in the larger branches is favoured, or, at all events, a free and open passage is left for it.

But that this truth may be made the more apparent, let an arm be tied up above the elbow as if for phlebotomy (A, A, fig. 1). At intervals in the course of the veins, especially in labouring people and those whose veins are large, certain knots or elevations (B, C, D, E, F) will be perceived, and this not only at the places where a branch is received (E, F), but also where none enters (C, D): these knots or risings are all formed by valves, which thus show themselves externally. And now if you press the blood from the space above one of the valves, from H to O, (fig. 2,) and keep the point of a finger upon the vein inferiorly, you will see no influx of blood from above; the portion of the vein between the point of the finger and the valve O will be obliterated; yet will the vessel continue sufficiently distended above the valve (O, G). The blood being thus pressed out, and the vein emptied, if you now apply a finger of the other hand upon the distended part of the vein above the valve O, (fig. 3,) and press downwards, you will find that you cannot force the blood through or beyond the valve; but the greater effort you use, you will only see the portion of vein that is between the finger and the valve become more distended, that portion of the vein which is below the valve remaining all the while empty (H, O, fig. 3).

It would therefore appear that the function of the valves in the veins is the same as that of the three sigmoid valves which we find at the commencement of the aorta and pulmonary artery, viz., to prevent all reflux of the blood that is passing over them.

[NOTE.—Woodcuts of the veins of the arm to which these letters and figures refer appear here in the original.—C. N. B. C.]

Farther, the arm being bound as before, and the veins looking full and distended, if you press at one part in the course of a vein with the point of a finger (L, fig. 4), and then with another finger streak the blood upwards beyond the next valve (N), you will perceive that this portion of the vein continues empty (L N), and that the blood cannot retrograde, precisely as we have already seen the case to be

in fig. 2; but the finger first applied (H, fig. 2, L, fig. 4), being removed, immediately the vein is filled from below, and the arm
becomes as it appears at D C, fig. 1. That the blood in the veins
therefore proceeds from inferior or more remote parts, and towards
the heart, moving in these vessels in this and not in the contrary
direction, appears most obviously. And although in some places
the valves, by not acting with such perfect accuracy, or where there
is but a single valve, do not seem totally to prevent the passage of the
blood from the centre, still the greater number of them plainly do
so; and then, where things appear contrived more negligently,
this is compensated either by the more frequent occurrence or
more perfect action of the succeeding valves, or in some other
way: the veins in short, as they are the free and open conduits
of the blood returning *to* the heart, so are they effectually prevented from serving as its channels of distribution *from* the
heart.

But this other circumstance has to be noted: The arm being
bound, and the veins made turgid, and the valves prominent, as
before, apply the thumb or finger over a vein in the situation of one
of the valves in such a way as to compress it, and prevent any blood
from passing upwards from the hand; then, with a finger of the
other hand, streak the blood in the vein upwards till it has passed
the next valve above (N, fig. 4), the vessel now remains empty;
but the finger at L being removed for an instant, the vein is immediately filled from below; apply the finger again, and having
in the same manner streaked the blood upwards, again remove
the finger below, and again the vessel becomes distended as
before; and this repeat, say a thousand times, in a short space of
time. And now compute the quantity of blood which you have
thus pressed up beyond the valve, and then multiplying the assumed quantity by one thousand, you will find that so much blood
has passed through a certain portion of the vessel; and I do now
believe that you will find yourself convinced of the circulation of the
blood, and of its rapid motion. But if in this experiment you say
that a violence is done to nature, I do not doubt but that, if you
proceed in the same way, only taking as great a length of vein as

possible, and merely remark with what rapidity the blood flows up-wards, and fills the vessel from below, you will come to the same conclusion.

CHAPTER XIV

CONCLUSION OF THE DEMONSTRATION OF THE CIRCULATION

And now I may be allowed to give in brief my view of the circula-tion of the blood, and to propose it for general adoption.

Since all things, both argument and ocular demonstration, show that the blood passes through the lungs, and heart by the force of the ventricles, and is sent for distribution to all parts of the body, where it makes its way into the veins and porosities of the flesh, and then flows by the veins from the circumference on every side to the centre, from the lesser to the greater veins, and is by them finally dis-charged into the vena cava and right auricle of the heart, and this in such a quantity or in such a flux and reflux thither by the arteries, hither by the veins, as cannot possibly be supplied by the ingesta, and is much greater than can be required for mere purposes of nutrition; it is absolutely necessary to conclude that the blood in the animal body is impelled in a circle, and is in a state of ceaseless motion; that this is the act or function which the heart performs by means of its pulse; and that it is the sole and only end of the motion and contraction of the heart.

CHAPTER XV

THE CIRCULATION OF THE BLOOD IS FURTHER CONFIRMED BY PROBABLE REASONS

It will not be foreign to the subject if I here show further, from certain familiar reasonings, that the circulation is matter both of convenience and necessity. In the first place, since death is a corruption which takes place through deficiency of heat,* and since all living things are warm, all dying things cold, there must be a particular seat and fountain, a kind of home and hearth, where the cherisher of nature, the original of the native fire, is stored and preserved; from which heat and life are dispensed to all parts as from a fountain head; from which sustenance may be derived; and upon which concoction and nutrition, and all vegetative energy may depend. Now, that the heart is this place, that the heart is the principle of life, and that all passes in the manner just mentioned, I trust no one will deny.

The blood, therefore, required to have motion, and indeed such a motion that it should return again to the heart; for sent to the external parts of the body far from its fountain, as Aristotle says, and without motion, it would become congealed. For we see motion generating and keeping up heat and spirits under all circumstances, and rest allowing them to escape and be dissipated. The blood, therefore, becoming thick or congealed by the cold of the extreme and outward parts, and robbed of its spirits, just as it is in the dead, it was imperative that from its fount and origin, it should again receive heat and spirits, and all else requisite to its preservation—that, by returning, it should be renovated and restored.

We frequently see how the extremities are chilled by the external cold, how the nose and cheeks and hands look blue, and how the blood, stagnating in them as in the pendent or lower parts of a corpse, becomes of a dusky hue; the limbs at the same time getting torpid, so that they can scarcely be moved, and seem almost to have lost their vitality. Now they can by no means be so effectually, and especially so speedily restored to heat and colour and life, as by a new efflux and contact of heat from its source. But how can parts attract in which the heat and life are almost extinct ? Or how should they whose passages are filled with condensed and frigid blood, admit fresh aliment—renovated blood—unless they had first got rid of their old contents ? Unless the heart were truly that fountain where life and heat are restored to the refrigerated fluid, and whence new blood, warm, imbued with spirits, being sent out

* Aristoteles De Respiratione, lib. ii et iii: De Part. Animal. et alibi.

by the arteries, that which has become cooled and effete is forced on, and all the particles recover their heat which was failing, and their vital stimulus wellnigh exhausted.

Hence it is that if the heart be unaffected, life and health may be restored to almost all the other parts of the body; but if the heart be chilled, or smitten with any serious disease, it seems matter of necessity that the whole animal fabric should suffer and fall into decay.   When the source is corrupted, there is nothing, as Aristotle says,* which can be of service either to it or aught that depends on it.   And hence, by the way, it may perchance be why grief, and love, and envy, and anxiety, and all affections of the mind of a similar kind are accompanied with emaciation and decay, or with disordered fluids and crudity, which engender all manner of diseases and consume the body of man.   For every affection of the mind that is attended with either pain or pleasure, hope or fear, is the cause of an agitation whose influence extends to the heart, and there induces change from the natural constitution, in the temperature, the pulse and the rest, which impairing all nutrition in its source and abating the powers at large, it is no wonder that various forms of incurable disease in the extremities and in the trunk are the consequence, inasmuch as in such circumstances the whole body labours under the effects of vitiated nutrition and a want of native heat.

Moreover, when we see that all animals live through food digested in their interior, it is imperative that the digestion and distribution be perfect, and, as a consequence, that there be a place and receptacle where the aliment is perfected and whence it is distributed to the several members.   Now this place is the heart, for it is the only organ in the body which contains blood for the general use; all the others receive it merely for their peculiar or private advantage, just as the heart also has a supply for its own especial behoof in its coronary veins and arteries.   But it is of the store which the heart contains in its auricles and ventricles that I here speak.   Then the heart is the only organ which is so situated and constituted that it can distribute the blood in due proportion to the several parts of the body, the quantity sent to each being according to the dimensions

* De Part. Animal. iii.

of the artery which supplies it, the heart serving as a magazine or fountain ready to meet its demands.

Further, a certain impulse or force, as well as an impeller or forcer, such as the heart, was required to effect this distribution and motion of the blood; both because the blood is disposed from slight causes, such as cold, alarm, horror, and the like, to collect in its source, to concentrate like parts to a whole, or the drops of water spilt upon a table to the mass of liquid; and because it is forced from the capillary veins into the smaller ramifications, and from these into the larger trunks by the motion of the extremities and the compression of the muscles generally. The blood is thus more disposed to move from the circumference to the centre than in the opposite direction, even were there no valves to oppose its motion; wherefore, that it may leave its source and enter more confined and colder channels, and flow against the direction to which it spontaneously inclines, the blood requires both force and impelling power. Now such is the heart and the heart alone, and that in the way and manner already explained.

CHAPTER XVI

The Circulation of the Blood is Further Proved from Certain Consequences

There are still certain problems, which, taken as consequences of this truth assumed as proven, are not without their use in exciting belief, as it were, *a posteriore;* and which, although they may seem to be involved in much doubt and obscurity, nevertheless readily admit of having reasons and causes assigned for them. Of such a nature are those that present themselves in connexion with contagions, poisoned wounds, the bites of serpents and rabid animals, lues venerea and the like. We sometimes see the whole system contaminated, though the part first infected remains sound; the lues venerea has occasionally made its attack with pains in the shoulders and head, and other symptoms, the genital organs being all the while unaffected; and then we know that the wound made by a rabid dog having healed, fever and a train of disastrous symptoms may nevertheless supervene.   Whence it appears that the contagion impressed upon or deposited in a particular part, is by-and-by carried by the returning current of blood to the heart, and by that organ is sent to contaminate the whole body.

In tertian fever, the morbific cause seeking the heart in the first instance, and hanging about the heart and lungs, renders the patient short-winded, disposed to sighing, and indisposed to exertion, because the vital principle is oppressed and the blood forced into the lungs and rendered thick.   It does not pass through them, (as I have myself seen in opening the bodies of those who had died in the beginning of the attack,) when the pulse is always frequent, small, and occasionally irregular;   but the heat increasing, the matter becoming attenuated, the passages forced, and the transit made, the whole body begins to rise in temperature, and the pulse becomes fuller and stronger.   The febrile paroxysm is fully formed, whilst the preternatural heat kindled in the heart is thence diffused by the arteries through the whole body along with the morbific matter, which is in this way overcome and dissolved by nature.

When we perceive, further, that medicines applied externally exert their influence on the body just as if they had been taken internally, the truth we are contending for is confirmed.   Colocynth and aloes in this way move the belly, cantharides excites the urine, garlic applied to the soles of the feet assists expectoration, cordials strengthen, and an infinite number of examples of the same kind might be cited.   Perhaps it will not, therefore, be found unreasonable, if we say that the veins, by means of their orifices, absorb some of the things that are applied externally and carry this inwards with the blood, not otherwise, it may be, than those of the mesentery imbibe the chyle from the intestines and carry it mixed with the blood to the liver.   For the blood entering the mesentery by the cœliac artery, and the superior and inferior mesenterics, proceeds to the intestines, from which, along with the chyle that has been attracted into the veins, it returns by their numerous ramifications into the

vena portæ of the liver, and from this into the vena cava, and this in
such wise that the blood in these veins has the same colour and consistency as in other veins, in opposition to what many believe to be
the fact.   Nor indeed can we imagine two contrary motions in any
capillary system—the chyle upwards, the blood downwards.   This
could scarcely take place, and must be held as altogether improbable.   But is not the thing rather arranged as it is by the con-
summate providence of nature?   For were the chyle mingled with
the blood, the crude with the digested, in equal proportions, the
result would not be concoction, transmutation, and sanguification,
but rather, and because they are severally active and passive, a
mixture or combination, or medium compound of the two, precisely
as happens when wine is mixed with water and syrup.   But when
a very minute quantity of chyle is mingled with a very large quantity
of circulating blood, a quantity of chyle that bears no kind of proportion to the mass of blood, the effect is the same, as Aristotle says,
as when a drop of water is added to a cask of wine, or the contrary;
the mass does not then present itself as a mixture, but is still sensibly either wine or water.

So in the mesenteric veins of an animal we do not find either chyme
or chyle and blood, blended together or distinct, but only blood, the
same in colour, consistency, and other sensible properties, as it appears in the veins generally.   Still as there is a certain though small
and inappreciable portion of chyle or incompletely digested matter
mingled with the blood, nature has interposed the liver, in whose
meandering channels it suffers delay and undergoes additional
change, lest arriving prematurely and crude at the heart, it should
oppress the vital principle.   Hence in the embryo, there is almost
no use for the liver, but the umbilical vein passes directly through, a
foramen or an anastomosis existing from the vena portæ.   The
blood returns from the intestines of the fœtus, not through the liver,
but into the umbilical vein mentioned, and flows at once into
the heart, mingled with the natural blood which is returning from
the placenta; whence also it is that in the development of the fœtus
the liver is one of the organs that is last formed.   I have observed
all the members perfectly marked out in the human fœtus, even the

genital organs, whilst there was yet scarcely any trace of the liver. And indeed at the period when all the parts, like the heart itself in the beginning, are still white, and except in the veins there is no appearance of redness, you shall see nothing in the seat of the liver but a shapeless collection, as it were, of extravasated blood, which you might take for the effects of a contusion or ruptured vein.

' But in the incubated egg there are, as it were, two umbilical vessels, one from the albumen passing entire through the liver, and going straight to the heart; another from the yelk, ending in the vena portæ; for it appears that the chick, in the first instance, is entirely formed and nourished by the white; but by the yelk after it has come to perfection and is excluded from the shell; for this part may still be found in the abdomen of the chick many days after its exclusion, and is a substitute for the milk to other animals.

But these matters will be better spoken of in my observations on the formation of the fœtus, where many propositions, the following among the number, will be discussed; Wherefore is this part formed or perfected first, that last, and of the several members, what part is the cause of another? And there are many points having special reference to the heart, such as wherefore does it first acquire consistency, and appear to possess life, motion, sense, before any other part of the body is perfected, as Aristotle says in his third book, "De partibus Animalium"? And so also of the blood, wherefore does it precede all the rest? And in what way does it possess the vital and animal principle, and show a tendency to motion, and to be impelled hither and thither, the end for which the heart appears to be made? In the same way, in considering the pulse, why should one kind of pulse indicate death, another recovery? And so of all the other kinds of pulse, what may be the cause and indication of each? Likewise we must consider the reason of crises and natural critical discharges; of nutrition, and especially the distribution of the nutriment; and of defluxions of every description. Finally, reflecting on every part of medicine, physiology, pathology, semeiotics and therapeutics, when I see how many questions can be answered, how many doubts resolved, how much obscurity illustrated by the truth we have declared, the light we have made to shine, I see a field of such vast extent in which I might proceed so far, and expatiate so widely, that this my tractate would not only swell out into a volume, which was beyond my purpose, but my whole life, perchance, would not suffice for its completion.

In this place, therefore, and that indeed in a single chapter, I shall only endeavour to refer the various particulars that present themselves in the dissection of the heart and arteries to their several uses and causes; for so I shall meet with many things which receive light from the truth I have been contending for, and which, in their turn, render it more obvious. And indeed I would have it confirmed and illustrated by anatomical arguments above all others.

There is but a single point which indeed would be more correctly placed among our observations on the use of the spleen, but which it will not be altogether impertinent to notice in this place incidentally. From the splenic branch which passes into the pancreas, and from the upper part, arise the posterior coronary, gastric, and gastroepiploic veins, all of which are distributed upon the stomach in numerous branches and twigs, just as the mesenteric vessels are upon the intestines. In a similar way, from the inferior part of the same splenic branch, and along the back of the colon and rectum proceed the hemorrhoidal veins. The blood returning by these veins, and bringing the cruder juices along with it, on the one hand from the stomach, where they are thin, watery, and not yet perfectly chylified; on the other thick and more earthy, as derived from the fæces, but all poured into this splenic branch, are duly tempered by the admixture of contraries; and nature mingling together these two kinds of juices, difficult of coction by reason of most opposite defects, and then diluting them with a large quantity of warm blood, (for we see that the quantity returned from the spleen must be very large when we contemplate the size of its arteries,) they are brought to the porta of the liver in a state of higher preparation. The defects of either extreme are supplied and compensated by this arrangement of the veins.

CHAPTER XVII

The Motion and Circulation of the Blood are Confirmed from the Particulars Apparent in the Structure of the Heart, and from Those Things which Dissection Unfolds

I do not find the heart as a distinct and separate part in all animals; some, indeed, such as the zoöphytes, have no heart; this is because these animals are coldest, of no great bulk, of soft texture, or of a certain uniform sameness or simplicity of structure; among the number I may instance grubs and earth-worms, and those that are engendered of putrefaction and do not preserve their species. These have no heart, as not requiring any impeller of nourishment into the extreme parts; for they have bodies which are connate and homogeneous and without limbs; so that by the contraction and relaxation of the whole body they assume and expel, move and remove, the aliment. Oysters, mussels, sponges, and the whole genus of zoöphytes or plant-animals have no heart, for the whole body is used as a heart, or the whole animal is a heart. In a great number of animals,—almost the whole tribe of insects—we cannot see distinctly by reason of the smallness of the body; still in bees, flies, hornets, and the like we can perceive something pulsating with the help of a magnifying-glass; in pediculi, also, the same thing may be seen, and as the body is transparent, the passage of the food through the intestines, like a black spot or stain, may be perceived by the aid of the same magnifying-glass.

But in some of the pale-blooded and colder animals, as in snails, whelks, shrimps, and shell-fish, there is a part which pulsates,— a kind of vesicle or auricle without a heart,—slowly, indeed, and not to be perceived except in the warmer season of the year. In these creatures this part is so contrived that it shall pulsate, as there is here a necessity for some impulse to distribute the nutritive fluid, by reason of the variety of organic parts, or of the density of the substance; but the pulsations occur unfrequently, and sometimes in consequence of the cold not at all, an arrangement the best adapted to them as being of a doubtful nature, so that sometimes they appear to live, sometimes to die; sometimes they show the vitality of an animal, sometimes of a vegetable. This seems also to be the case with the insects which conceal themselves in winter, and lie, as it were, defunct, or merely manifesting a kind of vegetative existence. But whether the same thing happens in the case of certain animals that have red blood, such as frogs, tortoises, serpents, swallows, may be very properly doubted.

In all the larger and warmer animals which have red blood, there was need of an impeller of the nutritive fluid, and that, perchance, possessing a considerable amount of power. In fishes, serpents, lizards, tortoises, frogs, and others of the same kind there is a heart present, furnished with both an auricle and a ventricle, whence it is perfectly true, as Aristotle has observed,* that no sanguineous animal is without a heart, by the impelling power of which the nutritive fluid is forced, both with greater vigour and rapidity, to a greater distance; and not merely agitated by an auricle, as it is in lower forms. And then in regard to animals that are yet larger, warmer, and more perfect, as they abound in blood, which is always hotter and more spirituous, and which possess bodies of greater size and consistency, these require a larger, stronger, and more fleshy heart, in order that the nutritive fluid may be propelled with yet greater force and celerity. And further, inasmuch as the more perfect animals require a still more perfect nutrition, and a larger supply of native heat, in order that the aliment may be thoroughly concocted and acquire the last degree of perfection, they required both lungs and a second ventricle, which should force the nutritive fluid through them.

Every animal that has lungs has, therefore, two ventricles to its heart—one right, the other left; and wherever there is a right, there also is there a left ventricle; but the contrary of this does not hold good: where there is a left there is not always a right ventricle. The left ventricle I call that which is distinct in office, not in place from the other, that one, namely, which distributes the blood to the

* De Part. Animal., lib. iii.

body at large, not to the lungs only.   Hence the left ventricle seems to form the principal part of the heart; situated in the middle, more strongly marked, and constructed with greater care, the heart seems formed for the sake of the left ventricle, and the right but to minister to it.   The right neither reaches to the apex of the heart nor is it nearly of such strength, being three times thinner in its walls, and in some sort jointed on to the left (as Aristotle says), though, indeed, it is of greater capacity, inasmuch as it has not only to supply material to the left ventricle, but likewise to furnish aliment to the lungs.

It is to be observed, however, that all this is otherwise in the embryo, where there is not such a difference between the two ventricles.   There, as in a double nut, they are nearly equal in all respects, the apex of the right reaching to the apex of the left, so that the heart presents itself as a sort of double-pointed cone. And this is so, because in the fœtus, as already said, whilst the blood is not passing through the lungs from the right to the left cavities of the heart, it flows by the foramen ovale and ductus arteriosus directly from the vena cava into the aorta, whence it is distributed to the whole body.   Both ventricles have, therefore, the same office to perform, whence their equality of constitution.   It is only when the lungs come to be used and it is requisite that the passages indicated should be blocked up that the difference in point of strength and other things between the two ventricles begins to be apparent.   In the altered circumstances the right has only to drive the blood through the lungs, whilst the left has to propel it through the whole body.

There are, moreover, within the heart numerous braces, in the form of fleshy columns and fibrous bands, which Aristotle, in his third book on "Respiration," and the "Parts of Animals," entitles nerves.   These are variously extended, and are either distinct or contained in grooves in the walls and partition, where they occasion numerous pits or depressions.   They constitute a kind of small muscles, which are superadded and supplementary to the heart, assisting it to execute a more powerful and perfect contraction, and so proving subservient to the complete expulsion of the blood.

They are, in some sort, like the elaborate and artful arrangement of ropes in a ship, bracing the heart on every side as it contracts, and so enabling it more effectually and forcibly to expel the charge of blood from its ventricles. This much is plain, at all events, that in some animals they are less strongly marked than in others; and, in all that have them, they are more numerous and stronger in the left than in the right ventricle; and while some have them present in the left, yet they are absent in the right ventricle. In man they are more numerous in the left than in the right ventricle, more abundant in the ventricles than in the auricles; and occasionally there appear to be none present in the auricles. They are numerous in the large, more muscular and hardier bodies of countrymen, but fewer in more slender frames and in females.

In those animals in which the ventricles of the heart are smooth within and entirely without fibres of muscular bands, or anything like hollow pits, as in almost all the smaller birds, the partridge and the common fowl, serpents, frogs, tortoises, and most fishes, there are no chordæ tendineæ, nor bundles of fibres, neither are there any tricuspid valves in the ventricles.

Some animals have the right ventricle smooth internally, but the left provided with fibrous bands, such as the goose, swan, and larger birds; and the reason is the same here as elsewhere. As the lungs are spongy and loose and soft, no great amount of force is required to force the blood through them; therefore the right ventricle is either without the bundles in question, or they are fewer and weaker, and not so fleshy or like muscles. Those of the left ventricle, however, are both stronger and more numerous, more fleshy and muscular, because the left ventricle requires to be stronger, inasmuch as the blood which it propels has to be driven through the whole body. And this, too, is the reason why the left ventricle occupies the middle of the heart, and has parietes three times thicker and stronger than those of the right. Hence all animals—and among men it is similar—that are endowed with particularly strong frames, and with large and fleshy limbs at a great distance from the heart, have this central organ of greater thickness, strength, and muscularity. This is manifest and necessary. Those, on the con-

trary, that are of softer and more slender make have the heart more
flaccid, softer, and internally either less or not at all fibrous.
Consider, farther, the use of the several valves, which are all so
arranged that the blood, once received into the ventricles of the
heart, shall never regurgitate; once forced into the pulmonary
artery and aorta, shall not flow back upon the ventricles.   When
the valves are raised and brought together, they form a three-cornered
line, such as is left by the bite of a leech; and the more they are
forced, the more firmly do they oppose the passage of the blood.
The tricuspid valves are placed, like gate-keepers, at the entrance
into the ventricles from the venæ cavæ and pulmonary veins, lest
the blood when most forcibly impelled should flow back.   It is for
this reason that they are not found in all animals, nor do they appear
to have been constructed with equal care in all animals in which
they are found.   In some they are more accurately fitted, in others
more remissly or carelessly contrived, and always with a view to their
being closed under a greater or a slighter force of the ventricle.
In the left ventricle, therefore, in order that the occlusion may be
the more perfect against the greater impulse, there are only two
valves, like a mitre, and produced into an elongated cone, so that
they come together and touch to their middle; a circumstance which
perhaps led Aristotle into the error of supposing this ventricle to
be double, the division taking place transversely.   For the same
reason, and that the blood may not regurgitate upon the pulmonary
veins, and thus the force of the ventricle in propelling the blood
through the system at large come to be neutralized, it is that these
mitral valves excel those of the right ventricle in size and strength
and exactness of closing.   Hence it is essential that there can be
no heart without a ventricle, since this must be the source and store-
house of the blood.   The same law does not hold good in reference
to the brain.   For almost no genus of birds has a ventricle in the
brain, as is obvious in the goose and swan, the brains of which
nearly equal that of a rabbit in size; now rabbits have ventricles in
the brain, whilst the goose has none.   In like manner, wherever the
heart has a single ventricle, there is an auricle appended, flaccid,
membranous, hollow, filled with blood; and where there are two

ventricles, there are likewise two auricles. On the other hand, some animals have an auricle without any ventricle; or, at all events, they have a sac analogous to an auricle; or the vein itself, dilated at a particular part, performs pulsations, as is seen in hornets, bees, and other insects, which certain experiments of my own enable me to demonstrate, have not only a pulse, but a respiration in that part which is called the tail, whence it is that this part is elongated and contracted now more rarely, now more frequently, as the creature appears to be blown and to require a large quantity of air. But of these things, more in our "Treatise on Respiration."

It is in like manner evident that the auricles pulsate, contract, as I have said before, and throw the blood into the ventricles; so that wherever there is a ventricle, an auricle is necessary, not merely that it may serve, according to the general belief, as a source and magazine for the blood: for what were the use of its pulsations had it only to contain?

The auricles are prime movers of the blood, especially the right auricle, which, as already said, is "the first to live, the last to die"; whence they are subservient to sending the blood into the ventricles, which, contracting continuously, more readily and forcibly expel the blood already in motion; just as the ball-player can strike the ball more forcibly and further if he takes it on the rebound than if he simply threw it. Moreover, and contrary to the general opinion, neither the heart nor anything else can dilate or distend itself so as to draw anything into its cavity during the diastole, unless, like a sponge, it has been first compressed and is returning to its primary condition. But in animals all local motion proceeds from, and has its origin in, the contraction of some part; consequently it is by the contraction of the auricles that the blood is thrown into the ventricles, as I have already shown, and from there, by the contraction of the ventricles, it is propelled and distributed. Concerning local motions, it is true that the immediate moving organ in every motion of an animal primarily endowed with a motive spirit (as Aristotle has it*) is contractile; in which way the word νεῦρον is derived from νεύω, nuto, contraho; and if I am permitted to

* In the book de Spiritu, and elsewhere.

proceed in my purpose of making a particular demonstration of the organs of motion in animals from observations in my possession, I trust I shall be able to make sufficiently plain how Aristotle was acquainted with the muscles, and advisedly referred all motion in animals to the nerves, or to the contractile element, and, therefore, called those little bands in the heart nerves.

But that we may proceed with the subject which we have in hand, viz., the use of the auricles in filling the ventricles, we should expect that the more dense and compact the heart, the thicker its parietes, the stronger and more muscular must be the auricle to force and fill it, and vice versâ. Now this is actually so: in some the auricle presents itself as a sanguinolent vesicle, as a thin membrane containing blood, as in fishes, in which the sac that stands in lieu of the auricles is of such delicacy and ample capacity that it seems to be suspended or to float above the heart. In those fishes in which the sac is somewhat more fleshy, as in the carp, barbel, tench, and others, it bears a wonderful and strong resemblance to the lungs.

In some men of sturdier frame and stouter make the right auricle is so strong, and so curiously constructed on its inner surface of bands and variously interlacing fibres, that it seems to equal in strength the ventricle of the heart in other subjects; and I must say that I am astonished to find such diversity in this particular in different individuals. It is to be observed, however, that in the fœtus the auricles are out of all proportion large, which is because they are present before the heart makes its appearance or suffices for its office even when it has appeared, and they, therefore, have, as it were, the duty of the whole heart committed to them, as has already been demonstrated. But what I have observed in the formation of the fœtus, as before remarked (and Aristotle had already confirmed all in studying the incubated egg), throws the greatest light and likelihood upon the point. Whilst the fœtus is yet in the form of a soft worm, or, as is commonly said, in the milk, there is a mere bloody point or pulsating vesicle, a portion apparently of the umbilical vein, dilated at its commencement or base. Afterwards, when the outline of the fœtus is distinctly indicated and it begins to have greater bodily consistence, the vesicle in question becomes more fleshy and stronger, changes its position, and passes into the auricles, above which the body of the heart begins to sprout, though as yet it apparently performs no office. When the fœtus is farther advanced, when the bones can be distinguished from the fleshy parts and movements take place, then it also has a heart which pulsates, and, as I have said, throws blood by either ventricle from the vena cava into the arteries.

Thus nature, ever perfect and divine, doing nothing in vain, has neither given a heart where it was not required, nor produced it before its office had become necessary; but by the same stages in the development of every animal, passing through the forms of all, as I may say (ovum, worm, fœtus), it acquires perfection in each. These points will be found elsewhere confirmed by numerous observations on the formation of the fœtus.

Finally, it is not without good grounds that Hippocrates, in his book, "De Corde," entitles it a muscle; its action is the same; so is its function, viz., to contract and move something else—in this case, the charge of the blood.

Farther, we can infer the action and use of the heart from the arrangement of its fibres and its general structures, as in muscles generally. All anatomists admit with Galen that the body of the heart is made up of various courses of fibres running straight, obliquely, and transversely, with reference to one another; but in a heart which has been boiled, the arrangement of the fibres is seen to be different. All the fibres in the parietes and septum are circular, as in the sphincters; those, again, which are in the columns extend lengthwise, and are oblique longitudinally; and so it comes to pass that when all the fibres contract simultaneously, the apex of the cone is pulled towards its base by the columns, the walls are drawn circularly together into a globe—the whole heart, in short, is contracted and the ventricles narrowed. It is, therefore, impossible not to perceive that, as the action of the organ is so plainly contraction, its function is to propel the blood into the arteries.

Nor are we the less to agree with Aristotle in regard to the importance of the heart, or to question if it receives sense and motion from the brain, blood from the liver, or whether it be the origin of the veins and of the blood, and such like. They who affirm these propositions overlook, or do not rightly understand, the principal argument, to the effect that the heart is the first part which exists, and that it contains within itself blood, life, sensation, and motion, before either the brain or the liver were created or had appeared distinctly, or, at all events, before they could perform any function. The heart, ready furnished with its proper organs of motion, like a kind of internal creature, existed before the body. The first to be formed, nature willed that it should afterwards fashion, nourish, preserve, complete the entire animal, as its work and dwelling-place: and as the prince in a kingdom, in whose hands lie the chief and highest authority, rules over all, the heart is the source and foundation from which all power is derived, on which all power depends in the animal body.

Many things having reference to the arteries farther illustrate and confirm this truth. Why does not the pulmonary vein pulsate, seeing that it is numbered among the arteries? Or wherefore is there a pulse in the pulmonary artery? Because the pulse of the arteries is derived from the impulse of the blood. Why does an artery differ so much from a vein in the thickness and strength of its coats? Because it sustains the shock of the impelling heart and streaming blood. Hence, as perfect nature does nothing in vain, and suffices under all circumstances, we find that the nearer the arteries are to the heart, the more do they differ from the veins in structure; here they are both stronger and more ligamentous, whilst in extreme parts of the body, such as the feet and hands, the brain, the mesentery, and the testicles, the two orders of vessels are so much alike that it is impossible to distinguish between them with the eye. Now this is for the following very sufficient reasons: the more remote the vessels are from the heart, with so much the less force are they distended by the stroke of the heart, which is broken by the great distance at which it is given. Add to this that the impulse of the heart exerted upon the mass of blood, which must needs fill the trunks and branches of the arteries, is diverted, divided, as it were, and diminished at every subdivision, so that the ultimate capillary

divisions of the arteries look like veins, and this not merely in constitution, but in function.　They have either no perceptible pulse,
or they rarely exhibit one, and never except where the heart beats
more violently than usual, or at a part where the minute vessel is
more dilated or open then elsewhere.　It, therefore, happens that at
times we are aware of a pulse in the teeth, in inflammatory tumours,
and in the fingers; at another time we feel nothing of the sort.　By
this single symptom I have ascertained for certain that young persons whose pulses are naturally rapid were labouring under fever;
and in like manner, on compressing the fingers in youthful and
delicate subjects during a febrile paroxysm, I have readily perceived
the pulse there.　On the other hand, when the heart pulsates more
languidly, it is often impossible to feel the pulse not merely in the
fingers, but the wrist, and even at the temple, as in persons afflicted
with lipothymiæ asphyxia, or hysterical symptoms, and in the debilitated and moribund.

Here surgeons are to be advised that, when the blood escapes
with force in the amputation of limbs, in the removal of tumours, and
in wounds, it constantly comes from an artery; not always indeed
per saltum, because the smaller arteries do not pulsate, especially
if a tourniquet has been applied.

For the same reason the pulmonary artery not only has the structure of an artery, but it does not differ so widely from the veins in
the thickness of its walls as does the aorta.　The aorta sustains a
more powerful shock from the left than the pulmonary artery
does from the right ventricle, and the walls of this last vessel are
thinner and softer than those of the aorta in the same proportion as
the walls of the right ventricle of the heart are weaker and thinner
than those of the left ventricle.　In like manner the lungs are
softer and laxer in structure than the flesh and other constituents
of the body, and in a similar way the walls of the branches of the
pulmonary artery differ from those of the vessels derived from the
aorta.　And the same proportion in these particulars is universally
preserved.　The more muscular and powerful men are, the firmer
their flesh; the stronger, thicker, denser, and more fibrous their
hearts, the thicker, closer, and stronger are the auricles and arteries.
Again, in those animals the ventricles of whose hearts are smooth on

their inner surface, without villi or valves, and the walls of which are thin, as in fishes, serpents, birds, and very many genera of animals, the arteries differ little or nothing in the thickness of their coats from the veins.

Moreover, the reason why the lungs have such ample vessels, both arteries and veins (for the capacity of the pulmonary veins exceeds that of both the crural and jugular vessels), and why they contain so large a quantity of blood, as by experience and ocular inspection we know they do, admonished of the fact indeed by Aristotle, and not led into error by the appearances found in animals which have been bled to death, is, because the blood has its fountain, and storehouse, and the workshop of its last perfection, in the heart and lungs.   Why, in the same way, we find in the course of our anatomical dissections the pulmonary vein and left ventricle so full of blood, of the same black colour and clotted character as that with which the right ventricle and pulmonary artery are filled, is because the blood is incessantly passing from one side of the heart to the other through the lungs.   Wherefore, in fine, the pulmonary artery has the structure of an artery, and the pulmonary veins have the structure of veins.   In function and constitution and everything else the first is an artery, the others are veins, contrary to what is commonly believed; and the reason why the pulmonary artery has so large an orifice is because it transports much more blood than is requisite for the nutrition of the lungs.

All these appearances, and many others, to be noted in the course of dissection, if rightly weighed, seem clearly to illustrate and fully to confirm the truth contended for throughout these pages, and at the same time to oppose the vulgar opinion; for it would be very difficult to explain in any other way to what purpose all is constructed and arranged as we have seen it to be.

HARVEY'S WRITINGS WITH EDITIONS AND TRANSLATIONS *

Ollivier's Dictionnaire Historique de la Médecine, 1834–37, Exercitatio Anatomica de Motu Cordis et Sanguinis in Animalibus, Frankfort, 1628; Leyden, 1639. Exercitationes duae anatomicae de circulatione sanguinis ad Joh. Riolanum fil, Rotterdam, 1649.   Cum refutationibus Æ Parisani et Primerosii, Leyden, 1639; Padua, 1643; 1646; Lyons, 1647.

* See foot-note on page 113.

With Spigel, Amsterdam, 1645. With a preface by Sylvius, Rotterdam, 1648. Cum duplici indice . . . accessit diss. de corde doct. Jac. de Back (præf. Sylvii), Rotterdam, 1654, 1660, 1671; Geneva, 1685; Glasgow, 1751; Leyden, 1737. Translated into English, London, 1653.

Exercitationes de generatione Animalium, quibus accedunt quaedam de partu, de membranis ac humoribus uteri, et de conceptione, London, 1651; Amsterdam, 1651, 1662; Padua, 1666; The Hague, 1680. Translated into English, 1653.

Anatomical account concerning Thomas Parr, who died at the age of one hundred and fifty-two years and nine months, Philos. Trans., 1669.

Surgeon General's Library Index Catalogue.

De Motu Cordis et Sanguinis in Animalibus, anatomica exercitatio, cum refutationibus Æmylii Parisani et Jacobi Primirosii, 3 p. l., 267, 84 pp., 2 pl. SM. quarto, Lugd. Bat., J. Maire, 1639.

The same, Cui postrema hac editione accesserunt Johannis Walaei epistolae duae, quibus Harveii doctrina roboratur, 5 p.l., 227 pp., 24mo. Patavii apud S. Sardum, 1643.

The same, Ex recensione Joh Antonidæ van der Linden, fol, Amsterdami, 1645. In: Spigelius (Adrianus). Opera quæ extant, Omnia, fol Amsterdami, 1645, i, pp. xxxvii–lxiv.

The same, Accessit dissertatio de corde, Doct. Jacobi de Back, 14 p. l., 285 pp., 91, 16mo. Roterodami, A. Leers, 1654.

The same, 14 p. l., 285 pp., 10 l, 16mo., Roterodami, A. Leers, 1660.

The same, 10 p. l., 285 pp., 13 l, 16mo., Reterodami, A. Leers, 1671.

The same, Cui accedunt ejusdem auctoris exercitationes duae anatomicae de circulatione sanguinis ad Joannem Riolanum filium atque hisce præfationem addidit Bernardus Siegfried. Albinus, 6 p. l., 167 pp., 2 l, SM. quarto, Lugd. Bat., Apud J. Van Kerckhem, 1736.

The same, Cum refutationibus Æmylii Parisani . . . et Jacobi Primirosii . . . 1 p. l., 267 pp.; 84 pp. quarto, Lugd. Bat., J. Marie, 1739.

The same, Exercitationes de motu Cordis et Sanguinis quas notis pauculis instruendas curavit Thomas Hingston, xviii, 250 pp., 2 pl., octavo, Edinburgi, apud J. Carfrae et filium, 1824.

The same, Van de beweging van'l hert ende bloet. Uit het Latijn vertaalt door N. van Assendelft, ende nu tot nut en voordeel van alle chirurgijns en liefhebbers in't licht gebracht, 11 p. l., 97 pp., 1l, 24mo. t'Amsteldam, C. Last, 1650.

The same, La Circulation du sang; des Mouvements du coeur chez l'homme et chez les Annimaux; deux réponses à Riolan. Traduction française, avec une introduction historique et des notes par Charles Richet, iii, 287 pp., octavo, Paris, G. Masson, 1879.

The same, On the Motion of the Heart and Blood in Animals, Willis's translation, revised and edited by Alexander Bowie, xx, 147 pp., 12mo, London, G. Bell and Sons, 1889.

The same, An Anatomical Dissertation upon the Movement of the Heart and Blood in Animals, being a Statement of the Discovery of the Circulation of the Blood, x, 72 pp.; viii, 9–91 pp. SM. quarto, Canterbury,

G. Moreton, 1894. Privately reproduced in facsimile from the original edition printed at Frankfort on the Main in the year 1628, with a translation and Memoir.

Exercitationes de generatione animalium quibus accedunt quaedam de partu, de membranis ac humoribus uteri, et de conceptione. Ed. novissima a mendis repurgata, 13 p. l., 388 pp., 16mo, Amstelædami, Apud J. Ravesteynium, 1651.

The same, 13 p. l., 388 pp., 16mo. Amstelædami, Apud J. Ravesteynium,— 1662.

The same, Amstelædami, Apud J. Ravesteynium, 604 pp., 31, 24mo. Patavii, typ. hered. Pframbotte, 1666.

The same, Anatomical Exercitationes Concerning the Generation of Living Creatures, to which are added Particular Discourses of Births and of Conceptions, etc., 22 p. l., 566 pp., port., 12mo, London, J. Young, 1653.

Prælectiones Anatomiæ universalis. Edited with an autotype reproduction of the original by a committee of the Royal College of Physicians of London, viii, 98 pp., 196 Photolithog., pl. quarto, London, J. and A. Churchill, 1886.

British Museum Catalogue.

Notice of an unpublished MS of Harvey, 1850, Paget.

Exercitatio anatomica, etc. Preface by Sylvius, Accessit dissertatio de corde, J. de Back, 2 vols., Roterdami, 1648, 12mo.

Exercitationes de generatione animalium. Quibus accedunt, etc., London, 1651, 4to.

The same, Amsterdam, 1661, 12mo.

Editio Novissima a mendis repurgato (Edited by Sir G. Ent), MS. notes Amsterdam, 1662, 12mo.

Another edition, Hagae Comitis, 1680, 12mo.

Dictionary of National Biography.

Collected Edition of Harvey's Works, Edited by Dr. Lawrence, Published by College of Physicians (London) 1766.

Complete Translation of his works, published by Sydenham Society, London, 1847.

* List of Writings compiled from Ollivier's Dictionnaire Historique de la Méde cine, 1834–37, the Surgeon General's Library, Index Catalogue (Washington), the Dictionary of National Biography and the British Museum Catalogue.

Percussion of the Chest

Leopold Auenbrugger Edler von Auenbrugg
geb. zu Graz 1722 gest. zu Wien 1809

LEOPOLD AUENBRUGGER.
From Lithograph which appears in Dr. Clar Gratz's "Auenbrugger" Published
in 1867.

LEOPOLD AUENBRUGGER
1722–1809

Auenbrugger was born at Gratz, in Styria, Lower Austria, November 19, 1722. His father was an innkeeper of Gratz, but he provided a university education for his son in Vienna, the centre at that time of German literature and culture. At Vienna also his medical education was obtained, under a great authority at that time, Baron Van Swieten.

Van Swieten had been the pupil of Boerhaave at Leyden, and was called from Holland to the Austrian capital by the Empress Maria Theresa. He was the court physician, and by this support was enabled to found the great medical school of Vienna.

The efforts to educate Auenbrugger were not thrown away, for he was soon accepted among the literary and cultured society of Vienna. His first opportunity for medical observation was in the appointment as physician to the Spanish Military Hospital, the largest and finest in the Austrian capital at that time. This was 1751; Auenbrugger was twenty-nine years old. Ten years later he published in Latin in a small volume his epochal contribution on "Percussion of the Chest." He was led to publish this, he says, not on account of a "pruritus scribendi" nor of armchair theorizing, but as a result of seven years' observation and testing of the value of the method. The modesty of the observer may be gathered by reading the preface. Besides this epochal contribution, Auenbrugger wrote little, as the list of his writings shows. His opera, "The Chimney Sweep," is, of course, not upon this list. The cultivation of music was at that time one of the requirements of German culture, and living in the heart of this, it is not surprising that he should have ventured to contribute. He was well accepted at the Vienna Court, being an intimate friend of the Empress Maria Theresa, and was ennobled by Emperor Joseph II. This title, which corresponds to English knighthood, was selected by him in preference to a pension, as the former descended to his children, while the latter ceased with his death.

This title, "Edler Von Auenbrug," was conferred because of his popularity at court, and not on account of his discovery of percussion, as the new method was practically unrecognized by the clinicians of his time. His teacher, Van Swieten, ignored it. De Haen, like Van Swieten a disciple of Boerhaave at Leyden, and who succeeded Van Swieten as head of the medical teaching in Vienna, also ignores Auenbrugger's discovery. Van Swieten published his clinical observations in 16 volumes of the Aphorisms of his teacher, Boerhaave. De Haen published his "Ratio Medendi," 1757–1779, in 18 volumes. These writings are merely of historical interest to-day, while Auenbrugger's volume, consisting of not more than 1200 words in one volume of 95 pages, is a classic. What can be the explanation for the omission of so great a discovery from even a passing notice by these great arbiters of medical thought in Germany? Stoll succeeded De Haen at Vienna, and he appreciated the discovery. He speaks in his work of the great value of the method in detecting pleurisy, and especially in detecting empyæma, that operation may be performed. Eyerell, a pupil of Stoll, emphasizes the importance of the method. Stoll, however, on account of private difficulties never attained a position of authority equal to that of Van Swieten or De Haen.

From contemporary writings outside of Vienna there seems to have been an indifference or ignorance of the method. Hippocratic succussion was confused with percussion or the work was not mentioned. Dock* cites in support of this observation the following three references: Gottingen Gelehrten Auzeigen, the leading journal of the times, and R. A. Vogel's Fene Med. Bibliothek Gott., 1766, Bd. 6. In France Roziere (according to the same authority), of the medical faculty of Montpellier, translated the "Inventum Novum" and published it with a work of his own.

The "Inventum Novum" went through two editions. In 1775

---

* "Leopold Auenbrugger and the History of Percussion." Address by George Dock, M.D., Sept. 27, 1898.

the work again appeared, together with other medical writings. The discovery was, however, unappreciated until Corvisart, physician to Napoleon I, and leader of medical thought in France, the then center of scientific development, translated the "Inventum Novum" and yielded unstinted praise to its discoverer. Corvisart's translation together with observations of his own appeared in 1808. It is a volume of 440 pages. This was forty-seven years after Auenbrugger's unpretentious little volume of 95 pages appeared in Germany. From this time the pendulum swung the other way, and we have extravagant claims for percussion as set forth in the writings of Piorry, who, however, introduced mediate percussion and the pleximeter. Auenbrugger made all his observations by direct or immediate percussion.

The subject received scientific consideration by such authorities as Skoda, Flint and others, and percussion became an established method in accurate diagnosis.

Auenbrugger lived just long enough to see the beginning of a proper recognition of his discovery. He died on May 17, 1809, one year after Corvisart's translation was published.

LEOPOLDI AUENBRUGGER

MEDICINÆ DOCTORIS
IN CÆSAREO REGIO NOSOCOMIO NATIONUM
HISPANICO MEDICI ORDINARII.

INVENTUM NOVUM

EX

PERCUSSIONE THORACIS HUMANI

UT SIGNO

ABSTRUSOS INTERNI

PECTORIS MORBOS
DETEGENDI.

LABORE ET FAVORE.

VINDOBONÆ,

TYPIS JOANNIS THOMÆ TRATTNER, CÆS. REG.
MAJEST. AULÆ TYPOGRAPHI.

MDCCLXI.

1761

ON PERCUSSION OF THE CHEST:

BEING A TRANSLATION OF

AUENBRUGGER'S ORIGINAL TREATISE,

Entitled

"INVENTUM NOVUM EX PERCUSSIONE THORACIS
HUMANI, UT SIGNO, ABSTRUSOS INTERNI
PECTORIS MORBOS DETEGENDI"

Published in **1761**

TRANSLATED BY JOHN FORBES, M.D.

THE AUTHOR'S PREFACE

I here present the reader with a new sign which I have discovered for detecting diseases of the chest. This consists in the percussion of the human thorax, whereby, according to the character of the particular sounds thence elicited, an opinion is formed of the internal state of that cavity. In making public my discoveries respecting this matter I have been actuated neither by an itch for writing, nor a fondness for speculation, but by the desire of submitting to my brethren the fruits of seven years' observation and reflexion. In doing so, I have not been unconscious of the dangers I must encounter; since it has always been the fate of those who have illustrated or improved the arts and sciences by their discoveries to be beset by envy, malice, hatred, detraction, and calumny. This, the common lot, I have chosen to undergo; but with the determination of refusing to every one who is actuated by such motives as these all explanation of my doctrines. What I have written I have proved again and again, by the testimony of my own senses, and amid laborious and tedious exertions; still guarding, on all occasions, against the seductive influence of self-love.

And here, lest any one should imagine that this new sign has been thoroughly investigated, even as far as regards the diseases noticed in my Treatise, I think it necessary candidly to confess that there still remain many defects to be remedied—and which I expect will be remedied—by careful observation and experience. Perhaps, also, the same observation and experience may lead to the discovery of other truths, in these or other diseases, of like value in the diagnosis, prognosis, and cure of thoracic affections. Owing to this acknowledged imperfection it will be seen that, in my difficulties, I have had recourse to the Commentaries of the most illustrious Baron Van Swieten, as containing everything which can be desired by the faithful observer of nature; by which means I have not only avoided the vice of tedious and prolix writing, but have, at the same time, possessed myself of the firmest basis whereon to raise, most securely and creditably, the rudiments of my discovery. In submitting this to the public I doubt not that I shall be considered, by all those who can justly appreciate medical science, as having thereby rendered a grateful service to our art, inasmuch as it must be allowed to throw no small degree of light upon the obscurer diseases of the chest, of which a more perfect knowledge has hitherto been much wanted.

In drawing up my little work I have omitted many things that were doubtful and not sufficiently digested; to the due perfection of which it will be my endeavour henceforth to apply myself. To conclude, I have not been ambitious of ornament in my mode or style of writing, being contented if I shall be understood.

December 31, 1760.

ON PERCUSSION OF THE CHEST

FIRST OBSERVATION

Of the Natural Sound of the Chest, and Its Character in Different Parts

I. The thorax of a healthy person sounds, when struck. I deem it unnecessary to give in this place any description of the thorax. I think it sufficient to say that, by this term, I mean that cavity bounded above by the neck and clavicles, and below by the diaphragm: in the sound state, the viscera it contains are fitted for their respective uses.

II. The sound thus elicited (1) from the healthy chest resembles the stifled sound of a drum covered with a thick woollen cloth or other envelope.

III. This sound is perceptible on different parts of the chest in the following manner:

1. On the right side anteriorly it is observed from the clavicle to the sixth true rib; laterally, from the axilla to the seventh rib; and posteriorly, from the scapula to the second and third false ribs.

2. The left side yields this sound from the clavicle to the fourth true rib anteriorly; and on the back and laterally, in the same extent as the other side; over the space occupied by the heart the sound loses part of its usual clearness and becomes dull.

3. The whole sternum yields as distinct a sound as the sides of the chest, except in the cardiac region, where it is somewhat duller.

4. The same sound is perceptible over that part of the spinal column which contributes to form the chest.

The sound is more distinct in the lean, and proportionably duller in the robust; in very fat persons it is almost lost. The most sonorous region is from the clavicle to the fourth rib anteriorly; lower down, the mammæ and pectoral muscles deaden the sound. Sometimes, owing to the presence of muscle, the sound is dull beneath the axilla. In the scapular regions on the back, owing to the obstacle afforded by the bones and thick muscles there, it is also less distinct. Sometimes, but rarely, it exists over the third false rib—owing, I conceive, to a very unwonted length of the thoracic cavity.

SECOND OBSERVATION

OF THE METHOD OF PERCUSSION

IV. The thorax ought to be struck, slowly and gently, with the points of the fingers, brought close together and at the same time extended.

Robust and fat subjects require a stronger percussion; such, indeed, as to elicit a degree of sound equal to that produced by a slight percussion in a lean subject.

V. During percussion the shirt is to be drawn tight over the chest, or the hand of the operator is covered with a glove made of unpolished leather.

If the naked chest is struck by the naked hand, the contact of the polished surfaces produces a kind of noise which alters or obscures the natural character of the sound.

VI. During the application of percussion the patient is first to go on breathing in the natural manner, and then is to hold his breath after a full inspiration. The difference of sound during inspiration, expiration, and the retention of the breath is important in fixing our diagnosis.

VII. While undergoing percussion on the fore parts of the chest the patient is to hold his head erect, and the shoulders are to be thrown back, in order that the chest may protrude, and the skin and muscles be drawn tight over it; a clear sound is thus obtained.

VIII. While we are striking the lateral parts of the chest, the patient is to hold his arms across his head; as, thereby, the thoracic parietes are made more tense and a clearer sound obtained.

IX. When operating on the back you are to cause the patient to bend forwards, and draw his shoulders towards the anterior parts of the chest, so as to render the dorsal region rounded; and for the same reasons, as stated in VIII.

Any healthy person may make experience of percussion in his own person or that of other sound subjects; and will thus be convinced, from the variety of the sounds obtained, that this sign is not to be despised in forming a diagnosis.

THIRD OBSERVATION

OF THE PRETERNATURAL OR MORBID SOUND OF THE CHEST AND ITS GENERAL IMPORT

X. To be able justly to appreciate the value of the various sounds elicited from the chest in cases of disease it is necessary to have learned, by experience on many subjects, the modifications of sound, general or partial, produced by the habit of the body, natural confirmation as to the scapulæ, mammæ, the heart, the capacity of the thorax, the degree of fleshiness, fatness, etc., etc.; inasmuch as these various circumstances modify the sound very considerably.*

XI. If, then, a distinct sound, equal on both sides, and commensurate to the degree of percussion, is not obtained from the sonorous regions above mentioned, a morbid condition of some of the parts within the chest is indicated.

On this truth a general rule is founded, and from this certain predictions can be deduced, as will be shown in order. For I have learned from much experience that diseases of the worst description may exist within the chest unmarked by any symptoms, and undiscoverable by any other means than percussion alone.

A clear and equal sound elicited from both sides of the chest indicates that the air cells of the lungs are free, and uncompressed

---

* I have purposely avoided the literal translation of the text in this place, as it is difficult to know the precise meaning attached by the author to one or two of the epithets used by him to designate the particular modifications of sound alluded to.—TRANS.

either by a solid or liquid body.   (Exceptions to this rule will be mentioned in their place.)

XII and XIII.   If a sonorous part of the chest struck with the same intensity yields a sound duller than natural, disease exists in that part.

XIV.   If a sonorous region of the chest appears, on percussion, entirely destitute of the natural sound,—that is, if it yields only a sound like that of a fleshy limb when struck,—disease exists in that region.

The nature of the indications above pointed out will be understood by any one who attends to the difference of sound elicited by percussion of the chest and of the thigh in his own person.

XV.   The superficial extent of this unnatural sound (XIV) in a sonorous region is commensurate with the extent of the morbid affection.

XVI.   If a place naturally sonorous, and now sounding only as a piece of flesh when struck, still retains the same sound (on percussion) when the breath is held after a deep inspiration, we are to conclude that the disease extends deep into the cavity of the chest.

XVII.   If the same results (XVI) are obtained both before and behind on points precisely opposite, we are to conclude that the disease occupies the whole diameter of the chest.

These varying results depend on the greater or less diminution of the volume of air usually contained in the thorax (lungs); and the cause which occasions this diminution, whether solid or liquid, produces analogous results to those obtained by striking a cask, for example, in different degrees of emptiness or fulness: the diminution of sound being proportioned to the diminution of the volume of air contained in it.

FOURTH OBSERVATION

OF THE DISEASES IN GENERAL IN WHICH THE MORBID SOUND OF THE CHEST IS OBSERVED

XVIII.   The preternatural or morbid sound occurs in acute and chronic diseases; it always accompanies a copious effusion of fluid in the thoracic cavity.

It must be admitted that whatever diminishes the volume of air within the chest diminishes the natural sound of that cavity; but we know from the nature, the causes, and the effects of acute and chronic diseases of the chest that such a result is possible in these cases; and the fact is finally demonstrated by examinations after death. The effect of effused fluids in producing the morbid sound is at once proved by the injection of water into the thorax of a dead body; in which case it will be found that the sound elicited by percussion will be obscure over the portion of the cavity occupied by the injected liquid.

FIFTH OBSERVATION

OF ACUTE DISEASES IN WHICH THE CHEST YIELDS THE MORBID SOUND

XIX. The morbid sound which is observed in acute diseases occurs during their progress or at their termination.

This consideration ought to lead all medical men to use percussion in acute diseases; as they will, thereby, be enabled to form a more correct judgment, which in such cases is always a difficult matter. It has often occurred to me to see cases of acute diseases, apparently over, and imposing on the physician under the mask of intermittent or remittent fevers, and which have eventually ended in a fatal vomica or fatal scirrhus of the lungs.

XX. The preternatural sound which is perceived during the course of acute diseases of the chest occurs most frequently in inflammatory affections.

The reason of this observation (XX) will be obvious to any one acquainted with the nature of inflammation. The preternatural sound may also be observed sometimes in epidemic exanthematous diseases, previously to the eruption, as was the case in the petechial epidemic of 1757, 1758, 1759, and in the miliary epidemic of the present year (1760). In the latter instance I observed that the preternatural sound, when once present, continued to the termination of the eruption.

XXI. The morbid sound which occurs towards the termination of acute diseases is observed when the excretion of morbid matter is not adequate to the severity of the affection.

XXII. The morbid sound occurring in inflammatory diseases is observable commonly on the fourth day; it rarely precedes, but often follows, this period.

This sign occurs rarely on the third, and very often on the fourth, fifth and seventh day, but never later.* It is observed in those inflammatory affections of the pleura or lungs, or both, which are accompanied by a humid cough; but not in those attended by a dry cough,—such, e. g., as the dry pleurisy, and inflammation of the mediastinum, pericardium, and heart. At least in these latter affections the sound is not observed, until such time as they verge towards a fatal termination, or have degenerated into obvious abscesses or vomicæ.

XXIII. The morbid sound increases, from the time of its appearance, according to the nature, severity, and duration of the disease; it diminishes proportionably to the nature, duration, and copiousness of the excretions.

The progressive augmentation of the preternatural sound depends on the gradual deposition of the morbific matter, which I have often found in such quantity as to occupy the inferior two-thirds of the affected side.

XXIV. The disease in which the preternatural sound is once present either proves fatal (on a decretory day, reckoning from its origin); passes off with due excretion; or terminates in other affections.

XXV. The following corollaries are the result of my observations of inflammatory diseases of the chest, studied under the sign of morbid resonance:

1. The duller the sound, and the more nearly approaching that of a fleshy limb stricken, the more severe is the disease.

2. The more extensive the space over which the morbid sound is

* The author explains this on the principle of critical days. I have omitted this part of the text, as purely theoretical. I doubt not also that his theory has, in this and some other places, biased his judgment and observation.—TRANS.

perceived, the more certain is the danger from the disease.

3. The disease is more dangerous on the left than on the right side.

4. The existence of the morbid sound on the superior and anterior part of the chest (*i.e.*, from the clavicle to the fourth rib) indicates less danger than on the inferior parts of the chest.

5. 'The want of the natural sound behind indicates more danger than it does on the anterior and superior part of the chest.

6. The total destitution of sound over one whole side is generally (passim) a fatal sign.

7. The absence of sound along the course of the sternum is a fatal sign.

8. The entire absence of the natural sound over a large space in the region of the heart is a fatal sign.

I have sometimes observed that the fatal prognostics given in the corollaries 6 and 7 were not verified when the matter made its way outwards, or abscesses formed in parts less essential to life. And this natural process has been often happily imitated by the ancients, by cauterising or otherwise incising the affected parts.

SIXTH OBSERVATION

OF CHRONIC DISEASES IN WHICH THE PRETERNATURAL SOUND IS OBSERVED

XXVI. The preternatural sound observed in chronic diseases is owing either to—(1) some hidden condition of the organs, which disorders them with a slow progress and finally destroys them; or exists (2) when certain obvious causes have induced a slow disorganization of the same.

These are the general sources of chronic diseases of the chest; and from whichever of the two classes of causes these arise, the morbid sound will equally and always be present.

XXVII. The diseases of the first class are: (1) Those which depend on hereditary predisposition; (2) those which arise from affections of the mind, particularly ungratified desires, the principal of which is nostalgia; (3) those which affect certain artisans, naturally possessing weak lungs.

The influence of an hereditary taint in producing diseases we know by experience, though we cannot explain it (see Van Swieten).

2. Mental affections, we find, produce quite opposite effects, while acting as causes of pectoral diseases. Of these affections of the mind, I have observed none more powerful in rendering obscure the natural resonance of the chest than the destruction of the cherished hopes. And as among this class of diseases, nostalgia (commonly called Heimwehe—home-ail) occupies the first place, I shall here give a short history of it.

When young men, not yet arrived at their full growth, are forcibly impressed into the military service, and thereby at once lose all hope of returning safe and sound to their beloved home and country, they become sad, silent, listless, solitary, musing, and full of sighs and moans, and finally quite regardless of, and indifferent to, all the cares and duties of life. From this state of mental disorder nothing can rouse them—neither argument, nor promises, nor the dread of punishment; and the body gradually pines and wastes away, under the pressure of ungratified desires, and with the preternatural sound of one side of the chest. This is the disease nostalgia. I have examined the bodies of many youths who have fallen victims to it, and have uniformly found the lungs firmly united to the pleura, and the lobes on that side where the obscure sound had existed callous, indurated, and more or less purulent. Some years ago this disease was very common, but is now rarely met with, since the wise arrangement has been adopted of limiting the period of military service to a certain number of years only.

3. The various arts and occupations of life have their peculiar diseases in like manner as the ages, temperaments, and sexes have theirs. This truth is exemplified in the case of the man of letters, the husbandman, the worker in metals, painters, etc., etc. Our particular business, however, at present, is with those arts which dispose to diseases of the chest indicated by the sounds so often described. Thus I have remarked that tailors, millers, etc., who are forced to inhale, during their

labours, a fine dust, become phthisical, while shoemakers, weavers, etc., from the forced position or application of their weak chests, during their various occupations, become asthmatical, with scirrhous lungs, etc.*

I may here state a fact which I have frequently proved by dissection, but which I cannot well account for; it is this: in the abovementioned class of cases it is extremely rare to find both lungs affected at the same time; and, when this happens, one lung is always more diseased than the other.

XXVIII. The diseases mentioned (in XXVI, 2.) arise from—(1) a vitiated condition of the fluids, gradually produced; or (2) from acute affections imperfectly cured.

1. The vitiation of the humours arises from ingesta which cannot be assimilated, the effect of which, in producing chronic diseases, is well known.

2. An acute disease is said to be imperfectly cured when some morbid affection still remains after it in some part of the body. This morbid condition will be observed either in the site of the primary disease or, at least, in that portion of the chest which yields the morbid sound, namely, the pleura, or the lungs, or both these together, or the mediastinum or the pericardium. When the primary inflammatory disease is succeeded by a collection of pus in the chest the affection is readily recognized; but if the secondary affection is a scirrhus of the lung, how often and how grievously are medical men deceived. Often have I met with cases of fancied convalescence from acute fevers, in which there was hardly any cough or dyspnœa, or indeed any other sign of disease (as appeared to the attendants), but a trifling degree of irregular fever. In these cases, however, on percussion the preternatural sound was found over one whole side of the chest, and the final result was death, preceded either

---

* The author here admits that these cases are improperly placed under the head of affections produced by secret and occult causes; but excuses himself under the plea that the occurrence of such diseases and their imperceptible progress, only in some few of the numbers exposed to the noxious influences, is a proof of original debility of the affected organ.—TRANS.

by dropsy or extreme emaciation; the real seat of the disease remaining, perhaps, unknown to the very last.

XXIX. For the above reasons it may be received as a general rule in chronic diseases that when, together with the indication stated XXVI, there are emaciation and debility, the case is desperate.

This result is inevitable whensoever the disease does not yield to medicine. In such cases we may always conclude that the lung of the side which yields the preternatural sound is either compressed by some foreign body, is indurated by disease, or destroyed by some morbid acrimony developed within its own structure.

SEVENTH OBSERVATION

OF THE PRETERNATURAL SOUND OF THE CHEST WHICH RESULTS FROM COPIOUS EXTRAVASATION OF THE FLUIDS CONTAINED IN THE VESSELS OF THAT CAVITY

XXX. The fluids contained in the vessels of the chest are: 1, Chyle; 2, blood; 3, serum and lymph.

I must candidly admit that I have never seen a case of extravasated chyle. I however believe the thing possible, although I am well aware that the thoracic duct runs outside the pleura; the same causes that produce erosion and perforation of the thoracic parietes, may produce this.

XXXI. The extravasation of these fluids (XXX) may arise from the following causes: 1, Rupture of the containing vessels; 2, too great tenuity of contained fluids; 3, non-absorption of the same, etc., etc.

1. Under this head come wounds, contusions, etc.
2. Extravasations from internal causes arise from rupture of relaxed and debilitated vessels, during a state of plethora and over-activity of the circulation.
3. A third class of causes are obstructions originating in a bad habit of the body.

XXXII. When from these causes the fluids mentioned are

poured out in considerable quantity, the preternatural sound will exist over the space occupied by them.

The correctness of this statement is evinced by the experiment mentioned at the end of XVII.

According to the plan formerly proposed (XI) I shall now proceed to notice those affections of the chest which are not indicated by percussion.

EIGHTH OBSERVATION

Of those Affections of the Chest which are not Indicated by Percussion

XXXIII. Certain diseases attended by a violent cough, and thereby creating a suspicion that the lungs are certainly implicated, are, nevertheless, truly diseases of the abdomen, and affect the pulmonary organs merely sympathetically.

Under this head are ranged the gastric and convulsive cough of infants, pregnant women, and such other persons as have their abdominal viscera oppressed by the lentor of autumnal agues or a superfluity of phlegm.

XXIV. Violent coughs, dyspnœas, asthmas, and consumptions are also occasionally observed, which originate in some incomprehensible irritability of the nerves of the chest. Affections of this sort rarely give rise to the preternatural sound: from the absence of this, however, and the presence of a copious watery urine their existence may be pretty confidently presumed.

Under this head are arranged the coughs, dyspnœas, and asthmas so common in hysterical and hypochondriacal affections; the nervous consumption and asthma of old persons; and, perhaps we may add, the polypous concretions found near the heart in young subjects.

XXXV. A slight engorgement of the lung, a scirrhus of small extent, a small vomica, and a trifling extravasation are not detected by percussion, unless, sometimes, by the decreased resonance of the affected part.

These affections are not dangerous until they reach a size when they become more readily discoverable by means of percussion.

XXXVI. There is another class of diseases of the lungs (undiscoverable by percussion) in which the distinguishing symptoms are a very severe cough, with expectoration of fatty, chalky, gypseous, and stony matters.

These cases are known by the nature of the expectoration. I have frequently observed a cough of this kind, but without the peculiar expectoration, succeeding miliary fevers improperly treated.

NINTH OBSERVATION

OF THE APPEARANCES ON DISSECTION, IN CASES WHERE THE PRETERNATURAL SOUND OF THE CHEST HAD BEEN OBSERVED

XXXVII. These are the following:
1. Scirrhus of the lungs.
2. The conversion of this into an ichorous vomica.
3. A purulent vomica (simple or ruptured) in the pleura, lungs, mediastinum or pericardium.
4. Empyema.
5. Dropsy of the chest, in one or both cavities.
6. Dropsy of the pericardium.
7. Extensive extravasation of blood in the cavity of the pleura or pericardium.
8. Aneurism of the heart.

I will now proceed to notice these diseases in order, premising, occasionally, some account of the general symptoms.

TENTH OBSERVATION

OF SCIRRHUS OF THE LUNGS, AND ITS SYMPTOMS

XXXVIII. By scirrhus of the lungs I mean the degeneration of the natural spongy substance of the organ into an indolent, fleshy mass.

A portion of sound lung swims in water, but this carniform degeneration sinks. There is often observed a vast difference in the character of these scirrhi, in respect of hardness, color, and component parts. Thus in inflammatory diseases of the chest proving fatal on the fifth, seventh, or ninth day, the lung is very often found so completely gorged with blood as to resemble liver in every respect, both as to colour and consistence. One appearance deserves to be noticed: the lung is frequently invested with a purulent adventitious membrane, in those instances wherein the fatal peripneumony has succeeded an acute pleurisy. In chronic diseases of the lungs the appearances are extremely various. Frequently they are interspersed, and, as it were, marbled with a fatty kind of matter; frequently along with the fleshy appearance they have the consistence of cartilage; and very often they are found indurated by means of a thickened and black blood. These varieties, doubtless, depend on the varieties of the morbific matter.

XXXIX. The presence of scirrhus of the lungs, in its primary, unsoftened condition, may be suspected from the following signs:

Together with diminution or entire loss of the natural sound over the affected part, there is an infrequent cough without any expectoration, or with only a scanty excretion of viscid and crude sputa. During a state of quiescence there is nothing to be observed much amiss, either in the condition of the pulse or respiration; but upon any considerable bodily exertion, or after speaking for some time, these persons become speedily exhausted, anxious, and breathless, and complain of a sense of dryness and roughness in the throat. At the same time the pulse, which had previously been of moderate frequency, becomes quick and unequal; the respiration and speech are broken and interrupted by sighs; the temporal, sublingual, and the jugular veins of the affected side are more than usually distended; while it will be observed that this side of the chest is less moveable than the other during inspiration. Meanwhile the natural and animal functions continue to be well performed; and the patient can lie on either side indifferently.

All the above symptoms are more severe in proportion as the scirrhus is more extensive.

ELEVENTH OBSERVATION

OF VOMICAE IN GENERAL

XL. When an humour, sound or morbid, is deposited from the circulating mass in a solid form, and, together with the extreme vessels, is afterwards, by means of the vital powers, softened and converted into matter, and contained in a sort of capsule, I term this collection of matter a *vomica*.

This notion applies to every vomica, whether produced by a vice of the solids or fluids, as is clear from the history of *obstruction* and *inflammation*.

XLI. I have observed two kinds of vomica—the *ichorous* and *purulent*. The former occupies the lungs only; the latter, both the lungs and other thoracic viscera. They are both either close or communicating with the trachæa.

By the term *ichorous vomica* I mean a sac containing a thin fluid, frequently of a reddish yellow colour, frequently of a reddish brown, often of a colour between these, different from pus, and arising from the destruction of a scirrhous lung. By *purulent vomica* I understand an encysted abscess of the chest, resulting from the conversion of an inflamed spot into a white, thick, glutinous, fatty matter. When these communicate with the bronchia and discharge any of their contents by expectoration, they are called *open;* otherwise, *close* or *shut*.

XLII. 1. *Ichorous Vomica.*—If a scirrhus of the lung, recognised by its proper signs (XXXIX), is converted into matter, it presents the following symptoms: The patient begins to languish and waste away insensibly (although the usual quantity of food is taken), with a quick, contracted, and unequal pulse. The respiration, even during a state of quietude, is unnaturally anxious and frequent and is remarkably interrupted by sighing. The forehead, during the more severe attacks, is sometimes covered with a cold sweat. The eyes are dim; the veins of the cheeks and lips are livid, and the tongue, especially on the affected side, is of a leaden hue. At the same time there is neither pain nor thirst. The diseased side, however, is observed to be less mobile than natural, and the degree of immobility is proportioned to the bulk of the vomica into which the scirrhus has been resolved. The cough is infrequent, interrupted, and dry; or the expectoration, if any, is dirty or blackish (cænosum aut fuscum).

When things have got to this height, the appetite begins to fail, and at length is entirely lost; and whatever is eaten only produces an increase of anxiety during the process of digestion: this process, however, takes place without any hectic flushing, which always accompanies the purulent vomica.

In some cases, when there is a dissolution of the central parts of the scirrhus, the abdomen and hypochondres sink in; in a very few instances the same parts are slightly swollen, and with an indistinct feeling of fluctuation. The urine rarely presents any deviation from the natural state; sometimes, however, it is red, and with a sediment, if any exists, of a cinnabar colour. The stools are of natural character, except under the influence of medicine. The extremities, even when of a livid colour, are never hotter than natural until a few days before death; the affected side is, moreover, observed to swell, and the hand and foot in the first place. The patient now suffers from frequent sinkings and faintings; and from having hitherto been able to lie easily on either side, he is able to remain on the affected side only.

2. *Close Purulent Vomica.*—The following are the symptoms of this affection: While the abdominal organs still continue to perform their functions well, there is often present a very troublesome, frequent, dry cough, so severe as to irritate the fauces, to render the voice hoarse, and often to excite vomiting. At this time are observed frequent irregular chills, followed by heat, and strong flushing of the cheeks and lips, particularly of the affected side. A degree of lassitude is experienced, more remarkable after a full meal; and at the same time there is perceived a degree of quickness and straitness of the respiration, sufficient to excite suspicion of some morbid affection of the chest. The pulse is also found to be contracted, frequent, somewhat hard, and unequal during the period of digestion; and even at other times it is never in a perfectly

natural state—more especially under the influence of bodily motion, laughing, or speaking.

If at this time the vomica has reached a size to be detected by percussion, the following additional signs exist: The patient is not nourished by the food taken, partly because it is, in a greater or less degree, rejected by vomiting, and partly on account of the imperfect assimilation of what is retained. As the disease increases the whole process of respiration is at length carried on by one lung; an incessant state of anxiety prevails, and the patient remains fixed on the diseased side, through dread of impending suffocation if he turn on the other. The face, hands, feet, and the affected side are œdematous; while the opposite part of the body, from deficient assimilation, hectic heat, and nocturnal perspirations, is extenuated. The urine now becomes scanty, red, turbid, with a copious branny sediment, and soon putrefies; and the scene is finally closed, with short and asthmatic breathlessness, lividity of the cheeks, lips, and nails, etc.

3. *Purulent Vomica Communicating with the Trachea.*—When a vomica of considerable size, discoverable by percussion, bursts into the trachea, or rather bronchia, by a large opening, it produces instant suffocation; if by a small aperture, it is recognised by the following marks: By means of a violent cough, pus is expectorated, which is, in different cases, white, yellow, saffron, green, brown, bloody; which sinks in water, and, when thrown on hot coals, emits a stinking, nidorous smell. If at this time, while the patient is coughing and spitting, the palm of the hand be placed over the site of the vomica, *i. e.*, over the place where its existence had been detected by percussion,—the noise of fluid within the chest will be sufficiently manifest. This kind of expectoration will cease for some days, with relief to the patient; but it speedily returns, and is always preceded, for four and twenty hours, by an increase of the febrile state. During this state of things, and before the return of the expectoration, if percussion is applied over the site of the vomica, a sound exactly like that from a fleshy limb is obtained; but if this is delayed until the evacuation of the accumulated pus, then there is perceived a distinct, though obtuse sound. The slow fever which in-

variably accompanies this condition is increased after eating, and is still higher during the night; and at these times the forehead, neck, and chest are covered with perspiration. With the increase of these symptoms and the continuation of the purulent expectoration the breath becomes tainted, insomuch as to be extremely disagreeable both to the patient and the attendants. The thirst continues great, but the appetite is lost, even for the greatest delicacies, which, however, sparingly taken, produce, in place of refreshment, languor and anxiety. (The case is very different with them whose sputa are inodorous, the appetite in many being even great.) The urine is uniformly frothy, grows speedily putrid, and deposits a viscid, tenacious, white sediment. The patient now daily grows more emaciated,—the bones almost pierce the skin,—the hair falls off, the nails become curved, the legs swell; at length a colliquative diarrhœa supervening first lessens, and then suppresses, the expectoration, and the sufferer finally dies suddenly, on the third day after that on which he began to remain obstinately fixed on his back, with his legs drawn under him.

XLIII. *Empyema.*—When a vomica (XXXVII), ascertained by percussion, discharges its contents into the cavity of the pleura and upon the diaphragm, empyema is produced.

I premise this definition to prevent the affection now in question from being confounded with a vomica that has discharged its contents into the trachæa.

XLIV. If a large vomica, whose superficial and central extent is supposed to have become recognised by the marks pointed out (*OBSERVATION THIRD*, XV, XVI, XVII), shall have burst as above mentioned (XLIII), it may be recognised by the following signs:

The patient, who had usually lain on the affected side, starts up with a sudden pain, as if nearly suffocated, and begs to be held in the erect posture.

If percussion is now applied, it will be found that the natural sound, which had been nearly lost in the site of the vomica, has in some degree been restored in that place; while it is more or less destroyed (according to the quantity of pus effused) over the posterior and inferior parts of the chest.

There is now a very frequent cough, which is either dry or with a scanty, frothy, and noisy expectoration. The respiration becomes very laborious, with frequent faintings, and a cold sweat bedews the forehead and throat; the cheeks and lips are of an ominous red, while the nails grow livid, the pupils dilate, and death (which follows in a few hours the rupture of a large vomica) is finally preceded by dimness of sight, etc.

A small vomica, ruptured in the same manner, produces the same symptoms and is equally fatal. This issue, however, is of later occurrence and is preceded by the marks of pleuro-peripneumony.

TWELFTH OBSERVATION

OF DROPSY OF THE CHEST

XLV. When water is collected in the cavity of the chest, between the pleura (costalis) and the lungs, the disease is called dropsy of the chest; and this is said to be of two kinds, namely, according as the fluid occupies one or both sides.

This is ascertained by percussion in the living subject; and is demonstrated by anatomical examination after death. The general symptoms of the disease are chiefly the following:

1. Difficult and laborious respiration.

2. A cough at intervals, which is dry, or only attended by sputa of a thin, watery nature, or occasionally somewhat viscid.

3. A pulse contracted, somewhat hard, frequent, unequal, and often intermitting.

4. A sense of breathlessness and suffocation on the slightest motion.

5. An incipient dislike of warm food.

6. Perpetual anxiety about the scrobiculus cordis.

7. Great pressure on the chest, and distension of the stomach during the period of digestion.

8. A murmuring noise about the hypochondres, and frequent eructation of flatus, with momentary relief.

9. Scarcely any thirst.

10. Urine very scanty, and rarely made, red, with a lateritious sediment.

11. Swelling of the abdomen, more especially in the epigastrium, and particularly in that point on which the incumbent water gravitates.

12. A sub-livid swelling of the extremities, especially of the feet, which are, moreover, cold to the touch.

13. Œdematous tumescence of the inferior palpebræ.

14. A pallid, or, according to the nature of the affection, a sub-livid, discoloration of the cheeks, lips, and tongue.

15. Inability to lie down; anxious, distressing nights, with heaviness, yet frequently sleepless.

All these symptoms vary in a wonderful manner according to the disease.

FIRST KIND.—Dropsy of One Side of the Chest.—Beside the general signs of this disease above enumerated, the affected side, if completely filled with water, is enfeebled (*effœminatum*) and appears less movable during inspiration. In this case, also, the affected side yields nowhere the natural sound on percussion. If the chest is only half filled, a louder sound will be obtained over the parts to which the fluid does not extend, and, in this case, the resonance will be found to vary according to the position of the patient and the consequent level which the liquid attains. The hypochondre of the affected side is also unusually tumid, and more resisting to pressure than the rest of the abdomen. The palpebra, hand, and foot of the affected side are slightly œdematous. It is a remarkable fact that the reclining posture (*decubitus declivis*) is easily borne when the chest is entirely full; while the contrary is the case when there remains space for the fluctuation of the water.

SECOND KIND.—Dropsy of Both Sides of the Chest.—If fluid is contained in both sides of the chest, the following specific signs, in addition to the general symptoms, exist: The natural sound is destroyed over the space occupied by the water in either side. The patients uniformly become asthmatic, and resemble, in many respects, those labouring under ascites, only that the former have their inferior palpebræ and hands swollen. They cannot lie in an horizontal posture, and are equally threatened with suffocation on whichever side they turn; on which account they are forced to remain sitting, day and night, to prevent the pressure of the fluid from being felt on the upper part of the chest (which would be the case on lying down), in the same degree on which it now gravitates on the abdomen.   The effect of this state of things might lead to the suspicion of ascites, only that we find, on examining the patient in the erect position, that the hypochondriac regions are more swollen than the inferior parts, which is not the case in ascites.

All these subjects die as if from peripneumony, that is to say, the pulse fails, the whole body, except the chest and head, grows cold, the cheeks and extremities become livid, the respiration is at first laborious, then interrupted, and finally ceases altogether.

XLVI. *Dropsy of the Pericardium.*—When the liquor percardii is morbidly increased, so as to be capable of disturbing the natural action of the heart, the disease is called dropsy of the pericardium; of this there are two species, as the fluid is purulent or serous.

The fluid naturally present in the pericardium accumulates in still greater quantity in those who suffer a long protracted mortal agony, as we find on examination after their death.   But it is not to this accumulation, originating in the relaxation of death, but to that produced by obstruction during life, that I apply the term dropsy. I have ventured to divide the affection into two species, because I have often witnessed both of them.   In the first variety the heart is rough, and, as it were, shagged, with a coating of the purulent matter; while in the latter the organ is only of a paler colour than natural.   Many may be of opinion that the purulent dropsy would be better classed under the head of empyema; but I shall never quarrel about words when there are appearances to instruct us.

Signs of Hydropericardium.—Almost all the symptoms which have already been enumerated as accompanying dropsy of the chest generally accompany this species also; in addition to these, however, I have observed the following specific signs of the dropsy of the pericardium:

The sound in the cardiac region, which I have already stated (III, 2, 3) to be naturally more obscure than in the other parts of the chest, is now as completely deadened as if the percussion were applied to a fleshy limb. A swelling is perceived in the præcordia, which can readily be distinguished by its superior resistance from the stomach distended by flatus.

The patients fall asleep while sitting, the body being inclined forwards; but they soon are roused by the unconscious dropping of the head. On this account they complain to all around them of the distressing propensity to sleep which they experience. At the same time they suffer from faintings (accompanied by a pulse frequently unequal in respect both of its rhythm and volume), and, indeed, continue to undergo, to the end of their wretched life, and in every position of the body, the greatest distress. A few days before death, in many cases, the neck is swollen, and the eyes become extremely red, as if from crying. This state of things is sometimes terminated suddenly by a stroke of apoplexy, or more slowly by leipothymia.

The same signs are furnished by percussion in the purulent, as in the proper dropsy of the pericardium; but in the former the other symptoms are precisely the same as those which exist in the close *purulent vomica*. In the purulent dropsy the fluid commonly resembles turbid whey, the thicker portions of it (quod purulentum est) being found adhering to the heart like fringes.

THIRTEENTH OBSERVATION

OF THE SYMPTOMS OF A COPIOUS EXTRAVASATION OF BLOOD

XLVII. The causes of a large extravasation of blood into the cavity of the chest have been noticed in XXXI. The following are the symptoms of this affection.

There is incessant and indescribable anxiety and oppression at the præcordia and on the chest, while there is constant jactitation of the body and complete intolerance of the horizontal posture. Percussion elicits none of the natural sounds over the space occupied by the extravasated blood. In all cases the pulse is extremely contracted, frequent, and irregular in every way. The respiration is extremely laborious, with a frequent cough, and broken by profound sighing. All the veins become flaccid, and the eyes are at first red, but ultimately pale. Cold sweats, etc., follow, and the patient dies stertorous.

These are the symptoms when the blood flows into the cavity of the pleura without any accompanying lesion of the lungs; when these are wounded, there is also bloody expectoration and a passage of air to and from the wound in the parietes of the chest.

FOURTEENTH OBSERVATION

OF ANEURISM OF THE HEART

XLVIII. When the heart becomes so much distended by blood, accumulated in its auricles and ventricles, as to be unequal to propel forwards its contents, it frequently becomes thereby enormously dilated. This dilatation has been called aneurism of the heart.

We frequently observe this state of the heart on dissection—(1) in sudden and extensive peripneumonias of both lobes at the same time, and (2) in those fatal inflammatory diseases which are noticed towards the end of XXII.

The pathognomonic sign of this affection is the complete fleshy sound on percussion existing over a considerable space in the region of the heart. Whenever this sound is perceptible in the acute peripneumony, it is a sign that the patient will not survive twenty-four hours; in fact, he is already at the last gasp, and is speedily carried off as in apoplexy, unconscious of his fate.

In the second class of inflammation the sign is equally fatal, but is attended by different symptoms. In this case the patients suffer dreadful anxiety, and by the constant jactitation of their limbs, are perpetually uncovering themselves. Older persons, indeed, bear more tranquilly their sufferings; but the younger are pertinaciously restless and violent, struggling and talking, attempting to get out of bed, demanding their clothes, and endeavouring to walk or go about their usual occupations. Meanwhile the eyes become dull, the cheeks livid, and the nails and extremities are tinged with a leaden hue, and death is ushered in by cold sweats and the gradual extinction of the pulse and respiration.

CEDANT HAEC MISERIS IN SOLIATIUM, VERIS AUTEM MEDICINÆ CULTORIBUS IN INCREMENTUM ARTIS: QUOD OPTO.

LIST OF WRITINGS—EDITIONS *

————Inventum novum ex percussione thoracis humani, ut signo, abstrusos interni pectoris morbos detegendi, 1761. In: De Wasserberg. Op. min. med. et diss. octavo, Vindob, 1775, i, 316–361.

————The same. Nouvelle méthode pour reconnaître les maladies internes de la portrine par la percussion de cette cavité. Ouvrage traduit du latin et commenté par J. N. Corvisart (1808). In: Ecycl d. sc. méd., 41 v, octavo, Paris, 1834–46; 7 div. [v. 12], 177–347.

————The same. Trattato della percussione di . . . suo inventore. Prima versione italiana col testo a fronte, del dott. Giovanni Piccardi, 77 pp. 1l. octavo, Milano, presso la libreria Bravetta, 1844. Latin and Italian text.

————De inwendige razernij, of drift tot zelfmord, als eene wezenlijke ziekte beschouwd; met oorspronglijke waerneemingen, en aenmerkingen bevestigd, uit het Hoogduitsch vertaeld en met verscheiden aentekeningen vermeerderd door Lambertus Nolst. iv, 129 pp., octavo, Dordrecht, J. Krap, A. Z., 1788. See, also, Essai sur les maladies et les lésions organiques du cœur (etc.), octavo, Paris, 1855.

* As they appear in the Surgeon General's Library, Index Catalogue (Washington).

Auscultation and the Stethoscope

RENÉ·THEOPHILE·HYACINTHE·LAENNEC
M.D.

*Portrait from Sir John Forbes'
Life of Laennec. 1827.*
Asclepiad. No 14. Vol V.   London August. 1888.

Kindly loaned by Dr. Charles E. Quimby.

RÉNÉ THÉOPHILE HYACINTHE LAËNNEC
1781-1826

Laënnec was born at Quimper, Lower Brittany, February 17, 1781. His mother died of pulmonary tuberculosis when Réné was not quite five years of age, a fact of importance when it is remembered that this disease seriously handicapped and terminated his career. His father, an advocate of considerable education, appears to have had no sense of responsibility in the bringing up of his children, for, after the mother's death, they were placed in the care of an uncle, a curé. From this influence Laënnec soon passed to that of another uncle, Guillaume François Laënnec, a professor in the faculty of the medical school at Nantes. Thus while receiving a thorough education, in which the classics and his native language occupied his especial attention, he was from an early age in a medical atmosphere. The practical side of medicine he saw in the military hospitals established at Nantes, to which, though an undergraduate, he was attached through the influence of his uncle. At nineteen years of age (1800) he went to Paris to complete his medical education. In Paris at La Charité he attended the clinics of Corvisart. It will be remembered that these were the stirring times of the Revolution, and a few years later of the first empire. Napoleon, with his remarkable insight into human capabilities, was appointing men of exceptional qualities to civil as well as military posts. Corvisart was Napoleon's physician. The influence of this astute clinician upon Laënnec was similar to that of Hunter upon Jenner. The older man encouraged and talked with Laënnec and he became a warm advocate of the theories advanced by his young pupil. One recalls a different relationship between teacher and pupil in Van Swieten

and Auenbrugger. Auenbrugger was a student under Van Swieten, but, unlike Corvisart, Van Swieten either failed to appreciate
or did not wish to emphasize the importance of the method evolved
by his pupil (see Percussion, Auenbrugger biographical sketch,
p. 118).   At the time Laënnec went to Paris it was the Continental
seat of learning. The spirit of materialism which followed the
revolution was felt more keenly in science than in any other branch
of human thought. Scientists were discarding superstition and
arm-chair philosophy, and instead were carrying on careful research.
Chemists and physicists were demonstrating some of the most
fundamental principles of nature. With such standards set by
the savants even society in general had replaced the ball-room
by the scientific saloon.   From his simple surroundings in Brittany
this was the world into which Laënnec came at nineteen years
of age. It was to him, at it was to Holmes, some years later, a
"great harvest." Into these exceptional opportunities Laënnec
threw himself, and though of a delicate constitution, manifested
a remarkable capacity for work, which, combined with system,
enabled him to accomplish at his age what men twenty years his
senior would consider more than commensurate with their years.
During the first three years of his attendance as pupil at La Charité
he drew up careful histories of 400 cases seen by him. These
histories, according to Dr. Meriadec Laënnec, his cousin, formed
the groundwork of his future research and discovery. He won
the first two prizes in surgery and medicine at the Concours in
1801 and in 1802, and while still an undergraduate, he published
a report upon a case of diseased heart; histories of inflammation
of the peritoneum; a review of Bell's "Treatise on Venereal
Disease"; a treatise on peritonitis and a treatise on the capsule
of the liver.   On June 11, 1804, at the age of twenty-three, he took
his doctor's degree. For five years after graduation he was
chief editor of the *Journal de Médecine*, and for two years he
lectured upon pathological anatomy. Each year saw two or three
important contributions from him, either to journals or to larger
works. It was the age of the encyclopædia and dictionary, and he

contributed extensively to these. Reference to the biblio-graphical list below will show the extent of his authorship during the next ten years. In 1816, being thirty-five years of age, he was appointed visiting physician to the Necker Hospital in Paris. Till now the discovery for which he is known had not formulated itself in his mind. He was, however, already well known in the medical world for his pathological observations, which he had been compelled upon several occasions to defend in open meeting and in his writings. His most lasting contribution to the study of pathology was his method of correlating clinical with post-mortem findings. The careful records which he kept in carrying out this method would in themselves probably have kept his name, like that of Morgagni, prominent in the history of medi-cine. His hospital appointment came, however, just at a time when he was in need of clinical opportunity. In his administration of this new position he immediately established a system of obser-vation which is given in his own words as follows:

"When a patient enters the hospital it is the duty of a pupil to collect from him those anamnestic facts which he can give con-cerning his disease, and to follow their course. On examining the patient myself, I dictate the principal symptoms which I observe—those especially which may serve to establish the diagnosis or indication for treatment. And I confirm my conclusion, unless I may have changed it, by subsequent observations. This dicta-tion, which is made in Latin, for reasons easily appreciated, is taken down by the pupil in charge of the patient, and at the same time on a separate sheet, which I call the "diagnostic leaf," to keep which, in order that it may be shown to me and read whenever required at each visit, is the especial duty of another pupil. If a new sign appears, such as might modify the first diagnosis, I have that also added. If a patient die, the account of the autopsy is col-lected by the pupil in charge of the case. I read this account before all those who have been present at the autopsy, and if any correction is to be made, I make it on the spot, after having con-sulted with them."

In the same year (1816) as his appointment to the hospital the idea of the stethoscope occurred to him. The account of how he evolved the principle underlying mediate auscultation is given in the preface to his essay (printed below, p. 162). At this time the only methods employed in the examination of the chest were *palpation* to a very limited extent, *percussion* and *immediate auscultation* (the ear directly to the chest). Percussion was but recently employed in clinical medicine, for it will be remembered that it was Corvisart, Laënnec's teacher, who introduced it, and reclaimed it from obscurity by translating from the Latin Auenbrugger's essay published in 1761. In May, 1816, Laënnec presented a report upon his method before the Société de l'école, and a few days later gave a public demonstration- of the stethoscope. He now devoted himself to the task of accumulating evidence in support of the value of his instrument, and in June, 1818, he communicated his results to the Academy of Sciences. A committee consisting of Portal, Pellentan, and Percy was appointed, and rendered the following report:

"Your committee, in extending to Dr. Laënnec, who is already very favorably known by learned researches upon divers medical subjects, all the justice which is his due, have further the honor to assure the Academy that this physician, of whose titles to public confidence and esteem it is well aware, has merited its particular appreciation and an especial testimonial of its satisfaction for the new work by which he has done it honor."

He now set about the publication, in book form, of his findings, which till then had been communicated to societies only. So closely did he apply himself that he broke down, and was compelled to retire to his country house at Quimper. On November 15, 1818, he returned from his retreat in Brittany to resume his duties at the Necker Hospital. By 1819 his book appeared. The following is a copy of the title-page to this first edition:

Auscultation Mediate
ou
Traité du Diagnostic des Maladies
des Poumons et du Cœur,
Fonde Principalement sur ce nouveau
Moyen D'Eploration.
Par R. T. H. Laennec,
D. M. P., Médecin de l'Hôpital Necker, Médecin
honoraire des Dispensaires, Membre de la
Sociéte de la Faculté Médecin de
Paris et de plusieurs autres
nationales et étrangères.
Μέγα δὲ ἡγεῦμαι τῆς τέχνης εἶναι τὸ δύνασθαι σκοπεῖν.
Pouroir explorer est, à mon avis, une
grande partie de l'art.—Hipp. Epid. III.
Paris—J. A. Brosson et J. S. Chaude, Libraires,
rue Pierre-Sarrazin, No. 9.
1819.

In 1822, being in his forty-first year, he was appointed to the chair of medicine in the College of France, and in 1823 was made full professor of medicine, to succeed his teacher, Corvisart. In 1826 he brought out a second edition of his work on mediate auscultation. This entailed an immense amount of very hard work, and he again broke down. From his student days he was always delicate, not merely of frail constitution, but often actually incapacitated for carrying out the plans of his otherwise indomitable ambition, and he is to be grouped with that long list of men who worked through illness and achieved success. Among these are Lancisi and Corvisart, both sufferers from heart disease; Darwin, Huxley, John Hunter, Matthew Arnold, Charles Sumner, the last three, victims of angina pectoris; Max Müller, Parkman the historian, and many others who struggled silently and whose sufferings history may never record. In 1826 he returned to his home. The constant association with cases of pulmonary disease, his mother's early death from tuberculosis, and his close application to hospital and literary work for twenty-five years well indicate the nature of his malady. On reaching his home, the dry cough from which he had long suffered became more severe and was accompanied by pain in the right side, fever, dyspnœa, and great emaciation. On August 13, 1826, he died, being in his forty-fifth year.

Note: I wish to acknowledge my indebtedness, for much valuable information, to Forbes' "Life of Laënnec" and to W. S. Thayer's "Laënnec."—(C. N. B. C.)

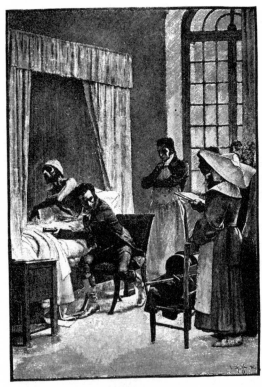

Laënnec Making a Ward Visit in the Necker Hospital, Paris, 1816. The Stethoscope may be seen in His Left Hand. (From a Painting in La Sorbonne, and Reproduced in *Harper's Monthly Magazine*, 1899.)

1818

A TREATISE ON THE DISEASES OF THE CHEST AND ON MEDIATE AUSCULTATION*

By R. T. H. LAËNNEC, M.D.

Translated from the Latest French Edition*
By JOHN FORBES, M.D., F.R.S.

FIRST FRENCH EDITION PUBLISHED SEPTEMBER, 1818*

* Though this is not strictly Laënnec's first publication, it represents his final conclusions on the subject. From the treatise, which is an exhaustive work on Diseases of the Chest, is selected for the present volume the Introduction and Chapter IV, which deals with Mediate Auscultation and the Stethoscope.—(C. N. B. C.)

INTRODUCTION

Of all the diseases which are essentially local, those of the thoracic organs are unquestionably the most frequent; while in point of danger they can only be compared with organic affections of the brain. The heart, lungs, and brain constitute, according to the happy expression of Bordeu, *the tripod of life;* and none of these organs can sustain any considerable or extensive morbid change without the greatest danger. The delicacy of their organization and their incessant motion account for the frequency and severity of their diseases. In no other texture of the animal system is idiopathic and primary inflammation so frequent a source of severe disorder and death as in the lungs; and no other is so liable to become the seat of *accidental productions* of every kind, more especially of tubercles, the most common of all. The heart, although of a less delicate texture, is equally obnoxious to morbid changes. Of these, it is true, some are only of rare occurrence; but others are extremely common—for instance, thickening of its muscular substance and dilatation of its cavities.

Diseases of the chest, in respect of their frequency and severity, hold also the first rank among those affections which, either as complications or effects, are found to accompany other diseases of a general nature. Thus in idiopathic fevers a slight degree of peripneumony, a determination of blood to the lungs, or a catarrh occasioning redness and thickening of the internal membrane of the bronchi and pouring into them an augmented secretion of mucus, are local affections quite as constant in their occurrence as the redness, thickenings or ulcerations of the mucous membrane of the intestines, in which several authors, ancient and modern, have fancied they discovered the *cause* of these diseases. It may even be asserted that in maladies of every sort, whatever be their seat, death scarcely ever occurs without the chest becoming affected in one way or an-

159

other; and that, in most cases, life does not seem in peril until the supervention of a congested state of the lungs, serous effusion into the pleura, or a great disorder of the circulation. The brain in general becomes affected only subsequently to these changes; and frequently remains undisturbed even to the last moment of life.

However dangerous diseases of the chest may be, they are, nevertheless, more frequently curable than any other severe internal affection. For this double reason medical men in all ages have been desirous of obtaining a correct diagnosis of them. Hitherto, however, their efforts have been attended by little success, a circumstance which must necessarily result from their having confined their attention to the observation and study of the deranged functions only. From the continued operation of the same cause we must even now confess, with Baglivi, that the diagnosis of the diseases of this cavity is more obscure than that of those of any other internal organ. Diseases of the brain, not in themselves numerous, are distinguished, for the most part, by constant and striking symptoms; the soft and yielding walls of the abdomen allow us to examine, through the medium of touch, the organs of that cavity, and thus to judge, in some measure, of their size, position, and degree of sensibility, and also of the extraneous substances that may be formed in them. On the other hand, the diseases of the thoracic viscera are very numerous and diversified, and yet have almost all the same class of symptoms. Of these, the most common and prominent are cough, dyspnœa, and, in some, expectoration. These, of course, vary in different diseases; but their variations are by no means of that determinate kind which can enable us to consider them as certain indications of known variations in the diseases. The consequence is that the most skilful physician who trusts to the pulse and general symptoms is often deceived in regard to the most common and best known complaints of this cavity. Nay, I will go so far as to assert, and without fear of contradiction from those who have been long accustomed to the examination of dead bodies, that, before the discovery of Auenbrugger, one-half of the acute cases of peripneumony and pleurisy, and almost all the chronic pleurisies, were mistaken by practitioners; and that, in such instances as the superior tact of a physician enabled him to suspect the true nature of the disease, his conviction was rarely sufficiently strong to prompt and justify the application of very powerful remedies. The percussion of the chest, according to the method of the ingenious observer just mentioned, is one of the most valuable discoveries ever made in medicine. By means of it several diseases which had hitherto been cognisable by general and equivocal signs only, are brought within the immediate sphere of our perceptions, and their diagnosis, consequently, rendered both more easy and more certain. It is not to be concealed, however, that this mode of exploration is very incomplete. Confined, in a great measure, to the indication of *fulness* or *emptiness*, it is only applicable to a limited number of organic lesions; it does not enable us to discriminate some which are very different in their nature or seat; it scarcely affords any indication except in extreme cases, and cannot, therefore, enable us to detect, or even to suspect, diseases in their very commencement. It is more particularly in diseases of the heart that we regret the insufficiency of this method and wish for something more precise. The general symptoms of disease in this organ greatly resemble those produced by many nervous complaints and by the diseases of other organs. The application of the hand affords some indications as to the extent, strength, and rhythm of the heart's motions; but these in general are by no means distinct, while in cases of considerable fatness or anasarca they become very obscure, or are altogether imperceptible. Within these few years some few physicians have, in those cases, attempted to gain further information by the application of the ear to the cardiac region. In this way the pulsations of the heart, perceived at once by the ear and touch, become, no doubt, more distinct. But even this method comes far short of what might be expected from it. Bayle was the first who, to my knowledge, had recourse to it at the time when we were attending the lectures of Corvisart. This great man himself never used it: he says only that he had several times heard the pulsation of the heart in *listening very close* to the chest.* We shall afterwards find that this phenomenon is different from auscultation, properly so

* Essai sur les Maladies du Cœur, 3e. ed., p. 396.

called, and is only observable in some particular cases.   But neither
Bayle nor any other of our fellow-students, who, with myself, might,
in imitation of him, employ this immediate auscultation (of which,
by the way, the first notion is derived from Hippocrates), obtained
any other result from it than that of perceiving more distinctly the
action of the heart, in the cases where this was not very perceptible to
the touch.   The reason of this limited application will be stated
hereafter.   But, independently of its deficiencies, there are other objections to its use: it is always inconvenient, both to the physician
and patient; in the case of females it is not only indelicate, but often
impracticable; and in that class of persons found in hospitals it is
disgusting.   For these various reasons this measure can but rarely
be had recourse to, and cannot, therefore, become practically useful,
since it is only by numerous observations and the comparison of
numerous facts of the same kind that we can ever, in medicine,
separate the truth from the errors which are constantly derived from
the inexperience of the observer, from the varying fitness of his per-
ceptive powers, the illusions of his senses, and the inherent difficulties of the method of exploration which he employs.   Observations made after long intervals can never overcome difficulties of this kind.   Nevertheless, I had been in the habit of using
this method for a long time, in obscure cases, and where it was
practicable; and it was the employment of it which led me to the
discovery of one much better.

In 1816 I was consulted by a young woman labouring under
general symptoms of diseased heart, and in whose case percussion
and the application of the hand were of little avail on account of the
great degree of fatness.   The other method just mentioned being
rendered inadmissible by the age and sex of the patient, I happened
to recollect a simple and well-known fact in acoustics, and fancied
it might be turned to some use on the present occasion.   The fact I
allude to is the great distinctness with which we hear the scratch of a
pin at one end of a piece of wood on applying our ear to the other.
Immediately, on this suggestion, I rolled a quire of paper into a
kind of cylinder and applied one end of it to the region of the heart
and the other to my ear, and was not a little surprised and pleased

to find that I could thereby perceive the action of the heart in a manner much more clear and distinct than I had ever been able to do by the immediate application of the ear. From this moment I imagined that the circumstance might furnish means for enabling us to ascertain the character, not only of the action of the heart, but of every species of sound produced by the motion of all the thoracic viscera and consequently for the exploration of the respiration, the voice, *the rhonchus*,* and perhaps even the fluctuation of fluid extravasated in the pleura or the pericardium. With this conviction I forthwith commenced at the Hospital Necker a series of observations from which I have been able to deduce a set of new signs of diseases of the chest, for the most part certain, simple, and prominent, and calculated, perhaps, to render the diagnoses of the diseases of the lungs, heart, and pleura, as decided and circumstantial as the indications furnished to the surgeon by the introduction of the finger or sound, in the complaints wherein these are used.

The following work, which contains the result of these observations, I shall divide into three parts. In the first I shall detail the various methods of exploration by which we obtain a knowledge of the diseases of the chest; the second will contain an account of the diseases of the bronchi, lungs, and pleura; the third, of the diseases of the heart and its appendages.

But before proceeding with my subject it may be well to say something on the attempts I have made to perfect my instrument of exploration, both as to its materials and shape, in order that others, who may entertain a like design, may follow a different route.

The first instrument which I used was a cylinder of paper, formed of three quires, compactly rolled together, and kept in shape by paste. The longitudinal aperture which is always left in the centre of paper thus rolled led accidentally in my hands to an important discovery. This aperture is essential to the exploration of the voice. A cylinder without any aperture is best for the exploration of the heart: the same kind of instrument will, indeed, suffice for the respiration and rhonchus; but both these are most distinctly perceived by means of a cylinder which is perforated throughout and

* See note †, p. 167.—(C. N. B. C.)

excavated into somewhat of a funnel shape, at one of its extremities, to the depth of an inch and a half.   The most dense bodies do not, as might have been expected from analogy, furnish the best materials for these instruments.   Glass and metals, exclusively of their weight and the sensation of cold occasioned by their application in winter, convey the sounds less distinctly than bodies of inferior density. Upon making this observation, which at once surprised me, I wished to give a trial to materials of the least possible density, and, accordingly, caused to be constructed a cylinder of gold-beater's skin, inflated with air, and having the central aperture formed of pasteboard.   This instrument I found to be inferior to all the others, as well from its communicating the sounds of the thoracic organs more imperfectly, as from its giving rise to foreign sounds, from the contact of the hand, etc.

Bodies of a moderate density, such as paper, the lighter kinds of wood, or Indian cane, are those which I always found preferable to others.   This result is perhaps in opposition to an axiom in physics; it has, nevertheless, appeared to me one which is invariable.   In consequence of these various experiments I now employ a cylinder of wood, an inch and a half in diameter and a foot long, perforated longitudinally by a bore three lines wide, and hollowed out into a funnel shape to the depth of an inch and a half at one of the extremities.   It is divided into two portions, partly for the convenience of carriage and partly to permit its being used of half the usual length.   The instrument in this form—that is, with the funnel-shaped extremity—is used in exploring the respiration and rhonchus: when applied to the exploration of the heart and the voice it is converted into a simple tube with thick sides by inserting into its excavated extremity a stopper or plug traversed by a small aperture, and accurately adjusted to the excavation.   This instrument I have denominated *the stethoscope.**   The dimensions mentioned are not a matter of indifference.   A greater diameter renders its exact application to certain parts of the chest impracticable; greater length renders its retention in exact apposition more difficult, and when shorter, it is not so easy to apply it to the axilla,

---

* From στῆθος, pectus, and σκοπέω, exploro.

while it exposes the physician too closely to the patient's breath, and, besides, frequently obliges him to assume an inconvenient posture, a thing above all others to be avoided if we wish to observe accurately. The only case in which a shorter instrument is useful is where the patient is seated in bed or on a chair, the head or back of which is close to him: then it may be more convenient to employ the half-length instrument.

In speaking of the different modes of exploration, I shall notice the particular positions of the patient, and also of the physician, most favourable to correct observation. At present I shall only observe that, on all occasions, the cylinder should be held in the manner of a pen, and that the hand of the observer should be placed very close to the body of the patient to insure the correct application of the instrument.

The end of the instrument which is applied to the patient—that, namely, which contains the stopper or plug—ought to be slightly concave, to insure its greater stability in application; and when there is much emaciation, it is sometimes, though rarely, necessary to insert between the ribs a piece of lint or cotton covered with cloth, on which the instrument is to be placed, as, otherwise, the results might be affected by its imperfect application.

Some of the indications afforded by mediate auscultation are very easily acquired, so that it is sufficient to have heard them once to recognise them ever after: such are those which denote ulcers in the lungs, hypertrophy of the heart when existing in a great degree, fistulous communication between the bronchi and cavity of the pleura, etc. There are others, however, which require much study and practice for their effectual acquisition.

The use of this new method must not make us forget that of Auenbrugger; on the contrary, the latter acquires quite a fresh degree of value through the simultaneous employment of the former, and becomes applicable in many cases wherein its solitary application is either useless or hurtful. It is by this combination of the two methods that we obtain certain indications of emphysema of the lungs, pneumo-thorax, and of the existence of liquid extravasations in the cavity of the pleura. The same remark may be extended to some other means, of more partial application—such, for example, as the *Hippocratic succussion*, the *mensuration* of the thorax, and *immediate* auscultation; all of which methods, often useless in themselves, become of great value when combined with the results procured through the medium of the stethoscope.

In conclusion, I would beg to observe that it is only in an hospital that we can acquire, completely and certainly, the practice of this new art of observation; inasmuch as it is necessary to have occasionally verified, by examination after death, the diagnostics established by means of the cylinder in order that we may acquire confidence in the instrument and in our own observation, and that we may be convinced, by ocular demonstration, of the correctness of the indications obtained. It will be sufficient, however, to study any one disease in two or three subjects to enable us to recognise it with certainty; and the diseases of the lungs and heart are so common that a very brief attendance on an hospital will put it in the power of any one to obtain all the knowledge necessary for his guidance in this important class of affections.

It would, no doubt, be expecting too much of physicians actively engaged in private practice to devote much time to the acquisition of this knowledge in an hospital; but they may readily and compendiously obtain the necessary opportunities through the kindness of friends attached to these establishments, who can make them acquainted with rare or interesting cases as they occur. In this way there is no physician who may not, in a very little time, learn to recognise with certainty not only the cases above mentioned, but peripneumony, pleurisy, latent catarrhs, and even the very rudiments of these affections: and this last-mentioned circumstance is unquestionably the chief practical benefit of auscultation, inasmuch as these diseases are the more easily cured, according as they are subjected to early treatment.

OF MEDIATE AUSCULTATION*

The signs afforded by mediate auscultation in the diseases of the lungs and pleura are derived from the changes presented by the sound of respiration, by that of the voice and coughing, within the chest, and also by the *rhonchus*† as well as certain other sounds which occasionally are heard in the same situation.   Of these signs we shall now proceed to give some account.   The notice of those which refer to the diseases of the heart will be deferred until we come to treat of the affections of this organ.

The general precautions which the practice of auscultation requires are the following: 1. The stethoscope must be applied very exactly and perpendicularly to the surface on which it rests, so as to leave no interval between the skin and any part of the extremity applied. 2. We must be careful not to produce pain by too strong pressure; this precaution is most necessary when the instrument is used without the stopper, and when the person is lean. 3. Although it is not necessary that the chest should be uncovered,—as all the positive stethoscopic signs, and frequently also the negative ones, may be perceived through clothes of considerable thickness, provided they are applied closely to the body,—still it is better that the clothing should only be light; for example, a flannel waistcoat and shirt.   Silks and also woollen stuffs are often inadmissible on account of the noise occasioned by their friction against the instrument.   The examiner ought to be careful, above all things, not to place himself in an uncomfortable posture, nor yet to stoop too much, nor turn his head backwards by a forced extension of the neck.   These positions determine the blood to the head and thus obscure the sense of hearing: they may sometimes be properly

---

*Only that portion of Laënnec's work dealing with mediate auscultation is given below; the original communication from which this is taken is an exhaustive treatise on the Diseases of the Thoracic Viscera.

† This word has improperly been given a separate meaning from that of râle. It is merely the word selected by Forbes to render into English the French word *râle* (from *raale*, old French).   Rhonchus, ῥόγχυς, snoring; *râle*, rattle—the words are synonymous.—C. N. B. C.

avoided by kneeling on one knee. In examining the fore parts of the chest we ought to place the patient on his back in a recumbent position, or in a chair, and gently reclining backwards. When we examine the back, we cause the patient to lean forwards and to keep his arms forcibly crossed in front; and when we examine the side, we cause him to lean gently to the opposite one and to place the forearm on the head.

SECTION I

AUSCULTATION OF THE RESPIRATION

In exploring the respiration we use the instrument without its stopper. In commencing our examination it is a proper precaution to cause the patient to take a few inspirations of moderate force and frequency, followed by expirations as nearly as may be of the same length. It sometimes happens that perfectly sound lungs give hardly any, or at most a very feeble, respiratory sound; and in these cases it is commonly found that the sound is weak in proportion to the effort made by the patient to make it audible. At other times our patients, fancying that something uncommon is expected from them, expand their chests to the very utmost extent; or they make several strong inspirations, one after another, without any intervening expiration; these unnatural efforts produce hardly any respiratory sound. In such cases, and indeed in all others where the sound of respiration is found to be weak, we desire the patient to cough. The act of coughing, particularly intentional coughing, is commonly preceded or followed by a real inspiration, which is then found to be as sonorous as the particular condition of the organ admits; and in these cases we are frequently surprised to perceive the ready penetration of the air into the lungs which we should have considered as impermeable, if we had relied on our first trials. We sometimes obtain a similar end in making the patient speak, and, still more, in making him read or recite. I state this fact not only because it is of practical importance, but because it tends to the conclusion that the lungs are themselves possessed of an inherent power of action, the seat of which is probably in the smaller bronchial ramifications.

The sound of respiration is different in the lungs, the trachea, and the larger bronchial tubes respectively. These differences we shall now describe.

1. *Vesicular Respiration.*—On applying the cylinder, with its funnel-shaped cavity open, to the breast of a healthy person, we hear, during inspiration and expiration, a slight but extremely distinct murmur, answering to the entrance of the air into, and its expulsion from, the air-cells of the lungs. This murmur may be compared to that produced by a pair of bellows whose valve makes no noise, or, still better, to that emitted by a person in a deep and placid sleep, who makes now and then a profound inspiration. We perceive this sound almost equally distinct in every part of the chest, but more particularly in those points where the lungs, in their dilatation, approach nearest to the thoracic parietes—for instance, the anterior-superior, the lateral, and the posterior-inferior regions. The hollow of the axilla, and the space between the clavicle and superior edge of the trapezius muscle, exhibit the phenomenon in its greatest intensity.

To judge correctly of the state of respiration by this method we must not rely on the results of the first moments of examination. The sort of buzzing sensation often caused by the first application of the instrument, the fear, restraint, and agitation of the patient, which mechanically lessen the force of respiration, the frequently inconvenient posture of the observer, and the great sensation occasionally produced by the action of the heart, are all causes which may at first prevent us from correctly appreciating, or even from hearing at all, the sound of inspiration and expiration. We must, therefore, allow some seconds to pass before we attempt to form an opinion. I need hardly observe that there must be no noise whatever in the vicinity of the patient.

I have already mentioned the necessity of the observer avoiding uneasy postures. Besides the inconveniences stated, this may also mislead by occasioning the auscultator to hear the sound of the contraction of his own muscles. We must be equally on our guard that the patient does not excite this sound in his own muscles by too strong a contraction of them in crossing the arms, leaning forward, or resting on the elbow. On this account, in the examination of weak subjects, it is always better to have them supported by assistants than to make them exhaust their remaining strength in keeping themselves in the erect position. It is right to observe, however, that all these precautions are only necessary to beginners. After one or two months' experience the ear becomes accustomed to the sound it is in search of, and is able to discriminate it from all the others with which it may be combined, even when weaker than they are.

The intervention of clothing, even when of considerable thickness, provided it be of a compact texture and fit the body well, does not sensibly diminish the sound of respiration; but we must be careful that there is no friction between this and the instrument, as this circumstance, especially if the clothes be of silk or of fine hard, woollen stuff, may mislead us by exciting a sensation analogous to that produced by respiration. Fatness, even when excessive, and anasarca of the chest, seem to have no effect in diminishing the peculiar sound. The sound is more distinct in proportion as the respiration is more frequent. A very deep inspiration, made very slowly, will sometimes be scarcely audible, while an imperfect respiration—such, for instance, as hardly at all elevates the chest, provided it be made quickly—may produce a very loud sound. On this account, when examining a patient, more especially if we have had but slight practice with the instrument, we should desire the respiration to be performed rather quickly. This is, however, a very unnecessary precaution in most diseases of the chest, as the frequent presence of dyspnœa necessarily renders the respiration quick. The same is true of fever and the agitation caused by nervous affections.

Many other causes, and especially the age of the individual, alter the intensity of the sound. In children respiration is very sonorous, even noisy, and can be heard easily, even through very thick clothing. In them the close and forcible application of the instrument to prevent the friction of the garments is unnecessary, as any noise that might arise from this cause is lost in the intensity of the other. The respiration of children differs, also, from that of adults in other respects besides its intensity. It is impossible to describe this peculiarity, but it will easily be understood by comparative trials. It appears as if, in children, we could distinctly hear the dilatation of all the air-cells to their full extent; whilst, in adults, these seem as if, from their stiffness, they could only bear a partial dilatation. This difference of sound is much less marked in expiration than inspiration. The dilatation of the chest in inspiration is also greater in the child; and both the peculiarities are more remarkable as the child is younger; they continue, in a greater or less degree, to the period of puberty or a little beyond it.

The sound produced by respiration varies, also, very much in its intensity in different adults. In some men it is scarcely perceptible unless they make a very deep inspiration, and even then, although sufficiently distinct, it is not one-half so audible as in the majority of persons. These individuals have generally a rather slow respiration and are little subject to dyspnœa, or breathlessness, from any cause. Others, however, have the respiration very distinct, even during a common inspiration, without being, on this account, at all more subject to shortness of breath than the former. Some few individuals, again, preserve through life a state of respiration resembling that of children, and which I shall, therefore, denominate *puerile*, in whatever age it may be perceptible. Such persons are almost all women, or men of a nervous temperament, and they preserve, in some other respects, the character of childhood. Some of these cannot be said to have any actual disease of the lungs, but they soon get out of breath, even though lean, by exercise, and are very liable to catch cold. Others of this class are affected with a chronic catarrh, attended by dyspnœa, a condition constituting one of those cases to which the name of *asthma* is usually given. With these exceptions an adult cannot, by any effort, give to his respiration the sonorous character it has in childhood; but in some morbid states the respiration spontaneously acquires it, without being, at the time, performed more forcibly than usual. This is particularly the case when one whole lung, or a considerable portion of both lungs, is rendered impermeable to air through disease, especially acute disease. In the sound portion of the lungs, in these cases, the respiration is perfectly similar to that of children. The same thing is observable throughout the whole extent of the lungs in some cases of fever and in certain nervous diseases.

At first we are tempted to believe that the superior intensity of the respiratory murmur in children may be owing to the tenuity of the muscles covering the chest, and to the superior suppleness of the texture of the lungs. But the first cause must have scarcely any effect in this way, since we find that, even in the fattest children, and in those most thickly clothed, the respiration is much more distinct than in the leanest adult examined uncovered; whilst of the adults who possess the *puerile* respiration, many are very robust and full of flesh. Neither does the quieter respiration of the adult depend on any induration or loss of pliability in the pulmonary texture, since it sometimes accidentally returns to the character it had in infancy. I am rather disposed to believe that the difference of result depends on the fact of children requiring a greater proportion of air, and consequently a fuller inspiration, than adults, whether this necessity arises from the greater activity of their circulation or from some difference in the chemical composition of the blood. The respiration which is most audible to the ear is not that which produces the greatest sound in the interior of the chest. I do not here allude to that species of respiration which is accompanied with a rattling or wheezing, or any other foreign sound, but to that kind of respiration which is simply loud, and which is so frequent in dyspnœa. This noise is merely the aggravation of the natural sound made by many persons in sleep, and is caused by the mode in which the air impinges upon the parts in the fauces. We can imitate it at will. I am acquainted with an asthmatic patient whose habitual respiration can be heard at the distance of twenty feet, and whose respiration, as heard in the interior of the chest, is, nevertheless, weaker than in the majority of men. The same remark applies to the noise (*snoring*) emitted by many healthy persons during sleep; and also to the imitative sounds of jugglers and ventriloquists, all of which are produced in the throat and posterior nares, and are quite unconnected with the sound of respiration in the interior of the chest.

When we can distinctly perceive, and with a uniform intensity, the respiratory sound in every part of the chest, we may be assured that there exists neither effusion into the cavity of the pleura nor any species of obstruction in the substance of the lungs. On the other hand, when we find the respiration is not to be distinguished in any particular point, we may safely conclude that the corresponding portion of the lungs within is become impermeable to the air from some cause or other. This sign is as easy to be perceived as the presence or absence of the sound, in the percussion of Auenbrugger, and affords precisely the same indications. With the exception of some peculiar cases, in which the simultaneous employment of the two different methods gives us signs which are completely pathognomonic, we may state it as a general fact that the absence of the sound on percussion coincides uniformly with the absence of respiration as ascertained by the stethoscope. Auscultation, as we shall find, has this advantage over percussion, that it points out more correctly the various degrees of pulmonary obstruction. It has certainly the inconvenience of requiring a little more time in its application; but, on the other hand, it demands less care and attention, and, moreover, can be employed in all cases, even in those wherein percussion affords no results whatever.

2. *Bronchial Respiration.*—By this term I designate the sound of respiration as observed in the larynx, trachea, and larger bronchial trunks. When we apply the stethoscope upon the larynx or cervical portion of the trachea we perceive that the respiratory sound is without that slight degree of crepitation which accompanies the dilatation of the air-cells of the lungs; the idea of a *drier* sound seems to be suggested to us, and we at the same time feel distinctly that the air is passing through a large empty space. This modification of the respiratory sound may be perceived over the greater part of the neck; it is strongly marked on the side of the neck; and we must be on our guard against it when exploring the acromion region, insomuch that if we direct the extremity of the cylinder to-

wards the lower portion of the neck we run the risk of hearing the tracheal respiration only, and may thereby, if not well versed in the distinctive characters of the different kinds of respiration, be led to consider the upper lobes as quite sound when they are, in fact, altogether impermeable to air. When a person inspires strongly by the nostrils, a like sound, originating in the nasal canal and fauces, may be heard over the whole surface of the head. In certain subjects, especially if very lean, the respiration possesses somewhat of this character when examined over the sternum and at the roots of the lungs—that is, between the scapulæ, and particularly near their upper and inner angle; but here the bronchial sound is not so readily distinguished, because of its intermixture with the common respiratory or vesicular murmur. Still less are we able, in the healthy condition of the lungs, to distinguish this peculiar modification of the respiration in the smaller bronchial tubes in other points of the chest. When, however, the texture of the lungs becomes indurated or condensed from any cause, such as pleuritic effusion, or the changes occasioned by a severe peripneumony or hæmoptysis, the vesicular respiration having then disappeared, or being much lessened, we can frequently perceive distinctly the bronchial respiration, not only in the large, but even in the small, ramifications of the bronchi. In such cases, although this peculiar modification of the respiratory sound is perceived in other parts, still it is nowhere so distinct as at the roots of the lungs. Next to the roots, the upper lobes exhibit it most frequently; and it is here, as we shall afterwards find, that the bronchi are most apt to become dilated. The cause of this bronchial respiration appears to me very obvious; in fact, when the air is prevented from penetrating the cells, this is the only kind of respiration that can exist; and it is found to be louder and more distinct in proportion as the lung is more condensed, and thereby becomes a better conductor of sound.

It is of great consequence to distinguish accurately the bronchial from the vesicular or pulmonary respiration, not only on account of the great errors of diagnosis which must result from their being confounded, but because the former becomes a pathognomonic sign in several cases of importance. In peripneumony it is one of the first indications of hepatization, and commonly precedes the loss of the natural sound on percussion; it is likewise one of the earliest signs of an accumulation of tubercles in the upper lobes of the lungs.

3. *Cavernous Respiration.*—I understand by this term the sound produced by inspiration and expiration in an excavation formed in the substance of the lungs, whether arising from the softening of a tubercle, from gangrene, from abscess (or from extensive dilatation of the bronchi). This variety has the same character as the preceding, only that it further conveys the idea of air entering into a larger cavity than a bronchial tube; and when there exists any doubt as to this being really the case, other circumstances connected with the sound of the voice and cough remove all uncertainty.

4. *Blowing or Puffing Respiration.*—In those cases wherein either the *bronchial* or *cavernous* respiration exists it is sometimes observed that when the patient is breathing quickly and by fits, during inspiration the air appears as if drawn from the auscultator's ear, while in expiration it seems blown into it. This species of respiration is one of those phenomena which serve to confirm the existence of an excavation near the surface of the lungs, but there are others yet more precise, which will be noticed hereafter. This sort of puffing or blowing is equally produced during coughing and speaking. The illusion of blowing into the ear in these cases is so perfect that it is only from the absence of the feeling of titillation, and of warmth or coldness, which a blast of air so impelled must necessarily occasion, that we are led to doubt its reality. This phenomenon is found to take place equally in the bronchi which adjoin the surface of the lungs, and particularly in the large branches at their roots, when the substance of the lung around is condensed, as in pneumonia or by a pleuritic effusion. In the case of excavations, this variety of respiration always indicates that they are very close to the surface of the lungs. It sometimes also presents a further modification, which I call the *veiled puff* (*souffle voilé*). In this case it seems to us as if every vibration of the voice, cough, or respiration agitates a sort of movable veil interposed between the excavation and the ear. This particular modification obtains under the following conditions: (1) In tuberculous excavations of

which the walls are very thin, at least in some points, and which are unconnected by adhesions with the costal pleura; (2) in peripneumonic abscesses of which the walls are unequally indurated, and in some places only congested; (3) in cases of peripneumony, when some part of a large bronchial ramification passes through a portion of lung still sound or only slightly congested; (4) in dilatation of the bronchi and also sometimes in pleurisy, when the affected branch has some part much less dense than the rest. We must be careful not to confound this phenomenon with a variety of mucous rhonchus which sometimes accompanies it.

SECTION II

AUSCULTATION OF THE VOICE

In the very earliest period of my researches on mediate auscultation I attempted to ascertain the differences which the sound of the voice within the chest might occasion. In examining several subjects with this view I was struck with the discovery of a very singular phenomenon. In the case of a woman, affected with a slight bilious fever and a recent cough having the character of a pulmonary catarrh, on applying the cylinder below the middle of the right clavicle, while she was speaking, her voice seemed to come directly from the chest, and to reach the ear through the central canal of the instrument. This peculiar phenomenon was confined to a space about an inch square, and was not discoverable in any other part of the chest. Being ignorant of the cause of this singularity, I examined, with the view to its elucidation, the greater number of the patients in the hospital, and I found it in about twenty. Almost all these were consumptive cases in an advanced stage of the disease. In some the existence of tubercles was still doubtful, though there was reason to suspect them. Two or three, like the woman above mentioned, had no symptom of this disease, and their robustness seemed to put all fears of it out of the question. Notwithstanding this I began immediately to suspect that this phenomenon might be occasioned by tuberculous excavations in the lungs. The observation of the same thing in patients who had no other symptoms of phthisis did not appear to me conclusive against the correctness of my suspicions, because I knew it to be by no means unusual to find in the lungs of persons carried off by some acute disease, and who had never shown any sign of consumption, tubercles not only softened, but excavated, and forming the very case denominated ulceration of the lungs. The subsequent death, in the hospital, of the greater number of the individuals who had exhibited this phenomenon enabled me to ascertain the correctness of my supposition: in every case I found excavations in the lungs of various sizes, the consequence of the dissolution of tubercles, and all communicating with bronchial tubes of variable size.

I found this peculiar phenomenon (which I have denominated *pectoriloquy*) to be more perceptible according to the density of the walls of the excavation and its proximity to the superfices of the lungs; and that it was most striking when these adhered to the pleura in such a manner as to render the thoracic parietes almost a part of the walls of the ulcerous excavation—a case of very frequent occurrence.

This circumstance naturally led me to think that *pectoriloquy* is occasioned by the superior vibration produced by the voice, in parts having a comparatively more solid and wider extent of surface than the air-cells and small bronchial tubes; and I imagined that, if this were so, the same effect ought to result from the application of the cylinder to the larynx or trachea of a person in health. My conjecture proved correct. There is an almost perfect identity of effect between pectoriloquy and the sound of the voice as heard through the tube resting on the larynx; and this experiment offers an excellent means for giving us an exact notion of the phenomenon when we have not the proper subjects for observation.

The sound of the voice in the different parts of the organs of respiration, and in the different conditions of these, in health and in disease, offers several important varieties which we shall now consider. In a healthy lung it is very slight, whether examined by the naked ear or stethoscope, being only a slight vibration analogous to that felt on applying the hand. I have already noticed the character of the voice on the larynx and trachea: it resounds strongly, traverses the tube of the stethoscope, and prevents the unarmed ear from hearing that issuing from the mouth. The same thing takes place over nearly the whole lateral surface of the neck, and even, in some individuals, towards the nape. On this account, in examining the acromion region, we must remember the precautions stated when speaking of the exploration of the respiration in the same place. The natural resonance of the voice in the throat and nasal fossæ is perceptible, more or less, over the whole surface of the head. In that portion of the trachea lying beneath the sternum it sounds loudly, but does not traverse the tube; on this account we must distrust *doubtful* pectoriloquy when it exists only about the upper portion of the sternum.

Bronchophony.—The sound of the voice is, in most cases, still more obscure in the larger bronchial trunks at the roots of the lungs—that is, in the interscapular region; nevertheless, it is always somewhat louder in this place, especially about the upper and inner angle of the scapula, than in the other parts of the chest. It is, indeed, very rare for it to be perceived distinctly traversing the stethoscope in a perfectly healthy subject; but it is found to resound so loudly at its extremity as to be more readily heard through the instrument than the voice issuing from the mouth is heard by the other ear. In persons, however, of a delicate and feeble frame, particularly in lean children, there frequently exists in this situation a *bronchophony* very similar to the *laryngophony* already noticed.

The sound of the voice is scarcely at all perceptible in the bronchi distributed through the lungs when these organs are healthy. This might be expected *a priori*, since the loose texture of the lungs, rendered still more rare by its intermixture with air, is a bad conductor of sound; and the softness of the bronchial branches, after they cease to be cartilaginous, renders them very unfit for its production; while the smallness of their calibre must render whatever sound is produced more acute and weaker in them than in the larger trunks. But if any one of these adverse conditions is removed, and, yet more, if several of them are so at the same time, the sound of the voice may become perceptible in the smaller bronchial tubes. Accordingly it is found that an attack of peripneumony, an extensive hæmoptysical induration, or the accumulation of a great number of tubercles in the same point, by condensing the texture of the lungs, gives occasion to a sound analogous to pectoriloquy. This phenomenon, which I denominate *accidental bronchophony*, is, as might be expected, most marked when the pulmonary induration has place near the roots of the lungs. This sign is one of those which serve best to measure the progress of a recent peripneumony.

The dilatation of the bronchi gives rise to the same phenomenon, and the more readily, because the substance of the lungs in the neighborhood of the dilated branches is often more compact than in the natural state. Sometimes two of the causes mentioned conspire to produce it; for instance, the cause just mentioned, and the accumulation of tubercles.

Bronchophony is rarely so like pectoriloquy as to deceive a person even of moderate experience. In the former the voice merely traverses the cylinder; its tone is somewhat like that of a speaking trumpet; and the sound is more diffused in its seat than pectoriloquy. Where any doubt exists, this is removed by the cough and the character of the respiration in the same point: neither of these has the *cavernous* character; we feel assured that the whole phenomena have for their site a series of tubes, and not a circumscribed space.

Pectoriloquy.—This phenomenon may be produced under very different circumstances: (1) by the softening of tubercles (by far the most common cause); (2) by the decomposition of a gangrenous eschar; (3) by an abscess, the consequence of peripneumony; (4) by the evacuation of a cyst into the bronchi; and probably also by a fistulous communication between the bronchi and an abscess of the mediastinum.

Pectoriloquy offers great varieties in respect of intensity and completeness. I divided it into *perfect*, *imperfect*, or *doubtful*.

Pectoriloquy is *perfect* when the transmission of the voice through the stethoscope is complete, and when it, as well as the corre-

sponding results obtained from the exploration of the cough and
rhonchus, are exactly circumscribed: in this case it can never be
confounded with bronchophony. It is *imperfect* when some one of
those characteristics is wanting, and particularly if the transmission
of the voice be not evident. It is *doubtful* when the sound of the voice
is very feeble, and when it can be distinguished from bronchophony
only by the aid of other signs derived from the consideration of its
site, the general symptoms, and the progress of the disease. These
last circumstances suffice, in almost every case, to enable us to distinguish the nature of the excavation.

The circumstances which concur to render pectoriloquy perfect
are: the complete emptiness of the excavation, the increased
density of the portion of lung which forms its walls, its ready communication with one or more bronchial tubes of a considerable size,
and its proximity to the walls of the chest. It is proper to state,
however, that whatever be the distance of the cavity from the surface
of the lungs, if it possesses the other qualities indicated, it will always
yield perfect pectoriloquy, unless, indeed, a very considerable
thickness of healthy lung be interposed, which, owing to its defective density, is necessarily a bad conductor of sound. The extent of the excavation contributes also to the completeness of the
phenomenon; it is most distinct when this is somewhat considerable; it is, however, often complete when the cavity is very
small. On the other hand, pectoriloquy is sometimes very indistinct where the excavations are very large—the size of the fist,
for instance—and when they communicate with the bronchi by
small openings.* It has several times been manifest to me that
when the number of fistulous openings, by which a very large excavation communicates with the bronchia, increases, pectoriloquy
becomes less evident or ceases altogether. It disappears also in
the two following cases, viz., when an excavation opens into the
pleura, particularly if the opening is large and direct; and when its
contents make their way through the walls of the chest into the
cellular membrane outside. Pectoriloquy may likewise be some-

* This fact may be explained on the principles of acoustics, and by a reference
to certain musical instruments.—AUTHOR.

times suspended for several hours, and even days, by the temporary obstruction of the communication of the cavity with the bronchi by the matter contained in it. We shall hereafter point out the method of obtaining pectoriloquy, or other equivalent signs, in cases of this kind.

Ægophony.—The phenomenon to which I have applied this name is, of all those furnished by auscultation, that which seems to me most complex in its causes. It may readily be confounded, by the inexperienced, with pectoriloquy; and still more so with bronchophony. I was myself long guilty of this mistake; and although the distinction is easy when the respective characters of each are strongly marked, there occur cases in which this is hardly practicable. My uncertainty as to the nature of ægophony was of longer duration, because it does not exist in every case of pleurisy; because the analogous phenomenon of bronchophony is still more frequently wanting in peripneumony; because these two diseases, and consequently the two phenomena in question, are frequently combined; and, finally, because the number of fatal cases of these diseases, more particularly of acute pleurisy, is too inconsiderable to afford many opportunities of verifying, by examination after death, the accuracy of the diagnosis derived from auscultation.*

Simple ægophony consists in a peculiar sound of the voice which accompanies or follows the articulation of words—it seems as if a kind of silvery voice, of a sharper and shriller tone than that of the patient, was vibrating on the surface of the lungs, sounding more like the echo of the voice than the voice itself. It rarely appears to enter the tube of the instrument, and scarcely ever passes through it entirely. It has, moreover, another character, so constant as to lead me to derive from it the appellation of the phenomenon—I mean a trembling or bleating sound like the voice of a goat, a character which is the more striking because the key or tone of it

---

* This assertion may seem strange to the practitioners who employ only bleeding and blisters in those diseases, but will be confirmed by the young physicians and students who have attended my *clinique* since I have been in the habit of using tartar emetic in large doses.—AUTHOR.

approaches that of this animal's voice.   When ægophony exists in
the vicinity of a large bronchial trunk, particularly towards the root
of the lungs, it is frequently combined with more or less of bronchophony.   The reunion of these affords numerous varieties, of
which we may have a good idea by recollecting the following
phenomena: (1) The sound of the voice through a metallic speaking trumpet or cleft reed; (2) that of a person speaking with a
counter between his lips and teeth; (3) the nasal intonations of the
juggler speaking in the character of Punch.   This last comparison
is frequently the most exact imaginable, particularly in persons
whose voice is somewhat bass (grave).   Very commonly, the same
individuals who exhibit at the roots of the lungs this combination of
the two phenomena yield simple ægophony about the outer and
lower edge of the scapula.

The sort of bleating so characteristic of ægophony seems, in
most cases, immediately connected with the articulation of the words,
although the patient's true voice has nothing of the sort: sometimes,
however, it seems unconnected with the articulation, so that we can
hear, at the same time, yet separately, the simple sound of the voice
and the bleating silvery sound of ægophony; which last appears to
be either nearer or more remote than the resonance of the simple
voice.   Sometimes, even, when the patient speaks slowly and interruptedly, we hear the bleating, like an imperfect echo, immediately after the voice.   These two last-named varieties have appeared
to me to exist only in cases of slight effusion.   To hear this sound
properly we must apply the cylinder strongly to the patient's chest,
and place the ear gently on the other end.   If the latter is forcibly
applied, the bleating sound is diminished one-half, and the phenomenon approaches nearer to bronchophony.

In comparing the results of my early and more recent experience
respecting ægophony, it seems to me certain that it exists only in
cases of pleurisy, either acute or chronic, attended by a moderate
effusion in the pleura, or in hydrothorax or other liquid extravasation in the same cavity.

All the cases in which I have observed ægophony since I have
been able to discriminate it from pectoriloquy and bronchophony

have, at the same time, afforded other undoubted signs of effusion into the chest.   In the examples of pleurisy which I have been able to attend to from their commencement to their close I found it as early as the first hours of the attack; but it has never been observed strongly marked until the second, third, or fourth day, and hardly ever until after the sound of respiration has become almost or altogether imperceptible in the affected side, and until this has yielded the dull sound on percussion.   I have observed ægophony in every case of pleurisy which has come under my care during the last five years, except in a few very slight acute cases, where the effusion (as proved by the auscultation of the respiration and by percussion) was inconsiderable, and in those which did not come under my notice until far advanced and when they were in progress towards recovery.   I have discovered this sign in cases where there did not exist above three or four ounces of fluid in the chest.   Ægophony decreases and gradually disappears as the effusion is absorbed.   In very acute cases it exists frequently two or three days only, and then totally disappears; in the chronic state of the disease with moderate effusion, I have found it sometimes continue for several months, with variations of intensity proportioned to the varying quantity of the effused fluid.   When this is very great, particularly when it is sufficient to cause dilatation of the chest, ægophony ceases entirely. I have never observed it in old cases of empyema in which the lungs were compressed upon the mediastinum; but have detected it, in an imperfect degree, in certain cases where the pleura contained from two to three pints of pus and where the lungs were prevented from being quite removed from the side by previous adhesions.   On the other hand, I have found that those cases which, when first seen, presented all the other signs of copious effusion except ægophony, yielded this sign also when the dilatation of the side diminished, and the other symptoms indicated the partial absorption of the fluid. In two cases of empyema operated on by my direction in 1821 and 1822 ægophony became much more manifest after the escape of a portion of the pus.

Ægophony is not like pectoriloquy, confined to one point, but extends over a certain continuous portion of the chest.   Most frequently it exists, at the same time, over the whole space between the scapula and spine, round the lower angle of the former bone, and in a zone from one to three fingers broad, following the line of the ribs from its middle to the nipple. This portion of the chest evidently corresponds with the internal parts where the effused fluid forms a thin layer on the surface of the lungs; it being well known that, in cases of moderate extravasation, the fluid collects principally in the lower part of the chest, when the patient is seated or resting on the back; and that, even in the cases where the whole surface of the lung is covered by it, the thickness of the layer progressively diminishes from below upwards, and is always much less before than behind. In a very few instances I have detected ægophony, at the commencement of the disease, over the whole affected side; in two of these I ascertained, by examination after death, that this peculiarity depended upon the retention of the lung in partial apposition with the chest, by means of pretty numerous adhesions, so that the lung became invested by a thin layer of fluid over its whole surface. In cases of this kind the sign in question is observable during the whole period of the disease.

I consider ægophony to be owing to the natural resonance of the voice in the bronchial tubes, rendered more distinct by the compression of the pulmonary texture, and by its transmission through a thin layer of fluid in a state of vibration. This opinion is supported by many facts and reasons. The points where it is constantly found correspond with the upper border of the fluid and where it is of least thickness. Moreover, if the patient turns on his face, the sound either disappears or is greatly diminished between the scapula and spine, while it continues on the side; and if he turns on the healthy side, the same result is obtained in the diseased side, now the uppermost. In respect of the influence of change of position upon this phenomenon, I have observed that the change was much less in cases where the quantity of fluid was either somewhat above or below the mean, than when it was of middling extent. The places formerly mentioned as yielding most distinct ægophony are those where the bronchial tubes are the largest and most numerous. This tends to confirm the truth of the opinion above stated, as

well as the fact of the cessation of the sign when the effusion becomes very copious, and its return on this being diminished: in the
former case it is evident that the bronchi, as well as the lungs, must
be compressed, while in the latter, they must be the first to recover
their natural shape on account of their superior elasticity. The
following circumstance, which I have now and then observed, leads
to the same conclusion. In cases where ægophony was very strongly
marked in the zone formerly mentioned, and where auscultation of
the respiration, percussion, and the general symptoms clearly
indicated an effusion, I have remarked from day to day the following changes take place in respect of this sign, and precisely at the
same moment that the other signs just enumerated gave evidence
of the progressive absorption of the fluid: it had become less loud
everywhere; it had lost three inches in extent, reckoning from above
downwards, in the interscapular region, and one inch on the side,
and had entirely disappeared in front; while, on the other hand, it
had become very distinct, though not loud, over the whole inferior
parts of the side and back, where it did not exist at all on the preceding day. These changes, I think, indicated the recession of the fluid
from the upper parts and its diminution in the lower. In fact,
I am of opinion that this phenomenon only exists when the lung is
enveloped with a thin layer of fluid; and that in the instances just
mentioned it became perceptible on the lower parts of the chest, only
because the quantity of this had diminished. This opinion is
further rendered probable by the fact of the respiration being always
very distinct in the places where ægophony exists, while it is not observed at all or very feebly below these places; and, by the additional observation, that when the ægophony descends, as above
mentioned, the respiration becomes stronger in the points which it
leaves, and reappears in those which it now occupies. I have already stated that in cases of very copious effusion there is usually no
ægophony, or if it exists at all, it is only near the roots of the lungs,
a situation where the fluid is necessarily less than anywhere else.

It will be difficult to fix, more precisely than I have now endeav-
oured to do, the exact relation between the bronchi and the thoracic
effusion which gives rise to ægophony. This will be the more

difficult on account of the small number of cases that prove fatal during the existence of this phenomenon. When death occurs from pleurisy, the effusion is generally very abundant, and ægophony has, therefore, disappeared. In looking for assistance from morbid anatomy, in this instance, we are, therefore, reduced to the very small number of cases that prove fatal from some concomitant disease, at the very time when the patients happened to be affected with pleurisy in that stage wherein ægophony exists.

I made an experiment with the view to ascertain the effect of an interposed fluid in modifying the voice to the character it possesses in ægophony, by applying a bladder, half filled with water, between the scapulæ of a young man who presented a well-marked natural bronchophony in this point. In this case it appeared to myself and several persons present that the voice, as transmitted through the liquid, became more acute, and also slightly tremulous, although less decidedly so than in real ægophony. The same experiment tried over the larynx gives a similar result.

It seems probable that the compression of the bronchial tubes by the pleuritic effusion contributes a good deal to the production of this phenomenon; since this must bring them into a form analogous to the *reeds* of certain wind instruments, such as the oboe and bassoon, which have something of the *bleating* sound of ægophony. This alteration of form, however, will not of itself account for the phenomenon without the presence of fluid, else it would exist in cases of contraction of the chest subsequent to pleurisy, which is not a fact. It would also be found in many cases of phthisis, wherein tubercles frequently compress the bronchi in the most decided manner.

I think there are only three cases of pleurisy in which this phenomenon will not be observed; these are: (1) Where a very rapid and copious effusion has suddenly compressed the lung against the mediastinum; (2) where a former attack of the same disease has firmly attached the posterior parts of the lung to the pleura; and (3) where there is hardly any liquid extravasation, but the formation, simply, of false membranes. This last case is very rare; and, besides, I have found ægophony where not more than two or three ounces of fluid existed.

From the preceding observations I think we are entitled to conclude that ægophony is a favourable sign in pleurisy, as it seems uniformly to indicate a moderate degree of effusion. Its continuance for some time is a favourable omen, as showing that the effusion does not increase; if it continues as long as the fever, or longer, we may be assured that the disease will not become chronic, as this never happens except when the effusion is extremely abundant. I have frequently drawn this prognostic, and have never been deceived in it. In every case where I have seen acute pleurisy terminate in chronic this phenomenon has ceased, or been much lessened, previously to the decrease of the febrile symptoms.

Ægophony, like pectoriloquy, is sometimes suspended for a longer or shorter time, reappearing after the patient has coughed or expectorated. But this happens much less frequently in the case of the former, as might be expected from the comparatively small bronchial secretion in pleurisy.

Some physicians have lately fancied that they have met with ægophony in cases of simple peripneumony without any pleuritic effusion; but I have no doubt they mistook bronchophony for it. It must be admitted that the two phenomena are likely to be confounded; I shall, therefore, in this place, compare them with each other, as well as with pectoriloquy:

1. Pectoriloquy being, in the great majority of cases, owing to the presence of tuberculous excavations, is almost always met with in the upper lobes. In whatsoever part, however, it may exist, it will always be readily distinguished by the accompanying cavernous rhonchus, respiration, and cough. In certain rare instances, namely, where the excavation is of a flattened shape with rather solid walls, pectoriloquy may assume something of the vibratory character of ægophony; but it will almost always be distinguished from it by the exact circumscription of the sound to a small space, by its situation, and by the consideration of the accompanying phenomena.

2. Bronchophony, being caused by the simple induration of the substance of the lungs, does not yield the clear transmission of the voice through the tube, except at the roots of the lungs. The sphere of this phenomenon is always over a certain extent, and no

one small point can be said to be its exclusive site. The same is true of the respiration and cough; the former is frequently found to be *bronchial*, and the latter to give the *mucous rhonchus*, but they are diffused over a certain space, and not, like those which are observed in cases of pectoriloquy, confined within a circumscribed spot. Bronchophony is less readily suspended than pectoriloquy, but more frequently than ægophony, for obvious reasons, depending on the relative condition of the bronchial secretion in the diseases in which each especially occurs. Finally, the tone or key of the speaking trumpet completes the list of the distinctive characters of bronchophony.

3. True and simple ægophony is characterised by the harsh, tremulous, silvery tones of the voice which is commonly more acute than the natural voice of the patient, and seems to be quite superficial, and to float, as it were, on the surface of the lungs, instead of coming from the interior, like pectoriloquy and bronchophony. It seems, moreover, to be rather the echo of the voice, repeating the words or their final syllables, in a small sharp and tremulous key, than the voice itself. This character of ægophony is especially marked when it exists in the anterior and lateral parts of the chest; since between the scapulæ and at their lower edge (to which situation, by the way, it is most commonly restricted) it is almost always conjoined with the natural bronchophony, rendered stronger by the compression of the lungs in that part. And it is here, in the space between the inner edge of the scapula and the spine, and in this part only, that we occasionally perceive the bleating ægophonic voice completely traversing the tube, with the most perfect resemblance of the squeaking of Punch. Ægophony and bronchophony are necessarily conjoined in cases of pleuro-peripneumony; and, indeed, pectoriloquy may co-exist with them when an abscess of the lung supervenes.

When I published the first edition* of this work I was not quite sure that ægophony might not exist in simple peripneumony: farther experience, however, has completely convinced me that this

* See foot-note, p. 157.—(C. N. B. C.)

cannot be the case. Whatever analogy there may be between this phenomenon and bronchophony, it is easy to distinguish them when they exist separately; and an experienced ear may recognise them, in most cases, when they co-exist in pleuro-peripneumony. Certain cases, however, will always be doubtful; and when it is so, we must be contented with the portion that is certain. The following positions seemed proved: (1) That ægophony exists in simple pleurisy, and in no case with more decided characters; (2) that bronchophony exists frequently in peripneumony, and with features sufficiently well marked to distinguish it from ægophony; (3) that both these co-exist in certain cases of pleuro-peripneumony.

When we meet with cases where the results obtained from percussion and the auscultation of the respiration leave reason to doubt as to the existence of pleurisy or peripneumony, if we find ægophony very complete and little mixed with bronchophony, we may conclude that the disease is exclusively the former, or nearly so; and, on the other hand, if the bronchophony is strongly marked, and with merely a shade of the stuttering cracked note of ægophony, we may decide upon peripneumony being the chief disease, conjoined, probably, with a slight pleuritic effusion. We may even conclude against the existence of any effusion if the characteristics of ægophony are observed only at the inner border of the scapula.

I have dwelt the longer upon these distinctions because they form perhaps the most difficult point in auscultation, and particularly because ægophony is the only one among the stethoscopic signs whose value has been called in question by competent judges. Cases of simple peripneumony, in which ægophony was supposed to exist, have been communicated to me by several of my colleagues and by many pupils. All these, as far as I had the means of ascertaining, were examples of bronchophony mistaken for ægophony, or a mixture of the two. In like manner I am constantly meeting with cases in the hospital where the two phenomena are confounded by the pupils; but when I have pointed out the distinction between them, and they have acquired more experience, they hesitate only in cases which are really doubtful.

SECTION III

Auscultation of the Cough

Coughing in a healthy state of the lungs excites no particular sound within the chest. When we listen with the cylinder on the larynx or trachea, and at the roots of the lungs where the chest is narrow, besides the shock communicated by the act of coughing we hear, at the same time, a sound as of the transmission of air in a tube. When the lungs are inflamed to the degree of hepatization, this peculiar sound becomes more manifest at the root of the lungs, and even in the bronchial tubes, not larger than a goose-quill, than it is in the trachea in a state of health; I, therefore, shall designate it *tubary cough*.* This cough is found also in cases of pleurisy, but at the roots of the lungs only. It exists equally in cases of dilatation of the bronchi, and may serve as a test of the degree of dilatation. Where there exists an excavation in the lungs communicating with the bronchi, the cough resounds in it as it does in the larynx, but is confined to a small space; it also gives rise to the *cavernous rhonchus*, and more readily than simple respiration does, particularly if there is still much matter contained in it, and not in a very liquid state. If the excavation is empty, this emptiness is indicated by the *cavernous cough*, better than any other phenomenon. Coughing gives also, in certain cases, the *metallic tinkling*, when it is not perceptible by the respiration or voice. When pectoriloquy is suspended in a tuberculous excavation, from obstruction of the bronchi by the sputa, coughing restores it by the expulsion of these, or excites the cavernous rhonchus, which is of the same import as a diagnostic sign: it clears in like manner the fistulous communications between the pleura and bronchi. In the excavations, where the tuberculous matter has only begun to be softened, and in the incipient abscess of peripneumony, while simple respiration is still unable to excite any rhonchus, coughing will often give a very strong

---

* Andral and Corvisart recommended "bronchial" instead of "tubary," a term now universally employed.—C. N. B. C.

guggling. And it may be stated as a general truth that all the sounds to be described in the next section are more audible during the act of coughing than during simple respiration. However, in deducing our indications from the auscultation of the cough, certain precautions are necessary. Sometimes a violent cough seems rather to close than open the pulmonary channels, producing a great commotion of the lungs and walls of the thorax without giving rise to any guggling. At other times, in timid patients, the cough seems confined to the throat, and excites no resonance in the bronchi.* One of the cases where this intentional cough is most useful is in that variety of the dry catarrh wherein the respiratory sound is inaudible under ordinary circumstances. Here the act of coughing, which, as we have formerly observed, is always either preceded or followed by a powerful inspiration, enables us to hear the sound of respiration, and thereby to judge of the condition of the lungs. The same measure is equally valuable in incipient peripneumony, especially if grafted on a chronic dry catarrh. In this case percussion elicits a sound which is either doubtful or delusive, and common respiration is inaudible; but the cough restores the respiratory murmur whenever the lungs are permeable, and enables us to detect the crepitous rhonchus, the pathognomonic sign of incipient peripneumony.

It is proper to observe that we ought not to have recourse to the factitious cough as a means of exploration, except where simple respiration is insufficient, as it may fatigue our patients. At the same time I may add that its inconveniences, in this respect, are less than may be imagined; as one single cough, and that rather moderate than otherwise, is sufficient to afford to an experienced observer all the signs which this phenomenon is capable of yielding.

* In this latter case we desire the patient to cough after taking a deep inspiration.—AUTHOR.

SECTION IV

AUSCULTATION OF SOUNDS NOT NECESSARILY ACCOMPANYING THE
RESPIRATION AND VOICE

Various sounds, foreign to the natural respiratory murmur or
resonance of the voice, may arise within the chest from various
accidental causes: I shall class these under two heads—*the rhonchus
and metallic tinkling.*

I. *Of the different kinds of rhonchus**

For want of a better or more generic term I use the word *rhonchus* to express all the sounds, besides those of health, which the act
of respiration gives rise to, from the passage of the air through
fluids in the bronchi or lungs, or by its transmission through any of
the air-passages partially contracted. These sounds likewise accompany the cough, and are made even more perceptible by it;
but in most cases the auscultation of the respiration suffices for their
exploration. They are extremely various; and although they possess, in general, very striking characters, it becomes difficult so to
describe them as to convey anything like a correct notion to those
who have never heard them. Sensations, we know, can only be
communicated to others by comparisons; and although those which
I shall employ may seem to myself sufficiently exact, they may not
be so to others. I expect, however, that my description will enable
any observer of ordinary application to recognise them when he
meets with them, as they are much more easily distinguished than
described.

We can distinguish five principal kinds of rhonchi: (1) The
moist crepitous rhonchus, or *crepitation;* (2) the mucous rhonchus,
or *guggling;* (3) the dry sonorous rhonchus, or *snoring;* (4) the dry
sibilous rhonchus, or *whistling;* (5) the dry crepitous rhonchus,
with large bubbles, or *crackling.*

*See foot-note, p. 167.—(C. N. B. C.)

1. *The moist crepitous rhonchus* has evidently its site in the substance of the lungs. It resembles the sound produced by the crepitation of salts in a vessel exposed to a gentle heat, or that produced by blowing into a dried bladder, or it is still more like that emitted by the healthy lungs when distended by air and compressed in the hand, only stronger. Besides the sound of crepitation, a sensation of humidity in the part is clearly conveyed. We feel that the pulmonary cells contain a watery fluid as well as air, and that the intermixture of the two fluids produces bubbles of extreme minuteness.

This species of rhonchus is one of the most important, and, fortunately, it is most easily distinguished, a single observation being sufficient to mark it ever after. It is the pathognomonic sign of the first stage of peripneumony, disappearing on the supervention of hepatization, and reappearing with the resolution of the inflammation. It is found also in œdema of the lungs, and sometimes in pulmonary apoplexy, but in these two cases *the bubbles* usually seem to be somewhat larger and moister than in the rhonchus of peripneumony. This variety I call subcrepitous.

2. *The Mucous Rhonchus.*—This is produced by the passage of the air through sputa accumulated in the bronchi, or through the softened matter of tubercles yet undischarged. It presents many varieties of character,which can hardly be defined, and of which, indeed, we can only form any notion by comparing the perceptions derived from the sense of hearing with such as we fancy might be conveyed by the sense of sight. In listening to it we receive the impression or idea of bubbles, such as are produced by blowing through a pipe into soapy water. The ear seems to appreciate most distinctly the consistence of the fluid which forms the bubbles, and also their varying sizes. The consistence of the fluid appears always greater in the mucous than in the crepitous rhonchus.

In respect of the size of the bubbles in the different rhonchi they may be estimated as *very large, large, middling, small*. The last term is especially applicable to the crepitous rhonchus of peripneumony, in which it seems as if an infinity of minute, equal-sized bubbles, formed at once, were thrilling or vibrating, rather than boiling, on the surface of a fluid. The mucous rhonchus, on the contrary, appears always larger, and most usually unequal, so as to convey the idea of a liquid into which some one is blowing, and thereby producing bubbles, of which some are of the size of a filbert, and others only as large as a cherry-stone or hempseed. We can estimate the quantity as well as the size of the bubbles, and may thus designate the rhonchus as *abundant* or *rare*. Accordingly, it sometimes seems that the point of lung beneath the stethoscope is filled with bubbles that touch each other; and at other times there seems to be only one here and there, while the intervening portion of lung yields the simple sound of respiration, or yields no sound at all, as the case may be. When the mucous rhonchus is very large and infrequent we can distinctly perceive the bubbles form and burst. When it exists at once copious, large, and constant, it is sometimes so noisy as to resemble the rolling of a drum.

A variety of the mucous is the *tracheal rhonchus*. It is observed when there is accumulated much mucus or other sputa in the larynx, trachea, or larger bronchial tubes, and may be readily heard by the unassisted ear, as in the case of the *dead-rattles* of the vulgar, from which I have derived the general appellation of the phenomenon. This species, or rather variety, may exist without there being any other perceived in the bronchi by the stethoscope; but the reverse of this is much more common, namely, that the instrument conveys to us a rhonchus, even a very loud one, when we perceive nothing by the unassisted ear. When examined by the cylinder, this rhonchus, which has its seat in the trachea, has almost always the character of the mucous rhonchus described above. The bubbles seem to be extremely numerous and very large. The sound is occasionally so loud as to resemble a drum or the noise of a carriage on the pavement. In these cases the rhonchus is perceived over the whole sternum, and is accompanied by a vibration very perceptible to the touch; we can even sometimes perceive it over the whole chest and through the interposed lung. In this last case, however, there is no vibration attending it, and we recognize, at once, that the sound originates in a remote point. This variety of rhonchus is sometimes so noisy as to mask the sound of the heart's action, and also of respiration, over a great portion of the chest; and in all cases where it exists in a certain degree of intensity we are unable to perceive the heart's pulsations under the sternum unless we request the patient to suspend respiration for a moment.

The tracheal rhonchus is only observed in this great degree in violent hæmoptysis, and in the severer paroxysms of the mucous catarrh of old persons, termed *suffocative catarrh.* It is found in most dying persons, particularly in cases of phthisis, peripneumony, diseases of the heart, and severe idiopathic fevers. In all cases, when it exists in a high degree, it may be regarded as of evil omen. In a lesser degree it exists in the acute pulmonary catarrh, in the severe cases of the chronic mucous catarrh, and in all diseases complicated with these. It may be reckoned as one of the worst symptoms which appear in fever. In concluding this notice of the tracheal rhonchus it ought to be observed that when too slight to be heard by the naked ear, it becomes very manifest on applying the stethoscope.

The mucous rhonchus, properly so called, exists principally in the pulmonary catarrh with copious secretion of mucus, and in hæmoptysis, and often also in peripneumony and phthisis. In the two former diseases it is caused by the transmission of air through the mucus or blood contained in the bronchi; in the two latter, it may have its seat in the same place, but it may also originate in cavities produced by an abscess or eschar of the lungs, or by softened tubercles. In the latter cases the rhonchus has a peculiar character which I shall denominate *cavernous.* It is more than usually *abundant and large,* and is confined also to a small space, within which we commonly observe, at the same time, both the cavernous respiration and pectoriloquism. It is more especially during the act of coughing that we detect this circumscribed or cavernous rhonchus. On some occasions we can even distinguish the consistence of the fluid contained in the excavation by means of the particular impulse communicated by the cough.

In certain rare instances the mucous rhonchus may be recognized, or at least suspected, independently of auscultation, either mediate or immediate.   I have sometimes noticed, while percussing the clavicle or neighbouring parts of the chest, in phthisical cases, a sort of vibration like that yielded by a cracked pot when gently struck, accompanied with an evident hollow resonance, and even with a humid crepitation or guggling.   The phenomenon indicates the presence of tuberculous excavations near the surface of the lungs. It is, however, by no means common, and has only been observed in subjects with very thin elastic chests, and, perhaps, with the clavicular ligaments more than usually lax.   Some of these patients are themselves conscious of the guggling of the tuberculous matter during percussion; and others can point out the seat of the excavation from the sensation occasioned by the detachment of the sputa from it during expectoration.   This last circumstance is, however, very uncommon.

I have sometimes also perceived in tuberculous excavations of the upper lobes a mucous rhonchus, or slight guggling, corresponding with, and no doubt caused by, the pulsation of the subclavian artery.   This case is extremely rare, as indeed it must be, when we consider the numerous circumstances that must conspire towards its production.   In an equally rare class of cases a strong mucous or cavernous rhonchus can sometimes be perceived by the naked ear, or on applying the hand to the part.   I do not here allude to the guggling rhonchus of the trachea or the bronchi already noticed, but to one confined to a small space, and this often at a distance from the larger bronchial tubes.   I have observed this phenomenon only in cases where the matter of an excavation had made its way through the walls of the chest, and formed a tumour beneath the skin; or where it had escaped into old cellular adhesions uniting the lungs to the chest; or, finally, where a large anfractuous excavation, half full of matter, lay near the surface of a lung closely united to the walls of the chest.*

* Sometimes when the sound of respiration is suspended or very weak, the *bubbles* of the mucous rhonchus become very small, few in number, and not perceptible, except on a deep inspiration; at other times, when the respiration is pretty good, it is found not to be *pure* or *clear*.   An inexperienced auscultator might be apt to confound these varieties (which may be named *obscure*) with a weak, crepitous rhonchus.—AUTHOR.

3. *The Dry Sonorous Rhonchus.*—This is more variable in its character than the two preceding kinds. It consists in a flat (grave) sound, sometimes extremely loud, resembling at times the snoring of a person asleep, at other times the sound produced by friction on a bass string, and occasionally the cooing of the wood-pigeon. This resemblance is sometimes so striking that we might be tempted to believe the bird concealed under the patient's bed. This last variety of sound is commonly confined to a small space. I have sometimes observed it in cases of pulmonary fistulæ of a middling size, and also in cases of dilated bronchi. I apprehend it can hardly exist in bronchial tubes of a small diameter. We must not confound the sonorous rhonchus with the guttural sounds formerly mentioned, which, unlike this, have their seat in the fauces, as may be ascertained by the application of the stethoscope.

It is difficult to ascertain the precise cause of this species of rhonchus. Neither the character of the sound nor the examination of the parts after death leads to the belief that it depends on the passage of the breath through any kind of matter. On the contrary, it would seem to depend rather on some alteration in the shape of the tubes through which the air passes, and I am disposed to attribute it in most cases to the contraction, from some cause or other, of the origin of a bronchial branch. This contraction may be either permanent or temporary, and may be occasioned by the pressure of an enlarged gland or of a circumscribed spot of inflammation, the presence of a tenacious clot of mucus, or the local thickening of the mucous membrane. It may not be easy on these grounds to explain the reason of the key of the sound being flatter instead of sharper, as might be expected from the contraction of the aperture; but we have an analogous case in the thickening of the membrane of the larynx and glottis in catarrh, when the voice, as we know, becomes hoarse and flatter than natural.

4. *The Dry Sibilous Rhonchus.*—This is also of very various character. Sometimes it is like a prolonged whistle, flat or sharp, dull or loud; sometimes it is very momentary, and resembles the chirping of birds, the sound emitted by suddenly separating two portions of smooth oiled stone, or by the action of a small valve.

The different kinds often exist together in different parts of the lungs or successively in the same part.   The peculiar nature of the sound, and the appearances on dissection, seem to prove the sibilant rattle to be owing to minute portions of very viscid mucus obstructing, more or less completely, the small bronchial ramifications. This explanation applies more especially to the variety resembling the sound of a valve, which is, indeed, only a variety of the mucous rhonchus; the kind more strictly sibilous is probably occasioned rather by a local contraction of the smaller bronchi from thickening of their inner membrane.

5. *The Dry Crepitous Rhonchus, with Large Bubbles.*—This species is observed only during inspiration. It conveys the impression as of air entering and distending lungs which had been dried,—and of which the cells had been very unequally dilated,—and entirely resembles the sound produced by blowing into a dried bladder.

This variety is the pathognomonic sign of emphysema of the pulmonary substance and of the interlobular emphysema. In the last disease it is much more distinct. We have a sound like this in the common subcutaneous emphysema, on pressing interruptedly with the ear on the stethoscope, or with the fingers, in the vicinity of the affected part.

Besides the peculiar sound produced by the various species of rhonchus, there is also to be noticed a slight vibration communicated to the cylinder when the seat of the phenomenon happens to be immediately beneath it. This sensation, like that occasioned by the voice, may sometimes be felt by the hand very distinctly. It is usually very strongly marked in the mucous and sonorous rhonchi, less in the crepitant, and still less in the sibilous. When the rhonchus has its seat remote from the point where the instrument rests, although it is heard very strongly, no vibration is felt; and when this can be discovered in no point of the surface of the chest, we may conclude that the cause of the rhonchus exists in the central parts of the lungs. This distinction may appear subtle, but I can assure the reader that it is one very easily made; and that a very little experience will enable any one to ascertain the distance of the rhonchus from the point of exploration.

Some of the species of rhonchus, especially the mucous and crepitous, cannot be distinguished at the distance of one or two inches from their site. The other kinds may frequently be perceived through the whole width of the chest, and are thus often combined with the former. In this manner, while we perceive a mucous rhonchus on one side of the chest, we may at the very same instant hear a dry sonorous rhonchus, which has its seat in the opposite lung. This complication is, however, very easily distinguished from a simple mucous rhonchus, however noisy.

From the very striking and conspicuous characters of the various *rhonchi* described it might be imagined that they would furnish some of the most valuable of our diagnostic signs. Taken singly, however, they are very inferior in this respect to the data supplied by auscultation of the respiration and the voice. Conjoined with other signs they become extremely valuable; the two crepitous rhonchi, and also and more especially the cavernous, are frequently more certain than any other of our signs.

II. *Of the metallic tinkling*

This phenomenon consists of a peculiar sound which bears a striking resemblance to that emitted by a cup of metal, glass, or porcelain, when gently struck with a pin, or into which a grain of sand is dropped. This sound does not at all depend on the nature of the materials of which the stethoscope is composed: it is perceived during respiration, speaking, and coughing; but is much more perceptible during the two latter than the former. The reverse of this is, however, sometimes the case. It is, in general, heard in a most striking manner during coughing; and when in any degree doubtful, this action ought to be performed.

The metallic tinkling produced by the voice differs according as pectoriloquy exists or not. In the former case *the tinkling*, as well as the voice, traverses the tube; in the latter, we merely hear within the chest a slight sharp sound like that occasioned by the vibration of a metallic cord touched by the finger.

The metallic tinkling always originates in a morbid excavation within the chest, containing partly air and partly liquid. It exists only, therefore, in two cases—viz., where a serous or purulent effusion co-exists with pneumo-thorax; or when a large tuberculous excavation of the lung is only partly filled with very liquid pus. It is further necessary, for the manifestation of this phenomenon, in cases of empyema or hydrothorax complicated with pneumo-thorax, that the cavity of the pleura should communicate directly with a bronchial tube by means of a fistula, such as has place when a tuberculous vomica, abscess, or eschar of the lungs opens into the chest. This sign may, on this account, be considered as pathognomonic of this triple lesion. From it we may also further have an idea of the size of the fistulous perforation, as well as of the relative proportion of air and liquid in the chest, since the phenomenon is more distinct according as the fistula is larger; while the extent of the vibrations of the sound corresponds with the extent of the spaces occupied by the air.*

Sometimes the tinkling assumes another character, and strikingly resembles the sound produced by blowing into a flask or bottle. This, like the tinkling, is equally produced by the cough, voice, or respiration; and in some cases the tinkling accompanies one of these and the buzzing of the other. I have named it from analogy, *utricular buzzing*, or *amphoric resonance (bourdonnement amphorique)*. This sound sometimes co-exists and sometimes alternates with metallic tinkling. Where the resonance or buzzing exists alone, or much more frequently than the tinkling, I have been led to attribute it either to there being more than one fistulous opening, or to the cavity in which it originates being very large, and containing only a very small quantity of liquid.†

* This may also be very exactly done by means of auscultation and percussion; the latter gives the sound of great emptiness, intermixed now and then with tinkling. I conceive that the phenomenon will be less distinct when the liquid is in *very small* quantity than where it is in more equal proportion with the air.—AUTHOR.

† The metallic tinkling is also sometimes heard independently of the voice, cough, or respiration; namely, when a patient affected with pneumo-thorax with liquid effusion is placed in the sitting posture, and some of the fluid which still adheres to the upper part of the cavity falls in drops into that beneath.—AUTHOR.

I had long suspected that the metallic tinkling and amphoric resonance would be heard after the operation of empyema, but it was not till April, 1822, that I was enabled to verify my conjecture, in the case of a patient who had been operated on about a month before. When an injection was thrown in by the wound, the fall of the liquid upon that previously in the cavity of the chest produced a well-marked tinkling. The stethoscope did not detect any respiratory sound in the part affected, but the entrance and escape of the air through the wound gave rise to an extremely distinct utricular buzzing. Upon plugging the wound a slight and dull hissing, occasioned by the passage of the air by the side of the tent, was only heard; but when the patient spoke, a distinct tinkling was perceived. This last fact would seem to show that a large communication with the external air converts the tinkling into simple buzzing. It is worthy of note in this case that there was no fistulous communication between the pleura and bronchi, and consequently that the tinkling sound could only be produced by the vibration occasioned by the resonance of the voice in the lung, which latter, it is further to be observed, was greatly compressed and covered with a strong false membrane. The metallic tinkling and utricular buzzing never exist unless when the air in the pleura communicates with the bronchi, except in the rare case mentioned in the note.*

I expect that future observations will discover other phenomena foreign to those naturally produced by the respiration, cough, and action of the heart, and which may prove useful signs in particular cases; yet I think it probable that such signs will be few in number, since, in the period that has elapsed since the publication of my first edition, my own researches, as well as those made in all the hospitals of Paris by a great many physicians and pupils, have discovered only a single one of the kind. I owe this to Dr. Honoré, who first perceived it in a case of pleuro-peripneumony in the spring

---

* There is a phenomenon of no value as a sign, but which an inexperienced observer might perhaps mistake for the metallic tinkling. If one percusses the chest at the same time that the stethoscope is applied, more especially close to the instrument, we perceive a sort of *metallic clicking* very like that produced by the handling of firearms in the military exercise. The same is sometimes perceived, in a less degree, during coughing.—AUTHOR.

of 1824, and afterwards in June of the same year. This latter
patient I saw, and made the following observations on his case:
the sound of respiration was feeble over the whole chest, and nearly
extinct in the inferior part of the left side, which had been the seat
of the effusion. On applying the stethoscope on the fourth rib,
about three inches from its cartilaginous portion, I perceived a dull
sound, such as would be produced under the stethoscope by the
friction of the finger against a bone, and further conveying the sensation as of a body rising and falling, and at the same time rubbing
somewhat harshly against another. The site of the phenomenon
was evidently very close to the walls of the chest. It was only very
distinct when the inspirations were deep; and at these times not only
was the patient sensible of the circumstance, but it was perceptible
to us on applying the hand over the part. I have since observed the
same thing in twelve or fifteen cases, under different circumstances,
and have been able to ascertain its most frequent cause. In most
cases, then, this phenomenon (which I shall call the *sound of
friction* of ascent and descent) is occasioned by the interlobular emphysema of the lungs. Together with the *crackling rhonchus*, or
dry crepitous rhonchus with large bubbles, it is indeed the pathognomonic sign of this lesion; and, as will be seen hereafter, may offer
many varieties of character.

In passing in review all the known lesions of the lungs and pleura,
there is one other which might possibly give occasion to this sound
of friction—the existence, namely, of a cartilaginous, bony, tuberculous, or other indurated tumor projecting from the surface of the
lung. This is, however, a mere conjecture; but should it prove
true, it is probable that the case in question would be readily dis-
tinguishable from emphysema, firstly, because it would present none
of the other signs of the last-mentioned disease; and, secondly,
because, owing to the accompanying humidity of the surfaces, the
resulting sounds would be duller and softer.

As the exploration of the heart and large vessels affords only
diagnostic signs in the diseases of these organs, I shall defer the
notice of this branch of auscultation until I come to treat of them,
and I shall transfer to the Appendix the application of the method

to the diagnosis of several cases unconnected with diseases of the chest.

LIST OF LAËNNEC'S WRITINGS AND EDITIONS *

Propositions sur la doctrine d'Hippocrate, relativement à la médecine pratique, 39 pp., quarto, Paris, an XII (1804), No. 241, v, 49.

1802–3.—A treatise on peritonitis in the *Journal de Médecine.*

1803–4.—A treatise on the capsule of the liver.

1804.—Description of an anatomical process by the aid of which the internal membrane of the ventricles of the brain can be dissected, of which the anatomists admitted the existence by analogy, but without having demonstrated it with the scalpel.

1804.—A treatise on pathological anatomy.

1805.—Monograph on vesicular worms, containing a description of several new species, and of the diseases and organic changes to which the presence of these worms gives rise in the human body.

1806.—A treatise on the melanoses, etc.

1806.—A treatise on angina of the chest; a treatise on a new species of hernia.

In the *Dictionary of the Medical Sciences* Laënnec also wrote on "Pathological Anatomy," "Hydatids," and "Encephaloides." In the *Journal de Médecine* there appeared essays on "Suicide," "Disease of the Heart," "Hydrocephalus," an article on the "Brunonian System of Medicine," and the "Works and Doctrines of Gall." (Thayer's "Laënnec.")

De l'auscultation médiate, ou traité du diagnostic des maladies des poumons et du cœur fondé principalement sur ce nouveau moyen d'exploration, 2 v, XLVIII, 456 pp., 4 l., 4 pl.; XVI, 472 pp., octavo, Paris, J. A. Brosson and J. S. Chaudé, 1819.

The same. Traité de l'auscultation médiate et des maladies des poumons et du cœur, 2. éd., 2 v, xxxvi, 728 pp., 4 pl.; 790 pp., 1 l., octavo, Paris, J. S. Chaudé, 1826.

The same. 3 éd., augmentée de notes par Mériadec Laënnec, 3 v, octavo, Paris, J. S. Chaudé, 1831.

The same. Avec les notes et addition de M. M.(eriadec) Laënnec, 4 éd. Considérablement augmentée par M. Andral, 3 v, octavo, Paris, J. S. Chaudé, 1837.

The same. A Treatise on the Diseases of the Chest in which they are Described According to their Anatomical Characters, and their Diagnosis Established on a New Principle by means of Acoustick Instruments, Transl. from the French, with a preface and notes by John Forbes, first Am. ed., VIII, 319 pp., 8 pl., octavo, Philadelphia, J. Webster, 1823.

The same. From the third revised London edition, with additional notes, XXVIII, 736 pp., 8 pl., octavo, New York, S. Wood and Sons, 1830.

The same. Transl. from the third French edition, with copious notes, a sketch of the author's life, and an extensive bibliography of the different diseases, by John Forbes. To which are added the notes of Prof. Andral, contained in the fourth and latest French edition, translated and accompanied with

* From various sources.

observations on Cerebral Auscultation by John D. Fisher, XLVIII, 784 pp., 2 pl., octavo, New York, S. S. and W. Wood, 1838.

The same. With the notes and additions of Mér(iadec) Laënnec, and of Andral. Transl. from the latest edition by a member of the College of Physicians. Edited by Theophilus Herbert, with practical notes condensed from the lectures of F. H. Ramadge, XXXI, 862 pp., 9 pl., octavo, London, H. Baillière, 1846.

Traité de l'auscultation médiate, et des maladies des poumons et du cœur, XXIV, 986 pp., 1 pl., octavo, Paris, Asselin and Cie, 1879.

Traité inédit sur l'anatomie pathologique, ou exposition des altérations visibles qu'éprouve le corps humain dans l'état de Maladie, introduction et premier chapitre précédés d'une préface par V. Cornil, XIII, 77 pp., 2 port., octavo, Paris, Germer-Baillière et Cie, 1884.

Mémoire sur les vers vésiculaires et principalement sur ceux qui se trouvent dans les corps humain, 176 pp., 4 pl., quarto (Paris, 1804).

Traitè de l'auscultation médiate et des maladies des poumons et du cœur. Nouvelle ed., publiée par les soins du . . . C. J. B. Comet, et augmentée d'une notice historique sur Laënnec, rédigée par M. Bayle, XXXII, 657 pp., 5 pl., 2 l., octavo, Bruxelles, 1828.

The same. De l'auscultation médiate de l'explorations de la poitrine, 142 pp., 12mo, Paris, G. Masson, 1893.

The same. Die mittelbare Auscultation . . . handlung über die Diagnostik der Krankheiten der Lunge und des Herzens, auf das neue . . . Nach dem Französischen im Auszuge bearbeitet, VI, XVI, 618 pp., 4 pl., octavo Weimar, 1822.

The same. A Treatise on the Diseases of the Chest and Mediate Auscultation, second edition, greatly enlarged. Translated from the French with notes and a sketch of the author's life, by John Forbes, 1 p. l., XXVIII, 722 pp., octavo, London, T. G. Underwood, 1827.

The same. Third edition, XXVIII, 736 pp., 8 pl., octavo, London, T. G. Underwood, 1829.

The same. From the fourth London edition, considerably enlarged and improved, with many additional notes and an extensive bibliography of the different diseases, XLIV, 675 pp., 2 pl., octavo, New York, S. Wood, 1835.

Vaccination against Smallpox

Engraved by Ridley from an original Painting by Northcote

EDWARD JENNER M.D.

Published by J. Asperne, at the Bible, Crown & Constitution Cornhill 1, Oct 1804.

EDWARD JENNER

1749–1823

Jenner was born in Berkeley, Gloucestershire, England, May 17, 1749. At nineteen years of age, after receiving a general education, he served apprenticeship under a country physician at Sodbury near Bristol. When thus engaged (1768) a young country woman applied to him for medical advice. In questioning her regarding smallpox she observed, "I cannot take that disease for I have had the cow-pox." Though this was a theory commonly accepted among country folk, it never had gained the least credence among physicians. Living in a farming district, Jenner must often have heard this rumoured about; but the particular instance here recorded marks the time when he first considered seriously its scientific possibilities, which he did not fully realize till nearly twenty-five years later. In 1770 he went to London to complete his medical studies at St. George's Hospital. While in London he lived at the house of John Hunter. The association with this great man exerted a lasting influence upon Jenner, and the friendship thus begun continued till Hunter's death. With Hunter he discussed the cow-pox question and was encouraged to pursue his investigation. This is of significance, for, as will be seen below, he was himself very sceptical, and everyone either ridiculed him or listened with the attention yielded those exploiting an absurd theory. Through his association with Hunter he had entered into the study of anatomy and natural history, and in consequence of his proficiency in these subjects was offered the position of naturalist on one of the expeditions of the navigator Cook. This offer, tempting to a physician of twenty-two years of age, recently qualified, he declined, and instead returned to his native village to take up practice. One questions how much his purpose to investigate the cow-pox had to do with this decision. In Gloucestershire, therefore, as a country practitioner he began, in 1773, to observe systematically and patiently the cow-pox and to keep those records which for accuracy of detail and simplicity of expression are models. His interests, however, embraced other studies, as will be seen by the bibliographic list below. Among these was angina pectoris. It will be remembered that John Hunter suffered from this disease and subsequently died in an attack of it. Doubtless Jenner had many opportunities of observing in his patron the characteristics of this disease. He presented his observations upon various subjects to the county medical societies, at which he received due attention, but was informed that if he continued to bring forward his views on cow-pox he would be requested to resign. It might be supposed that this was the opinion of country practitioners only, but it will be seen from the account given below that even the London societies and practitioners assumed the same attitude. It was not until 1780, ten years after his conversations with Hunter, that Jenner ventured even in private to prophesy the future of his beliefs. This appears in the following letter, written in confidence to his friend, Edward Gardener: "I have entrusted a most important matter to you, which I firmly believe will prove of essential benefit to the human race. I know you, and should not wish what I have stated brought into conversation; for, should anything untoward turn up in my experiments, I should be made, particularly by my medical brethren, the subject of ridicule—for I am the mark they all shoot at."

It should be remembered that all the important letters, records, etc., bearing upon the subject appeared in evidence before a committee of the House of Commons, just as similar papers in the ether controversy were submitted to the Congressional Committee. This establishes the historic value of all such documents, of which the above is one.

For sixteen years more he continued to observe, with the same scrutiny, the effects of the cow-pox as presented on the hands of the milkers and to keep records of those attacked and those immune to smallpox. By 1796 he seems to have acquired sufficient evidence to attempt a regular inoculation, for on May 14th of that year *he performed the first vaccination.* "Lymph taken from the hand of Sarah Holmes," affected with cow-pox, was inserted into the arm of James Phipps, a healthy boy about eight years of age. The boy went through an attack of cow-pox. The real test now came. Six weeks later (July 1st) matter from a smallpox pustule was introduced into his arm. The boy remained perfectly well. From this date Jenner devoted almost his entire attention to the investigation, as will be seen by the record reprinted below. Like Harvey and Morton, his practice and fortune were neglected, and for two years he conducted experiments to corroborate this first successful vaccination. His feelings during this time are well described in his own words. He says: "While the vaccine discovery was progressive, the joy I felt at the prospect before me of being the instrument destined to take away from the world one of its greatest calamities, blended with the fond hope of enjoying independence and domestic peace and happiness, was often so excessive that, in pursuing my favorite subject among the meadows, I have sometimes found myself in a kind of reverie. It is pleasant for me to recollect that these reflections always ended in devout acknowledgments to that Being from whom this and all other mercies flow."

In 1798, having, as he considered, completed his observations sufficiently to make them public, he applied to the Royal Society (London) for permission to present his conclusions before that body. To this request the following advice was given by the president of the Society, that he (Jenner) "should be cautious and prudent, that he had already gained some credit by his communications to the Royal Society, and ought not to risk his reputation by presenting to the learned body anything which appeared so much at variance with established knowledge, and withal so incredible."*

The communication was not made, but Jenner visited London in April of this year and remained until July. During this visit he endeavored to demonstrate his findings to professional friends. In June, 1796, while he was still in London, his monograph

* Baron, quoted by Pettigrew.

which is reprinted below appeared. He returned to the country in July, having failed to arouse any interest among the London physicians. He left, however, a supply of virus with Mr. Cline, of St. Thomas's Hospital. This surgeon employed it as a counter-irritant in a case of hip disease. The cow-pox having gone through the usual course in this case, Mr. Cline consented to try the effects of inoculating the child with smallpox matter. This was inserted in three places, each of which manifested a slight inflammation on the third day and then subsided. Smallpox did not subsequently develop in this child. Mr. Cline now became an enthusiastic advocate of the method and urged Jenner to settle in London, promising him £10,000 a year as an income from the practice he would acquire. Jenner was now nearing his fiftieth year and the following reply to the above suggestion is full of interest: "Shall I, who even in the morning of my days sought the lowly and sequestered paths of life, the valley, and not the mountain; shall I, now my evening is fast approaching, hold myself up as an object for fortune and for fame? Admitting it as a certainty that I obtain both, what stock should I add to my little fund of happiness? My fortune, with what flows in from my profession, is sufficient to gratify my wishes; indeed, so limited is my ambition, and that of my nearest connexions, that were I precluded from future practice, I should be enabled to obtain all I want. And as for fame, what is it? a gilded butt, forever pierced with the arrows of malignancy. * * * "

This statement shows that at this time his practice and his means were sufficient to supply the wants of himself and family. Unlike Morton, he was not at this or any time reduced to poverty, but his practice and fortune were seriously encroached upon by the immense amount of unremunerative business and travel it was necessary for him to do. On this account he was urged by friends to present an application to Parliament. On the 17th of March, 1802, the petition was presented and a committee appointed. As in the ether controversy, many persons were examined and much documentary evidence presented, and finally Jenner's claim openly disputed. Twenty-five years had been spent in investigation and examination of carefully kept records before Jenner ventured to make his conclusions public. To his sensitive disposition the opposition which he now met caused him bitter disappointment. This opposition was better, however, than the apathy and distrust of a few years before, for much of Jenner's laborious investigation was now proclaimed by a legislative body in a manner impossible in a tribunal composed of medical men. The following extract from a letter of 1802 to a friend expresses Jenner's feeling on this matter. He says: "I sometimes wish this business had never been brought forward. It makes me feel indignant to reflect that one who has, through a most painful and laborious investigation, brought to light a subject that will add to the happiness of every human being in the world, should appear among his countrymen as a supplicant for the means of obtaining a few comforts for himself and family."

Following the report of the Committee, the House voted £10,000 to Jenner. An amendment proposing £20,000 was lost by a majority of three. A public subscription was proposed, but was not carried out. It is of interest here to recall that though Morton failed in obtaining an award from Congress, he received a liberal sum from public subscription, in which the profession figured largely.

In 1813 Jenner received the degree of Doctor of Physic from the University of Oxford, but the College of Physicians of London refused to admit him without the usual examination.

On January 26, 1823, Jenner died, being in his seventy-fourth year. After his death there was found among his papers a letter, post marked January 14, 1823, with the following, probably part of a note to be written in full later: "My opinion of vaccination is precisely as it was when I first promulgated the discovery. It is not in the least strengthened by any event that has happened, for it could gain no strength; it is not in the least weakened, for if the failures you speak of had not happened, the truth of my assertions respecting those coincidences which occasioned them, would not have been made out."*

* *Note:* For this quotation, as well as for much valuble information appearing in the above sketch, the writer wishes to acknowledge his indebtedness to Pettigrew's "Medical Portrait Gallery."—C. N. B. C.

AN

INQUIRY

INTO

THE CAUSES AND EFFECTS

OF

THE VARIOLÆ VACCINÆ,

A DISEASE

DISCOVERED IN SOME OF THE WESTERN COUNTIES OF ENGLAND,

PARTICULARLY

GLOUCESTERSHIRE,

AND KNOWN BY THE NAME OF

THE COW POX.

BY EDWARD JENNER, M.D. F.R.S. &c.

———— QUID NOBIS CERTIUS IPSIS

SENSIBUS ESSE POTEST, QUO VERA AC FALSA NOTEMUS.

LUCRETIUS.

London:

PRINTED, FOR THE AUTHOR,

BY SAMPSON LOW, N°. 7, BERWICK STREET, SOHO:

AND SOLD BY LAW, AVE-MARIA LANE; AND MURRAY AND HIGHLEY, FLEET STREET.

1798.

1798

AN INQUIRY INTO THE CAUSES AND EFFECTS OF THE VARIOLÆ VACCINÆ, A DISEASE DISCOVERED IN SOME OF THE WESTERN COUNTIES OF ENGLAND, PARTICULARLY GLOUCESTERSHIRE, AND KNOWN BY THE NAME OF THE COW-POX.

By EDWARD JENNER, M.D., F.R.S. Etc.

.　.　.　.　.　. *quid nobis certius ipsis*
Sensibus esse potest, quo vera ac falsa notemus.
　　　　　　　　　　　　　　　　　　—Lucretius.

To

C. H. PARRY, M.D.

AT BATH

MY DEAR FRIEND:

In the present age of scientific investigation it is remarkable that a disease of so peculiar a nature as the cow-pox, which has appeared in this and some of the neighbouring counties for such a series of years, should so long have escaped particular attention. Finding the prevailing notions on the subject, both among men of our profession and others, extremely vague and indeterminate, and conceiving that facts might appear at once both curious and useful, I have instituted as strict an inquiry into the causes and effects of this singular malady as local circumstances would admit.

The following pages are the result, which, from motives of the most affectionate regard, are dedicated to you, by

Your sincere friend,

EDWARD JENNER.

BERKELEY, GLOUCESTERSHIRE,
June 21st, 1798.

The deviation of man from the state in which he was originally placed by nature seems to have proved to him a prolific source of diseases. From the love of splendour, from the indulgences of luxury, and from his fondness for amusement he has familiarised himself with a great number of animals, which may not originally have been intended for his associates.

The wolf, disarmed of ferocity, is now pillowed in the lady's lap.* The cat, the little tiger of our island, whose natural home is the forest, is equally domesticated and caressed. The cow, the hog, the sheep, and the horse, are all, for a variety of purposes, brought under his care and dominion.

There is a disease to which the horse, from his state of domestication, is frequently subject. The farriers have called it the grease. It is an inflammation and swelling in the heel, from which issues matter possessing properties of a very peculiar kind, which seems capable of generating a disease in the human body (after it has undergone the modification which I shall presently speak of), which bears so strong a resemblance to the smallpox that I think it highly probable it may be the source of the disease.

In this dairy country a great number of cows are kept, and the office of milking is performed indiscriminately by men and maid servants. One of the former having been appointed to apply dressings to the heels of a horse affected with the grease, and not paying due attention to cleanliness, incautiously bears his part in milking the cows, with some particles of the infectious matter adhering to his fingers. When this is the case, it commonly happens that a disease is communicated to the cows, and from the cows to the dairymaids, which spreads through the farm until the most of the cattle and domestics feel its unpleasant consequences. This

* The late Mr. John Hunter proved, by experiments, that the dog is the wolf in a degenerate state.

disease has obtained the name of the cow-pox. It appears on the nipples of the cows in the form of irregular pustules. At their first appearance they are commonly of a palish blue, or rather of a colour somewhat approaching to livid, and are surrounded by an erysipelatous inflammation. These pustules, unless a timely remedy be applied, frequently degenerate into phagedenic ulcers, which prove extremely troublesome.* The animals become indisposed, and the secretion of milk is much lessened. Inflamed spots now begin to appear on different parts of the hands of the domestics employed in milking, and sometimes on the wrists, which quickly run on to suppuration, first assuming the appearance of the small vesications produced by a burn. Most commonly they appear about the joints of the fingers and at their extremities; but whatever parts are affected, if the situation will admit, these superficial suppurations put on a circular form, with their edges more elevated than their centre, and of a colour distantly approaching to blue. Absorption takes place, and tumours appear in each axilla. The system becomes affected—the pulse is quickened; and shiverings, succeeded by heat, with general lassitude and pains about the loins and limbs, with vomiting, come on. The head is painful, and the patient is now and then even affected with delirium. These symptoms, varying in their degrees of violence, generally continue from one day to three or four, leaving ulcerated sores about the hands, which, from the sensibility of the parts, are very troublesome, and commonly heal slowly, frequently becoming phagedenic, like those from whence they sprung. The lips, nostrils, eyelids, and other parts of the body are sometimes affected with sores; but these evidently arise from their being heedlessly rubbed or scratched with the patient's infected fingers. No eruptions on the skin have followed the decline of the feverish symptoms in any instance that has come under my inspection, one only excepted, and in this case a very few appeared on the arms: they were very minute, of a vivid red

---

* They who attend sick cattle in this country find a speedy remedy for stopping the progress of this complaint in those applications which act chemically upon the morbid matter, such as the solutions of the vitriolum zinci and the vitriolum cupri etc.

colour, and soon died away without advancing to maturation; so that I cannot determine whether they had any connection with the preceding symptoms.

Thus the disease makes its progress from the horse to the nipple of the cow, and from the cow to the human subject.

Morbid matter of various kinds, when absorbed into the system, may produce effects in some degree similar; but what renders the cow-pox virus so extremely singular is that the person who has been thus affected is for ever after secure from the infection of the small pox; neither exposure to the variolous effluvia, nor the insertion of the matter into the skin, producing this distemper.

In support of so extraordinary a fact, I shall lay before my reader a great number of instances.*

CASE I.—Joseph Merret, now an under gardener to the Earl of Berkeley, lived as a servant with a farmer near this place in the year 1770, and occasionally assisted in milking his master's cows. Several horses belonging to the farm began to have sore heels, which Merret frequently attended. The cows soon became affected with the cow-pox, and soon after several sores appeared on his hands. Swellings and stiffness in each axilla followed, and he was so much indisposed for several days as to be incapable of pursuing his ordinary employment. Previously to the appearance of the distemper among the cows there was no fresh cow brought into the farm, nor any servant employed who was affected with the cow-pox.

* It is necessary to observe that pustulous sores frequently appear spontaneously on the nipples of cows, and instances have occurred, though very rarely, of the hands of the servants employed in milking being affected with sores in consequence, and even of their feeling an indisposition from absorption. These pustules are of a much milder nature than those which arise from that contagion which constitutes the true cow pox. They are always free from the bluish or livid tint so conspicuous in the pustules in that disease. No erysipelas attends them, nor do they shew any phagedenic disposition as in the other case, but quickly terminate in a scab without creating any apparent disorder in the cow. This complaint appears at various seasons of the year, but most commonly in the spring, when the cows are first taken from their winter food and fed with grass. It is very apt to appear also when they are suckling their young. But this disease is not to be considered as similar in any respect to that of which I am treating, as it is incapable of producing any specific effects on the human constitution. However, it is of the greatest consequence to point it out here, lest the want of discrimination should occasion an idea of security from the infection of the smallpox, which might prove delusive.

In April, 1795, a general inoculation taking place here, Merret was inoculated with his family; so that a period of twenty-five years had elapsed from his having the cow-pox to this time. However, though the variolous matter was repeatedly inserted into his arm, I found it impracticable to infect him with it; an efflorescence only, taking on an erysipelatous look about the centre, appearing on the skin near the punctured parts. During the whole time that his family had the smallpox, one of whom had it very full, he remained in the house with them, but received no injury from exposure to the contagion.

It is necessary to observe that the utmost care was taken to ascertain, with the most scrupulous precision, that no one whose case is here adduced had gone through the smallpox previous to these attempts to produce that disease.

Had these experiments been conducted in a large city, or in a populous neighborhood, some doubts might have been entertained; but here, where population is thin, and where such an event as a person's having had the smallpox is always faithfully recorded, no risk of inaccuracy in this particular can arise.

CASE II.—Sarah Portlock, of this place, was infected with the cow-pox when a servant at a farmer's in the neighbourhood, twenty-seven years ago.*

In the year 1792, conceiving herself, from this circumstance, secure from the infection of the smallpox, she nursed one of her own children who had accidentally caught the disease, but no indisposition ensued. During the time she remained in the infected room, variolous matter was inserted into both her arms, but without any further effect than in the preceding case.

CASE III.—John Phillips, a tradesman of this town, had the cowpox at so early a period as nine years of age. At the age of sixty-two I inoculated him, and was very careful in selecting matter in its most active state. It was taken from the arm of a boy just before the commencement of the eruptive fever, and instantly inserted. It very speedily produced a sting-like feel in the part. An efflorescence appeared, which on the fourth day was rather extensive, and some degree of pain and stiffness were felt about the shoulder; but on the fifth day these symptoms began to disappear, and in a

---

* I have purposely selected several cases in which the disease had appeared at a very distant period previous to the experiments made with variolous matter, to shew that the change produced in the constitution is not affected by time.

day or two after went entirely off, without producing any effect on the system.

CASE IV.—Mary Barge, of Woodford, in this parish, was inoculated with variolous matter in the year 1791. An efflorescence of a palish red colour soon appeared about the parts where the matter was inserted, and spread itself rather extensively, but died away in a few days without producing any variolous symptoms.* She has since been repeatedly employed as a nurse to smallpox patients, without experiencing any ill consequences. This woman had the cow-pox when she lived in the service of a farmer in this parish thirty-one years before.

CASE V.—Mrs. H——, a respectable gentlewoman of this town, had the cow-pox when very young. She received the infection in rather an uncommon manner: it was given by means of her handling some of the same utensils† which were in use among the servants of the family, who had the disease from milking infected cows. Her hands had many of the cow-pox sores upon them, and they were communicated to her nose, which became inflamed and very much swollen. Soon after this event Mrs. H—— was exposed to the contagion of the small pox, where it was scarcely possible for her to have escaped, had she been susceptible of it, as she regularly attended a relative who had the disease in so violent a degree that it proved fatal to him.

In the year 1778 the smallpox prevailed very much at Berkeley, and Mrs. H——, not feeling perfectly satisfied respecting her safety (no indisposition having followed her exposure to the smallpox), I inoculated her with active variolous matter. The same appearance followed as in the preceding cases—an efflorescence on the arm without any effect on the constitution.

---

* It is remarkable that variolous matter, when the system is disposed to reject it, should excite inflammation on the part to which it is applied more speedily than when it produces the smallpox. Indeed, it becomes almost a criterion by which we can determine whether the infection will be received or not. It seems as if a change, which endures through life, had been produced in the action, or disposition to action, in the vessels of the skin; and it is remarkable, too, that whether this change has been effected by the smallpox or the cow-pox that the disposition to sudden cuticular inflammation is the same on the application of variolous matter.

† When the cow-pox has prevailed in the dairy, it has often been communicated to those who have not milked the cows, by the handle of the milk pail.

CASE VI.—It is a fact so well known among our dairy farmers that those who have had the smallpox either escape the cow-pox or are disposed to have it slightly, that as soon as the complaint shews itself among the cattle, assistants are procured, if possible, who are thus rendered less susceptible of it, otherwise the business of the farm could scarcely go forward.

In the month of May, 1796, the cow-pox broke out at Mr. Baker's, a farmer who lives near this place. The disease was communicated by means of a cow which was purchased in an infected state at a neighbouring fair, and not one of the farmer's cows (consisting of thirty) which were at that time milked escaped the contagion. The family consisted of a man servant, two dairymaids, and a servant boy, who, with the farmer himself, were twice a day employed in milking the cattle. The whole of this family, except Sarah Wynne, one of the dairymaids, had gone through the smallpox. The consequence was that the farmer and the servant boy escaped the infection of the cow-pox entirely, and the servant man and one of the maid servants had each of them nothing more than a sore on one of their fingers, which produced no disorder in the system. But the other dairymaid, Sarah Wynne, who never had the smallpox, did not escape in so easy a manner. She caught the complaint from the cows, and was affected with the symptoms described in the fifth page in so violent a degree that she was confined to her bed, and rendered incapable for several days of pursuing her ordinary vocations in the farm.

March 28, 1797, I inoculated this girl and carefully rubbed the variolous matter into two slight incisions made upon the left arm. A little inflammation appeared in the usual manner around the parts where the matter was inserted, but so early as the fifth day it vanished entirely without producing any effect on the system.

CASE VII.—Although the preceding history pretty clearly evinces that the constitution is far less susceptible of the contagion of the cow-pox after it has felt that of the smallpox, and although in general, as I have observed, they who have had the smallpox, and are employed in milking cows which are infected with the cow-pox, either escape the disorder, or have sores on the hands without feeling any general indisposition, yet the animal economy is subject to some variation in this respect, which the following relation will point out:

In the summer of the year 1796 the cow-pox appeared at the farm of Mr. Andrews, a considerable dairy adjoining to the town of

Berkeley. It was communicated, as in the preceding instance, by an infected cow purchased at a fair in the neighbourhood. The family consisted of the farmer, his wife, two sons, a man and a maid servant; all of whom, except the farmer (who was fearful of the consequences), bore a part in milking the cows. The whole of them, exclusive of the man servant, had regularly gone through the small pox; but in this case no one who milked the cows escaped the contagion. All of them had sores upon their hands, and some degree of general indisposition, preceded by pains and tumours in the axillæ: but there was no comparison in the severity of the disease as it was felt by the servant man, who had escaped the small-pox, and by those of the family who had not, for, while he was confined to his bed, they were able, without much inconvenience, to follow their ordinary business.

February the 13th, 1797, I availed myself of an opportunity of inoculating William Rodway, the servant man above alluded to. Variolous matter was inserted into both his arms: in the right, by means of superficial incisions, and into the left by slight punctures into the cutis. Both were perceptibly inflamed on the third day. After this the inflammation about the punctures soon died away, but a small appearance of erysipelas was manifest about the edges of the incisions till the eighth day, when a little uneasiness was felt for the space of half an hour in the right axilla. The inflammation then hastily disappeared without producing the most distant mark of affection of the system.

CASE VIII.—Elizabeth Wynne, aged fifty-seven, lived as a servant with a neighbouring farmer thirty-eight years ago. She was then a dairymaid, and the cow-pox broke out among the cows. She caught the disease with the rest of the family, but, compared with them, had it in a very slight degree, one very small sore only breaking out on the little finger of her left hand, and scarcely any perceptible indisposition following it.

As the malady had shewn itself in so slight a manner, and as it had taken place at so distant a period of her life, I was happy with the opportunity of trying the effects of variolous matter upon her constitution, and on the 28th of March, 1797, I inoculated her by making two superficial incisions on the left arm, on which the matter was cautiously rubbed. A little efflorescence soon appeared, and a tingling sensation was felt about the parts where the matter was inserted until the third day, when both began to subside, and so early as the fifth day it was evident that no indisposition would follow.

CASE IX.—Although the cow-pox shields the constitution from the smallpox, and the smallpox proves a protection against its own future poison, yet it appears that the human body is again and again susceptible of the infectious matter of the cow-pox, as the following history will demonstrate.

William Smith, of Pyrton in this parish, contracted this disease when he lived with a neighbouring farmer in the year 1780. One of the horses belonging to the farm had sore heels, and it fell to his lot to attend him. By these means the infection was carried to the cows, and from the cows it was communicated to Smith. On one of his hands were several ulcerated sores, and he was affected with such symptoms as have been before described.

In the year 1791 the cow-pox broke out at another farm where he then lived as a servant, and he became affected with it a second time; and in the year 1794 he was so unfortunate as to catch it again. The disease was equally as severe the second and third time as it was on the first.*

In the spring of the year 1795 he was twice inoculated, but no affection of the system could be produced from the variolous matter; and he has since associated with those who had the smallpox in its most contagious state without feeling any effect from it.

CASE X.—Simon Nichols lived as a servant with Mr. Bromedge, a gentleman who resides on his own farm in this parish, in the year 1782. He was employed in applying dressings to the sore heels of one of his master's horses, and at the same time assisted in milking the cows. The cows became affected in consequence, but the disease did not shew itself on their nipples till several weeks after he had begun to dress the horse. He quitted Mr. Bromedge's service, and went to another farm without any sores upon him; but here his hands soon began to be affected in the common way, and he was much indisposed with the usual symptoms. Concealing the nature of the malady from Mr. Cole, his new master, and being there also employed in milking, the cow-pox was communicated to the cows.

Some years afterward Nichols was employed in a farm where the smallpox broke out, when I inoculated him with several other patients, with whom he continued during the whole time of their confinement. His arm inflamed, but neither the inflammation nor

* This is not the case in general—a second attack is commonly very slight, and so, I am informed, it is among the cows.

his associating with the inoculated family produced the least effect upon his constitution.

CASE XI.—William Stinchcomb was a fellow servant with Nichols at Mr. Bromedge's farm at the time the cattle had the cowpox, and he was, unfortunately, infected by them. His left hand was very severely affected with several corroding ulcers, and a tumour of considerable size appeared in the axilla of that side. His right hand had only one small tumor upon it, and no sore discovered itself in the corresponding axilla.

In the year 1792 Stinchcomb was inoculated with variolous matter, but no consequences ensued beyond a little inflammation in the arm for a few days. A large party were inoculated at the same time, some of whom had the disease in a more violent degree than is commonly seen from inoculation. He purposely associated with them, but could not receive the smallpox.

During the sickening of some of his companions their symptoms so strongly recalled to his mind his own state when sickening with the cow-pox that he very pertinently remarked their striking similarity.

CASE XII.—The paupers of the village of Tortworth, in this county, were inoculated by Mr. Henry Jenner, Surgeon, of Berkeley, in the year 1795. Among them, eight patients presented themselves who had at different periods of their lives had the cow-pox. One of them, Hester Walkley, I attended with that disease when she lived in the service of a farmer in the same village in the year 1782; but neither this woman, nor any other of the patients who had gone through the cow-pox, received the variolous infection either from the arm or from mixing in the society of the other patients who were inoculated at the same time. This state of security proved a fortunate circumstance, as many of the poor women were at the same time in a state of pregnancy.

CASE XIII.—One instance has occurred to me of the system being affected from the matter issuing from the heels of horses, and of its remaining afterwards unsusceptible of the variolous contagion; another, where the smallpox appeared obscurely; and a third, in which its complete existence was positively ascertained.

First, Thomas Pearce is the son of a smith and farrier near to this place. He never had the cow-pox; but, in consequence of dressing horses with sore heels at his father's, when a lad, he had sores on his fingers which suppurated, and which occasioned a pretty severe in-disposition. Six years afterwards I inserted variolous matter into his arm repeatedly, without being able to produce any thing more than slight inflammation, which appeared very soon after the matter was applied, and afterwards I exposed him to the contagion of the smallpox with as little effect.*

CASE XIV.—Secondly, Mr. James Cole, a farmer in this parish, had a disease from the same source as related in the preceding case, and some years after was inoculated with variolous matter. He had a little pain in the axilla and felt a slight indisposition for three or four hours. A few eruptions shewed themselves on the forehead, but they very soon disappeared without advancing to maturation.

CASE XV.—Although in the former instances the system seemed to be secured, or nearly so, from variolous infection, by the absorp-tion of matter from the sores produced by the diseased heels of horses, yet the following case decisively proves that this cannot be entirely relied upon until a disease has been generated by the mor-bid matter from the horse on the nipple of the cow, and passed through that medium to the human subject.

Mr. Abraham Riddiford, a farmer at Stone in this parish, in consequence of dressing a mare that had sore heels, was affected with very painful sores in both his hands, tumours in each axilla, and severe and general indisposition. A surgeon in the neighbour-hood attended him, who, knowing the similarity between the ap-pearance of the sores upon his hands and those produced by the cow-pox, and being acquainted also with the effects of that disease on the human constitution, assured him that he never need to fear the infection of the smallpox; but this assertion proved fallacious, for, on being exposed to the infection upwards of twenty years after-wards, he caught the disease, which took its regular course in a very mild way. There certainly was a difference perceptible, although it is not easy to describe it, in the general appearance of the pustules from that which we commonly see. Other practitioners who visited the patient at my request agreed with me in this point, though

---

* It is a remarkable fact, and well known to many, that we are frequently foiled in our endeavours to communicate the smallpox by inoculation to blacksmiths, who in the country are farriers. They often, as in the above instance, either resist the contagion entirely, or have the disease anomalously. Shall we not be able to account for this on a rational principle?

there was no room left for suspicion as to the reality of the disease, as I inoculated some of his family from the pustules, who had the smallpox, with its usual appearances, in consequence.

CASE XVI.—Sarah Nelmes, a dairymaid at a farmer's near this place, was infected with the cow-pox from her master's cows in May, 1796. She received the infection on a part of her hand which had been previously in a slight degree injured by a scratch from a thorn. A large pustulous sore and the usual symptoms accompanying the disease were produced in consequence. The pustule was so expressive of the true character of the cow-pox, as it commonly appears upon the hand, that I have given a representation of it in the annexed plate. The two small pustules on the wrists arose also from the application of the virus to some minute abrasions of the cuticle, but the livid tint, if they ever had any, was not conspicuous at the time I saw the patient. The pustule on the forefinger shews the disease in an earlier stage. It did not actually appear on the hand of this young woman, but was taken from that of another, and is annexed for the purpose of representing the malady after it has newly appeared.

CASE XVII.—The more accurately to observe the progress of the infection I selected a healthy boy, about eight years old, for the purpose of inoculation for the cow-pox. The matter was taken from a sore on the hand of a dairymaid,* who was infected by her master's cows, and it was inserted, on the 14th of May, 1796, into the arm of the boy by means of two superficial incisions, barely penetrating the cutis, each about half an inch long.

On the seventh day he complained of uneasiness in the axilla, and on the ninth he became a little chilly, lost his appetite, and had a slight headache. During the whole of this day he was perceptibly indisposed, and spent the night with some degree of restlessness, but on the day following he was perfectly well.

The appearance of the incisions in their progress to a state of maturation were much the same as when produced in a similar manner by variolous matter. The only difference which I perceived was in the state of the limpid fluid arising from the action of the virus, which assumed rather a darker hue, and in that of the efflorescence spreading round the incisions, which had more of an erysipelatous look than we commonly perceive when variolous matter has been made use of in the same manner; but the whole died

* From the sore on the hand of Sarah Nelmes. See the preceding case.

away (leaving on the inoculated parts scabs and subsequent eschars) without giving me or my patient the least trouble.

In order to ascertain whether the boy, after feeling so slight an affection of the system from the cow-pox virus, was secure from the contagion of the smallpox, he was inoculated the 1st of July following with variolous matter, immediately taken from a pustule. Several slight punctures and incisions were made on both his arms, and the matter was carefully inserted, but no disease followed. The same appearances were observable on the arms as we commonly see when a patient has had variolous matter applied, after having either the cow-pox or smallpox. Several months afterwards he was again inoculated with variolous matter, but no sensible effect was produced on the constitution.

Here my researches were interrupted till the spring of the year 1798, when, from the wetness of the early part of the season, many of the farmers' horses in this neighbourhood were affected with sore heels, in consequence of which the cow-pox broke out among several of our dairies, which afforded me an opportunity of making further observations upon this curious disease.

A mare, the property of a person who keeps a dairy in a neighbouring parish, began to have sore heels the latter end of the month of February, 1798, which were occasionally washed by the servant men of the farm, Thomas Virgoe, William Wherret, and William Haynes, who in consequence became affected with sores in their hands, followed by inflamed lymphatic glands in the arms and axillæ, shiverings succeeded by heat, lassitude, and general pains in the limbs. A single paroxysm terminated the disease; for within twenty-four hours they were free from general indisposition, nothing remaining but the sores on their hands. Haynes and Virgoe, who had gone through the smallpox from inoculation, described their feelings as very similar to those which affected them on sickening with that malady. Wherret never had had the smallpox. Haynes was daily employed as one of the milkers at the farm, and the disease began to shew itself among the cows about ten days after he first assisted in washing the mare's heels. Their nipples became sore in the usual way, with bluish pustules; but as remedies were early applied, they did not ulcerate to any extent.

CASE XVIII.—John Baker, a child of five years old, was inoculated March 16, 1798, with matter taken from a pustule on the hand of Thomas Virgoe, one of the servants who had been infected from the mare's heels. He became ill on the sixth day with symptoms similar to those excited by cow-pox matter. On the eighth day he was free from indisposition.

There was some variation in the appearance of the pustule on the arm. Although it somewhat resembled a smallpox pustule, yet its similitude was not so conspicuous as when excited by matter from the nipple of the cow, or when the matter has passed from thence through the medium of the human subject.

This experiment was made to ascertain the progress and subsequent effects of the disease when thus propagated. We have seen that the virus from the horse, when it proves infectious to the human subject, is not to be relied upon as rendering the system secure from variolous infection, but that the matter produced by it upon the nipple of the cow is perfectly so. Whether its passing from the horse through the human constitution, as in the present instance, will produce a similar effect, remains to be decided. This would now have been effected, but the boy was rendered unfit for inoculation from having felt the effects of a contagious fever in a workhouse soon after this experiment was made.

CASE XIX.—William Summers, a child of five years and a half old, was inoculated the same day with Baker, with matter taken from the nipples of one of the infected cows, at the farm alluded to. He became indisposed on the sixth day, vomited once, and felt the usual slight symptoms till the eighth day, when he appeared perfectly well. The progress of the pustule, formed by the infection of the virus, was similar to that noticed in Case XVII, with this exception, its being free from the livid tint observed in that instance.

CASE XX.—From William Summers the disease was transferred to William Pead, a boy of eight years old, who was inoculated March 28th. On the sixth day he complained of pain in the axilla, and on the seventh was affected with the common symptoms of a patient sickening with the smallpox from inoculation, which did not terminate till the third day after the seizure. So perfect was the similarity to the variolous fever that I was induced to examine the skin, conceiving there might have been some eruptions, but none appeared. The efflorescent blush around the part punctured in the boy's arm was so truly characteristic of that which appears on variolous inoculation that I have given a representation of it. The drawing was made when the pustule was beginning to die away and the areola retiring from the centre.

CASE XXI.—April 5th: Several children and adults were inoculated from the arm of William Pead. The greater part of them sickened on the sixth day, and were well on the seventh, but in three of the number a secondary indisposition arose in consequence of an extensive erysipelatous inflammation which appeared on the inoculated arms. It seemed to arise from the state of the pustule, which spread out, accompanied with some degree of pain, to about half the diameter of a sixpence. One of these patients was an infant of half a year old. By the application of mercurial ointment to the inflamed parts (a treatment recommended under similar circumstances in the inoculated smallpox) the complaint subsided without giving much trouble.

Hannah Excell, an healthy girl of seven years old, and one of the patients above mentioned, received the infection from the insertion of the virus under the cuticle of the arm in three distinct points. The pustules which arose in consequence so much resembled, on the twelfth day, those appearing from the infection of variolous matter, that an experienced inoculator would scarcely have discovered a shade of difference at that period. Experience now tells me that almost the only variation which follows consists in the pustulous fluids remaining limpid nearly to the time of its total disappearance; and not, as in the direct smallpox, becoming purulent.

CASE XXII.—From the arm of this girl matter was taken and inserted April 12th into the arms of John Macklove, one year and a half old, Robert F. Jenner, eleven months old, Mary Pead, five years old, and Mary James, six years old.

Among these, Robert F. Jenner did not receive the infection. The arms of the other three inflamed properly and began to affect the system in the usual manner; but being under some apprehensions from the preceding cases that a troublesome erysipelas might arise, I determined on making an experiment with the view of cutting off its source. Accordingly, after the patients had felt an indisposition of about twelve hours, I applied in two of these cases out of the three, on the vesicle formed by the virus, a little mild caustic, composed of equal parts of quick-lime and soap, and suffered it to remain on the part six hours.* It seemed to give the children but little uneasiness, and effectually answered my intention in preventing the appearance of erysipelas. Indeed, it seemed to do more, for in half an hour after its application the in-

---

* Perhaps a few touches with the lapis septicus would have proved equally efficacious.

disposition of the children ceased.* These precautions were perhaps unnecessary, as the arm of the third child, Mary Pead, which was suffered to take its common course, scabbed quickly, without any erysipelas.

CASE XXIII.—From this child's arm matter was taken and transferred to that of J. Barge, a boy of seven years old. He sickened on the eighth day, went through the disease with the usual slight symptoms, and without any inflammation on the arm beyond the common efflorescence surrounding the pustule, an appearance so often seen in inoculated smallpox.

After the many fruitless attempts to give the smallpox to those who had had the cow-pox, it did not appear necessary, nor was it convenient to me, to inoculate the whole of those who had been the subjects of these late trials; yet I thought it right to see the effects of variolous matter on some of them, particularly William Summers, the first of these patients who had been infected with matter taken from the cow. He was, therefore, inoculated with variolous matter from a fresh pustule; but, as in the preceding cases, the system did not feel the effects of it in the smallest degree. I had an opportunity also of having this boy and William Pead inoculated by my nephew, Mr. Henry Jenner, whose report to me is as follows: "I have inoculated Pead and Barge, two of the boys whom you lately infected with the cow-pox. On the second day the incisions were inflamed and there was a pale inflammatory stain around them. On the third day these appearances were still increasing and their arms itched considerably. On the fourth day the inflammation was evidently subsiding, and on the sixth day it was scarcely perceptible. No symptom of indisposition followed.

"To convince myself that the variolous matter made use of was in a perfect state I at the same time inoculated a patient with some of it who never had gone through the cow-pox, and it produced the smallpox in the usual regular manner."

These experiments afforded me much satisfaction; they proved that the matter, in passing from one human subject to another, through five gradations, lost none of its original properties, J. Barge being the fifth who received the infection successively from William Summers, the boy to whom it was communicated from the cow.

* What effect would a similar treatment produce in inoculation for the small-pox?

I shall now conclude this inquiry with some general observations on the subject, and on some others which are interwoven with it.

Although I presume it may be unnecessary to produce further testimony in support of my assertion "that the cow-pox protects the human constitution from the infection of the smallpox," yet it affords me considerable satisfaction to say that Lord Somerville, the President of the Board of Agriculture, to whom this paper was shewn by Sir Joseph Banks, has found upon inquiry that the statements were confirmed by the concurring testimony of Mr. Dolland, a surgeon, who resides in a dairy country remote from this, in which these observations were made. With respect to the opinion adduced "that the source of the infection is a peculiar morbid matter arising in the horse," although I have not been able to prove it from actual experiments conducted immediately under my own eye, yet the evidence I have adduced appears sufficient to establish it.

They who are not in the habit of conducting experiments may not be aware of the coincidence of circumstances necessary for their being managed so as to prove perfectly decisive; nor how often men engaged in professional pursuits are liable to interruptions which disappoint them almost at the instant of their being accomplished: however, I feel no room for hesitation respecting the common origin of the disease, being well convinced that it never appears among the cows (except it can be traced to a cow introduced among the general herd which has been previously infected, or to an infected servant) unless they have been milked by some one who, at the same time, has the care of a horse affected with diseased heels.

The spring of the year 1797, which I intended particularly to have devoted to the completion of this investigation, proved, from its dryness, remarkably adverse to my wishes; for it frequently happens, while the farmers' horses are exposed to the cold rains which fall at that season, that their heels become diseased, and no cow-pox then appeared in the neighbourhood.

The active quality of the virus from the horses' heels is greatly increased after it has acted on the nipples of the cow, as it rarely happens that the horse affects his dresser with sores, and as rarely that a milkmaid escapes the infection when she milks infected cows. It is most active at the commencement of the disease, even before it has acquired a pus-like appearance; indeed, I am not confident whether this property in the matter does not entirely cease as soon as it is secreted in the form of pus. I am induced to think it does cease,* and that it is the thin, darkish-looking fluid only, oozing from the newly-formed cracks in the heels, similar to what sometimes appears from erysipelatous blisters, which gives the disease. Nor am I certain that the nipples of the cows are at all times in a state to receive the infection. The appearance of the disease in the spring and the early part of the summer, when they are disposed to be affected with spontaneous eruptions so much more frequently than at other seasons, induces me to think that the virus from the horse must be received upon them when they are in this state, in order to produce effects: experiments, however, must determine these points. But it is clear that when the cow-pox virus is once generated, that the cows cannot resist the contagion, in whatever state their nipples may chance to be, if they are milked with an infected hand.

Whether the matter, either from the cow or the horse, will affect the sound skin of the human body, I cannot positively determine; probably it will not, unless on those parts where the cuticle is extremely thin, as on the lips, for example. I have known an instance of a poor girl who produced an ulceration on her lip by frequently holding her finger to her mouth to cool the raging of a cow-pox sore by blowing upon it. The hands of the farmers' servants here, from the nature of their employments, are constantly exposed to those injuries which occasion abrasions of the cuticle, to punctures from thorns, and such like accidents; so that they are always in a state to feel the consequences of exposure to infectious matter.

It is singular to observe that the cow-pox virus, although it renders the constitution unsusceptible of the variolous, should,

---

* It is very easy to procure pus from old sores on the heels of horses. This I have often inserted into scratches made with a lancet, on the sound nipples of cows, and have seen no other effects from it than simple inflammation.

nevertheless, leave it unchanged with respect to its own action. I have already produced an instance* to point out this, and shall now corroborate it with another.

Elizabeth Wynne, who had the cow-pox in the year 1759, was inoculated with variolous matter, without effect, in the year 1797, and again caught the cow-pox in the year 1798. When I saw her, which was on the eighth day after she received the infection, I found her affected with general lassitude, shiverings, alternating with heat, coldness of the extremities, and a quick and irregular pulse. These symptoms were preceded by a pain in the axilla. On her hand was one large pustulous sore, which resembled that delineated in Plate No. 1. (Plate appears in original.)

It is curious also to observe that the virus, which with respect to its effects is undetermined and uncertain previously to its passing from the horse through the medium of the cow, should then not only become more active, but should invariably and completely possess those specific properties which induce in the human constitution symptoms similar to those of the variolous fever, and effect in it that peculiar change which for ever renders it unsusceptible of the variolous contagion.

May it not then be reasonably conjectured that the source of the smallpox is morbid matter of a peculiar kind, generated by a disease in the horse, and that accidental circumstances may have again and again arisen, still working new changes upon it until it has acquired the contagious and malignant form under which we now commonly see it making its devastations amongst us? And, from a consideration of the change which the infectious matter undergoes from producing a disease on the cow, may we not conceive that many contagious diseases, now prevalent among us, may owe their present appearance not to a simple, but to a compound, origin? For example, is it difficult to imagine that the measles, the scarlet fever, and the ulcerous sore throat with a spotted skin have all sprung from the same source, assuming some variety in their forms according to the nature of their new combinations? The same question will apply respecting the origin of many

* See Case IX.

other contagious diseases which bear a strong analogy to each other.

There are certainly more forms than one, without considering the common variation between the confluent and distinct, in which the smallpox appears in what is called the natural way. About seven years ago a species of smallpox spread through many of the towns and villages of this part of Gloucestershire: it was of so mild a nature that a fatal instance was scarcely ever heard of, and consequently so little dreaded by the lower orders of the community that they scrupled not to hold the same intercourse with each other as if no infectious disease had been present among them. I never saw nor heard of an instance of its being confluent. The most accurate manner, perhaps, in which I can convey an idea of it is by saying that had fifty individuals been taken promiscuously and infected by exposure to this contagion, they would have had as mild and light a disease as if they had been inoculated with variolous matter in the usual way. The harmless manner in which it shewed itself could not arise from any peculiarity either in the season or the weather, for I watched its progress upwards of a year without perceiving any variation in its general appearance. I consider it then as a *variety* of the smallpox.*

In some of the preceding cases I have noticed the attention that was paid to the state of the variolous matter previous to the experiment of inserting it into the arms of those who had gone through the cow-pox. This I conceived to be of great importance in conducting these experiments, and, were it always properly attended to by those who inoculate for the smallpox, it might prevent much subsequent mischief and confusion. With the view of enforcing so necessary a precaution I shall take the liberty of digressing so far as to point out some unpleasant facts relative to mismanagement in this particular, which have fallen under my own observation.

A medical gentleman (now no more), who for many years inocu-

* My friend, Dr. Hicks, of Bristol, who, during the prevalence of this distemper, was resident at Gloucester, and physician of the hospital there (where it was seen soon after its first appearance in this country), had opportunities of making numerous observations upon it, which it is his intention to communicate to the public.

lated in this neighbourhood, frequently preserved the variolous matter intended for his use on a piece of lint or cotton, which, in its fluid state, was put into a vial, corked, and conveyed into a warm pocket; a situation certainly favourable for speedily producing putrefaction in it. In this state (not unfrequently after it had been taken several days from the pustules) it was inserted into the arms of his patients, and brought on inflammation of the incised parts, swellings of the axillary glands, fever, and sometimes eruptions. But what was this disease? Certainly not the smallpox; for the matter having from putrefaction lost or suffered a derangement in its specific properties, was no longer capable of producing that malady, those who had been inoculated in this manner being as much subject to the contagion of the smallpox as if they had never been under the influence of this artificial disease; and many, unfortunately, fell victims to it, who thought themselves in perfect security. The same unfortunate circumstance of giving a disease, supposed to be the smallpox, with inefficacious variolous matter, having occurred under the direction of some other practitioners within my knowledge, and probably from the same incautious method of securing the variolous matter, I avail myself of this opportunity of mentioning what I conceive to be of great importance; and, as a further cautionary hint, I shall again digress so far as to add another observation on the subject of inoculation.

Whether it be yet ascertained by experiment that the quantity of variolous matter inserted into the skin makes any difference with respect to the subsequent mildness or violence of the disease, I know not; but I have the strongest reason for supposing that if either the punctures or incisions be made so deep as to go *through* it and wound the adipose membrane, that the risk of bringing on a violent disease is greatly increased. I have known an inoculator whose practice was "to cut deep enough (to use his own expression) to see a bit of fat," and there to lodge the matter. The great number of bad cases, independent of inflammations and abscesses on the arms, and the fatality which attended this practice, was almost inconceivable; and I cannot account for it on any other principle than that of the matter being placed in this situation instead of the skin.

It was the practice of another, whom I well remember, to pinch up a small portion of the skin on the arms of his patients and to pass through it a needle, with a thread attached to it previously dipped in variolous matter. The thread was lodged in the perforated part, and consequently left in contact with the cellular membrane. This practice was attended with the same ill success as the former. Although it is very improbable that any one would now inoculate in this rude way by design, yet these observations may tend to place a double guard over the lancet, when infants, whose skins are comparatively so very thin, fall under the care of the inoculator.

A very respectable friend of mine, Dr. Hardwicke, of Sodbury in this county, inoculated great numbers of patients previous to the introduction of the more modern method by Sutton, and with such success that a fatal instance occurred as rarely as since that method has been adopted. It was the doctor's practice to make as slight an incision as possible *upon* the skin, and there to lodge a thread saturated with the variolous matter. When his patients became indisposed, agreeably to the custom then prevailing, they were directed to go to bed and were kept moderately warm. Is it not probable then that the success of the modern practice may depend more upon the method of invariably depositing the virus in or upon the skin, than on the subsequent treatment of the disease?

I do not mean to insinuate that exposure to cool air, and suffering the patient to drink cold water when hot and thirsty, may not moderate the eruptive symptoms and lessen the number of pustules; yet, to repeat my former observation, I cannot account for the uninterrupted success, or nearly so, of one practitioner, and the wretched state of the patients under the care of another, where, in both instances, the general treatment did not differ essentially, without conceiving it to arise from the different modes of inserting the matter for the purpose of producing the disease. As it is not the identical matter inserted which is absorbed into the constitution, but that which is, by some peculiar process in the animal economy, generated by it, is it not probable that different parts of the human body may prepare or modify the virus differently? Although the skin, for example, adipose membrane, or mucous membranes are all capable of producing the variolous virus by the stimulus given by the particles originally deposited upon them, yet I am induced to conceive that each of these parts is capable of producing some variation in the qualities of the matter previous to its affecting the constitution. What else can constitute the difference between the smallpox when communicated casually or in what has been termed the natural way, or when brought on artificially through the medium of the skin?

After all, are the variolous particles, possessing their true specific and contagious principles, ever taken up and conveyed by the lymphatics unchanged into the blood vessels? I imagine not. Were this the case, should we not find the blood sufficiently loaded with them in some stages of the smallpox to communicate the disease by inserting it under the cuticle, or by spreading it on the surface of an ulcer? Yet experiments have determined the impracticability of its being given in this way; although it has been proved that variolous matter, when much diluted with water and applied to the skin in the usual manner, will produce the disease. But it would be digressing beyond a proper boundary to go minutely into this subject here.

At what period the cow-pox was first noticed here is not upon record. Our oldest farmers were not unacquainted with it in their earliest days, when it appeared among their farms without any deviation from the phænomena which it now exhibits. Its connection with the smallpox seems to have been unknown to them. Probably the general introduction of inoculation first occasioned the discovery.

Its rise in this country may not have been of very remote date, as the practice of milking cows might formerly have been in the hands of women only; which I believe is the case now in some other dairy countries, and, consequently, that the cows might not in former times have been exposed to the contagious matter brought by the men servants from the heels of horses.* Indeed, a knowledge of the source of the infection is new in the minds of most of the farmers in this neighbourhood, but it has at length produced good consequences; and it seems probable, from the precautions they are now disposed to adopt, that the appearance of the cow-pox here may either be entirely extinguished or become extremely rare.

Should it be asked whether this investigation is a matter of mere curiosity, or whether it tends to any beneficial purpose, I should answer that, notwithstanding the happy effects of inoculation, with all the improvements which the practice has received since its first introduction into this country, it not very unfrequently produces deformity of the skin, and sometimes, under the best management, proves fatal.

These circumstances must naturally create in every instance some degree of painful solicitude for its consequences. But as I have never known fatal effects arise from the cow-pox, even when impressed in the most unfavourable manner, producing extensive inflammations and suppurations on the hands; and as it clearly appears that this disease leaves the constitution in a state of perfect security from the infection of the smallpox, may we not infer that a mode of inoculation may be introduced preferable to that at present adopted, especially among those families which, from previous circumstances, we may judge to be predisposed to have the disease unfavourably? It is an excess in the number of pustules which we chiefly dread in the smallpox; but in the cow-pox no pustules appear, nor does it seem possible for the contagious matter to produce the disease from effluvia, or by any other means than contact, and that probably not simply between the virus and the cuticle; so that a single individual in a family might at any time receive it without the risk of infecting the rest or of spreading a distemper that fills a country with terror.

----

* I have been informed from respectable authority that in Ireland, although dairies abound in many parts of the island, the disease is entirely unknown. The reason seems obvious. The business of the dairy is conducted by women only. Were the meanest vassal among the men employed there as a milker at a dairy, he would feel his situation unpleasant beyond all endurance.

Several instances have come under my observation which justify the assertion that the disease cannot be propagated by effluvia. The first boy whom I inoculated with the matter of cow-pox slept in a bed, while the experiment was going forward, with two children who never had gone through either that disease or the smallpox, without infecting either of them.

A young woman who had the cow-pox to a great extent, several sores which maturated having appeared on the hands and wrists, slept in the same bed with a fellow-dairymaid who never had been infected with either the cow-pox or the smallpox, but no indisposition followed.

Another instance has occurred of a young woman on whose hands were several large suppurations from the cow-pox, who was at the same time a daily nurse to an infant, but the complaint was not communicated to the child.

In some other points of view the inoculation of this disease appears preferable to the variolous inoculation.

In constitutions predisposed to scrophula, how frequently we see the inoculated smallpox rouse into activity that distressful malady! This circumstance does not seem to depend on the manner in which the distemper has shewn itself, for it has as frequently happened among those who have had it mildly as when it has appeared in the contrary way.

There are many who, from some peculiarity in the habit, resist the common effects of variolous matter inserted into the skin, and who are in consequence haunted through life with the distressing idea of being insecure from subsequent infection. A ready mode of dissipating anxiety originating from such a cause must now appear obvious. And, as we have seen that the constitution may at any time be made to feel the febrile attack of cow-pox, might it not, in many chronic diseases, be introduced into the system, with the probability of affording relief, upon well-known physiological principles?

Although I say the system may at any time be made to feel the febrile attack of cow-pox, yet I have a single instance before me where the virus acted locally only, but it is not in the least probable that the same person would resist the action both of the cow-pox virus and the variolous.

Elizabeth Sarfenet lived as a dairymaid at Newpark farm, in this parish. All the cows and the servants employed in milking had the cow-pox; but this woman, though she had several sores upon her fingers, felt no tumours in the axillæ, nor any general indisposition. On being afterwards casually exposed to variolous infection, she had the smallpox in a mild way. Hannah Pick, another of the dairymaids who was a fellow-servant with Elizabeth Sarfenet when the distemper broke out at the farm, was, at the same time, infected; but this young woman had not only sores upon her hands, but felt herself also much indisposed for a day or two. After this, I made several attempts to give her the smallpox by inoculation, but they all proved fruitless. From the former case then we see that the animal economy is subject to the same laws in one disease as the other.

The following case, which has very lately occurred, renders it highly probable that not only the heels of the horse, but other parts of the body of that animal, are capable of generating the virus which produces the cow-pox.

An extensive inflammation of the erysipelatous kind appeared without any apparent cause upon the upper part of the thigh of a sucking colt, the property of Mr. Millet, a farmer at Rockhampton, a village near Berkeley. The inflammation continued several weeks, and at length terminated in the formation of three or four small abscesses. The inflamed parts were fomented, and dressings were applied by some of the same persons who were employed in milking the cows. The number of cows milked was twenty-four, and the whole of them had the cow-pox. The milkers, consisting of the farmer's wife, a man and a maid-servant, were infected by the cows. The man-servant had previously gone through the smallpox, and felt but little of the cow-pox. The servant maid had some years before been infected with the cow-pox, and she also felt it now in a slight degree; but the farmer's wife, who never had gone through either of the diseases, felt its effects very severely.

That the disease produced upon the cows by the colt and from thence conveyed to those who milked them was the *true* and not the *spurious* cow-pox,* there can be scarcely any room for suspicion; yet it would have been more completely satisfactory had the effects of variolous matter been ascertained on the farmer's wife, but there was a peculiarity in her situation which prevented my making the experiment.

Thus far have I proceeded in an inquiry founded, as it must appear, on the basis of experiment; in which, however, conjecture has been occasionally admitted in order to present to persons well situated for such discussions objects for a more minute investigation. In the mean time I shall myself continue to prosecute this inquiry, encouraged by the hope of its becoming essentially beneficial to mankind.

* See note (immediately preceding Case I).

FURTHER OBSERVATIONS ON THE VARIOLÆ VACCINÆ OR COW-POX

By EDWARD JENNER, M.D., F.R.S., F.L.S., ETC.

PUBLISHED 1799

To
C. H. PARRY, M.D.
AT BATH

MY DEAR FRIEND:

The same motives which impelled me to dedicate to you my first essay on the Variolæ Vaccinæ, induce me to offer you my further observations on the same subject.

I am pleased at seeing the investigation so generally entered into, and I hope that the spirit with which this important inquiry will be prosecuted may be tempered with that calmness and moderation which should ever accompany philosophical researches.

With the greatest regard,
I remain,
Yours very sincerely,
EDWARD JENNER.

BERKELEY, GLOUCESTERSHIRE,
5th April, 1799.

FURTHER OBSERVATIONS

Although it has not been in my power to extend the inquiry into the causes and effects of the variolæ vaccinæ much beyond its original limits, yet, perceiving that it is beginning to excite a general spirit of investigation, I think it of importance, without delay, to communicate such facts as have since occurred, and to point out the fallacious sources from whence a disease imitative of the true variolæ vaccinæ might arise, with the view of preventing those who may inoculate from producing a spurious disease; and, further, to enforce the precaution suggested in the former treatise on the subject, of subduing the inoculated pustule as soon as it has sufficiently produced its influence on the constitution. From a want of due discrimination of the real existence of the disease, either in the brute or in the human subject, and also of that stage of it in which it is capable of producing the change in the animal economy which renders it unsusceptible of the contagion of the smallpox, unpleasant consequences might ensue, the source of which, perhaps, might not be suspected by one inexperienced in conducting such experiments.

My late publication contains a relation of most of the facts which had come under my own inspection at the time it was written, interspersed with some conjectural observations. Since then Dr. G. Pearson has established an inquiry into the validity of my principal assertion, the result of which cannot but be highly flattering to my feelings. It contains not a single case which I think can be called an exception to the fact I was so firmly impressed with—that the cow-pox protects the human body from the smallpox. I have myself received some further confirmations, which shall be subjoined. I have lately also been favoured with a letter from a gentleman of great respectability (Dr. Ingenhousz), informing me that, on making an inquiry into the subject in the county of Wilts, he discovered that a farmer near Calne had been infected with the smallpox after having had the cow-pox, and that the disease in each instance was so strongly characterised as to render the facts incontrovertible. The cow-pox, it seems, from the doctor's information, was communicated to the farmer from his cows at the time that they gave out *an offensive stench from their udders.*

Some other instances have likewise been represented to me of the appearance of the disease, apparently marked with its characteristic symptoms, and yet that the patients have afterwards had the smallpox. On these cases I shall, for the present, suspend any particular remarks, but hope that the general observations I have to offer in the sequel will prove of sufficient weight to render the idea of their ever having had existence, but as cases of spurious cow-pox, extremely doubtful.

Ere I proceed let me be permitted to observe that truth, in this and every other physiological inquiry that has occupied my attention, has ever been the object of my pursuit, and should it appear in the present instance that I have been led into error, fond as I may appear of the offspring of my labours, I had rather see it perish at once than exist and do a public injury.

I shall proceed to enumerate the sources, or what appear to me as such, of a spurious cow-pox.

First: That arising from pustules on the nipples or udder of the cow; which pustules contain no specific virus.

Secondly: From matter (although originally possessing the specific virus) which has suffered a decomposition, either from putrefaction or from any other cause less obvious to the senses.

Thirdly: From matter taken from an ulcer in an advanced stage, which ulcer arose from a true cow pock.

Fourthly: From matter produced on the human skin from contact with some peculiar morbid matter generated by a horse.

On these subjects I shall offer some comments: First, to what length pustulous diseases of the udder and nipples of the cow may extend it is not in my power to determine; but certain it is that these parts of the animal are subject to some variety of maladies of this nature; and as many of these eruptions (probably all of them) are capable of giving a disease to the human body, would it not be discreet for those engaged in this investigation to suspend controversy and cavil until they can ascertain with precision what *is* and what *is not* the cow-pox?

For example: A farmer who is not conversant with any of these maladies, but who may have heard of the cow-pox in general terms, may acquaint a neighbouring surgeon that the distemper appears at his farm. The surgeon, eager to make an experiment, takes away matter, inoculates, produces a sore, uneasiness in the axilla, and perhaps some affection of the system. This is one way in which a fallacious idea of security both in the mind of the inoculator and the patient may arise; for a disease may thus have been propagated from a simple eruption only.

One of the first objects then of this pursuit, as I have observed, should be, to learn how to distinguish with accuracy between that peculiar pustule which is the *true* cow pock, and that which is spurious. Until experience has determined this, we view our object through a mist. Let us, for instance, suppose that the smallpox and the chicken-pox were at the same time to spread among the inhabitants of a country which had never been visited by either of these distempers, and where they were quite unknown before: what confusion would arise! The resemblance between the symptoms of the eruptive fever and between the pustules in either case would be so striking that a patient who had gone through the chicken-pox to any extent would feel equally easy with regard to his future security from the smallpox as the person who had actually passed through that disease. Time and future observation would draw the line of distinction.

So I presume it will be with the cow-pox until it is more generally understood. All cavilling, therefore, on the mere report of those who *tell us* they have had this distemper, and are afterwards found susceptible of the smallpox, should be suspended. To illustrate this I beg leave to give the following history:

Sarah Merlin, of the parish of Eastington in this county, when about thirteen or fourteen years of age lived as a servant with farmer Clarke, who kept a dairy consisting of about eighteen cows

at Stonehouse, a neighbouring village. The nipples and udders of
three of the cows were extensively affected with large white blisters.
These cows the girl milked daily, and at the time she assisted, with
two others, in milking the rest of the herd. It soon appeared that the
disease was communicated to the girl. The rest of the cows escaped
the infection, although they were milked several days after the three
above specified, had these eruptions on the nipples and udders, and
even after the girl's hand became sore. The two others who were
engaged in milking, although they milked the cows indiscriminately,
received no injury. On the fingers of each of the girl's hands there
appeared several large white blisters—she supposes about three or
four on each finger. The hands and arms inflamed and swelled, but
no constitutional indisposition followed. The sores were anointed
with some domestic ointment and got well without ulcerating.

As this malady was called the cow-pox, and recorded as such in
the mind of the patient, she became regardless of the smallpox;
but, on being exposed to it some years afterwards she was infected,
and had a full burthen.

Now had any one conversant with the habits of the disease heard
this history, they would have had no hesitation in pronouncing
it a case of spurious cow-pox; considering its deviation in the
numerous blisters which appeared on the girl's hands; their termination without ulceration; its not proving more generally contagious
at the farm, either among the cattle or those employed in milking;
and considering also that *the patient felt no general indisposition,
although there was so great a number of vesicles.*

This is perhaps the most deceptious form in which an eruptive
disease can be communicated from the cow, and it certainly requires some attention in discriminating it. The most perfect criterion by which the judgment may be guided is perhaps that
adopted by those who attend infected cattle. These white blisters
on the nipples, they say, *never eat into the fleshy parts* like those
which are commonly of a bluish cast, and which constitute the
true cow-pox, but that they affect the skin only, quickly end in
scabs, and are not nearly so infectious.

That which appeared to me as one cause of spurious eruptions,

I have already remarked in the former treatise, namely, the transition that the cow makes in the spring from a poor to a nutritious diet, and from the udder's becoming at this time more vascular than usual for the supply of milk. But there is another source of inflammation and pustules which I believe is not uncommon in all the dairy counties in the west of England. A cow intended to be exposed for sale, having naturally a small udder, is previously for a day or two neither milked artificially nor is her calf suffered to have access to her. Thus the milk is preternaturally accumulated, and the udder and nipples become greatly distended. The consequences frequently are inflammation and eruptions which maturate.

Whether a disease generated in this way has the power of affecting the constitution in any *peculiar* manner I cannot presume positively to determine. It has been conjectured to have been a cause of the true cow-pox, though my inquiries have not led me to adopt this supposition in any one instance; on the contrary, I have known the milkers affected by it, but always found that an affection thus induced left the system as susceptible of the smallpox as before.

What is advanced in my second position I consider also of very great importance, and I could wish it to be strongly impressed on the minds of all who may be disposed to conclude hastily on my observations, whether engaged in their investigation by experiments or not. To place this in its clearest point of view (as the similarity between the action of the smallpox and the cow-pox matter is so obvious) it will be necessary to consider what we sometimes observe to take place in inoculation for the smallpox when imperfect variolous matter is made use of. The concise history on this subject that was brought forward respecting what I had observed in this neighbourhood* I perceive, by a reference since made to the Memoirs of the Medical Society of London, may be considered as no more than a corroboration of the facts very clearly detailed by Mr. Kite.† To this copious evidence I have to add still

* Inquiry into the Causes and Effects of the Variolæ Vaccinæ, p. 56 of the original article.

† See an account of some anomalous appearances consequent to the inoculation of the smallpox, by Charles Kite, Surgeon, of Gravesend, in the Memoirs of the Medical Society of London, vol. iv, p. 114.

more in the following communications from Mr. Earle, surgeon, of Frampton-upon-Severn, in this county, which I deem the more valuable, as he has with much candour permitted me to make them public:

"SIR:

"I have read with satisfaction your late publication on the Variolæ Vaccinæ, and being, among many other curious circumstances, particularly struck with that relating to the inefficacy of smallpox matter in a particular state, I think it proper to lay before you the following facts which came within my own knowledge, and which certainly tend to strengthen the opinions advanced in pages 56 and 57 of your treatise.

"In March, 1784, a general inoculation took place at Arlingham in this county. I inoculated several patients with active variolous matter, all of whom had the disease in a favourable way; but the matter being all used, and not being able to procure any more in the state I wished, I was under the necessity of taking it from a pustule which, experience has since proved, was advanced too far to answer the purpose I intended. Of five persons inoculated with this last matter, four took the smallpox afterwards in the natural way, one of whom died, three recovered, and the other, being cautioned by me to avoid as much as possible the chance of catching it, escaped from the disease through life. He died of another disorder about two years ago.

"Although one of these cases ended unfortunate, yet I cannot suppose that any medical man will think me careless or inattentive in their management; for I conceive the appearances were such as might have induced any one to suppose that the persons were perfectly safe from future infection. Inflammation in every case took place in the arm, and fever came on with a considerable degree of pain in the axilla. In some of their arms the inflammation and suppuration were more violent than is commonly observed when perfect matter is made use of; in one there was an ulcer which cast off several large sloughs. About the ninth day eruptions appeared, which died away earlier than common without maturation. From these circumstances I should suppose that no medical practitioner would scarcely have entertained a doubt but that these patients had been infected with a true smallpox; yet I must confess that some small degree of doubt presented itself to me at the speedy disappearance of the eruptions; and in order, as far as I could, to ascertain their safety, I sent one of them to a much older practitioner than myself. This gentleman, on hearing the circumstances of the case, pronounced the patient perfectly secure from future infection.

"The following facts are also a striking proof of the truth of your observations on this subject:

"In the year 1789 I inoculated three children of Mr. Coaley, of Hurst farm in this county. The arms inflamed properly, fever and pain in the axillæ came on precisely the same as in the former cases, and in ten days eruptions appeared, which disappeared in the course of two days. I must observe that the matter here made use of was procured for me by a friend; but no doubt it was in an improper state; for, from the similarity of these cases to those which happened at Arlingham five years before, I was somewhat alarmed for their safety, and desired to inoculate them again; which being permitted, I was particularly careful to procure matter in its most perfect state. All the children took the smallpox from this second inoculation, and all had a very full burthen. These facts I conceive strikingly corroborate your opinion relative to the different states of matter; for in both instances that I have mentioned it was capable of producing something strongly resembling the true smallpox, although it afterwards proved not to be so.

"As I think the communication of these cases is a duty I owe to the public, you are at liberty to make what use you please of this letter.

"I remain, &c.,

"John Earle.

" FRAMPTON-UPON SEVERN, GLOUCESTERSHIRE,
    November 10, 1798.

"P. S. I think it necessary to observe that I can pronounce, with the greatest certainty, that the matter with which the Arlingham patients were inoculated was taken from a true smallpox pustule. I took it myself from a subject that had a very full burthen."

Certain then it is that variolous matter may undergo such a change from the putrefactive process, as well as from some of the more obscure and latent processes of nature, as will render it incapable of giving the smallpox in such a manner as to secure the human constitution from future infection, although we see at the same time it is capable of exciting a disease which bears so strong a resemblance to it as to produce inflammation and matter in the incised skin (frequently, indeed, more violent than when it produces its effects perfectly), swelling of the axillary glands, general indisposition, and eruptions. So strongly persuaded was the gentleman, whose practice I have mentioned in page 56 of the late treatise, that he could produce a mild smallpox by his mode of managing the matter, that he spoke of it as a useful discovery until convinced of his error by the fatal consequence which ensued.

After this ought we to be in the smallest degree surprised to find, among a great number of individuals who, by living in dairies, have been casually exposed to the cow-pox virus when in a state analogous to that of the smallpox above described, some who may have had the disease so imperfectly as not to render them secure from variolous attacks? For the matter, when burst from the pustules on the nipples of the cow, by being exposed, from its lodgment there, to the heat of an inflamed surface, and from being at the same time in a situation to be occasionally moistened with milk, is often likely to be in a state conducive to putrefaction; and thus, under some modification of decomposition, it must, of course, sometimes find access to the hand of the milker in such a way as to infect him. What confusion should we have were there no other mode of inoculating the smallpox than such as would happen from handling the diseased skin of a person labouring under that distemper in some of its advanced and loathsome stages! It must be observed that every case of cow-pox in the human species, whether communicated by design or otherwise, is to be considered as a case of inoculation. And here I may be allowed to make an observation on the case of the farmer communicated to me by Dr. Ingenhousz. That he was exposed to the matter when it had undergone the putrefactive change is highly probable from the doctor's observing that the sick cows at the farm gave out *an offensive stench from their udders*. However, I must remark that it is unusual for cattle to suffer to such an extent, when disordered with the cow-pox, as to make a bystander sensible of any ill smell. I have often stood among a herd which had the distemper without being conscious of its presence from any particular effluvia. Indeed, in this neighbour-hood it commonly receives an early check from escharotic applica-tions of the *cow leech*. It has been conceived to be contagious with-out contact; but this idea cannot be well founded because the cattle in one meadow do not infect those in another (although there may be no other partition than a hedge) unless they be handled or milked by those who bring the infectious matter with them; and, of course, the smallest particle imaginable, when applied to a part sus-ceptible of its influence, may produce the effect. Among the human species it appears to be very clear that the disease is pro-duced by contact only. All my attempts, at least, to communicate it by effluvia have hitherto proved ineffectual.

As well as the perfect change from that state in which variolous matter is capable of producing full and decisive effects on the con-stitution, to that wherein its specific properties are entirely lost, it may reasonably be supposed that it is capable of undergoing a variety of intermediate changes. The following singular occur-rences in ten cases of inoculation, obligingly communicated to me by Mr. Trye, Senior Surgeon to the Infirmary at Glocester, seem to indicate that the variolous matter, previously to its being taken from the patient for the intended purpose, was beginning to part with some of its original properties, or, in other words, that it had suffered a partial decomposition. Mr. Trye says: "I inoculated ten children with matter taken at one time and from the same sub-ject. I observed no peculiarity in any of them previously to their inoculation, nor did any thing remarkable appear in their arms till after the decline of the disease. Two infants of three months old had erysipelas about the incisions, in one of them extending from the shoulders to the fingers' ends. Another infant had abscesses in the cellular substance in the neighbourhood of the incisions, and five or six of the rest had axillary abscesses. The matter was taken from the distinct smallpox late in its progress, and when some pustules had been dried. It was received upon glass and slowly dried by the fire. All the children had pustules which maturated, so that I suppose them all secure from future infection; at least, as secure as any others whom I have ever inoculated. My practice never afforded a sore arm before.''

In regard to my former observation on the improper and dangerous mode of preserving variolous matter, I shall here remark that it seems not to have been clearly understood. Finding that it has been confounded with the more eligible modes of preservation, I will explain myself further. When the matter is taken from a fit pustule and properly prepared for preservation, it may certainly be kept without losing its specific properties a great length of time; for instance, when it is previously dried in the open air on some compact body, as a quill or a piece of glass, and afterwards secured in a small vial.* But when kept several days in a state of moisture, and during that time exposed to a warm temperature, I do not think it can be relied upon as capable of giving a *perfect* disease, although, as I have before observed, the progress of the symptoms arising from the action of the imperfect matter bear so strong a resemblance to the smallpox when excited completely.

Thirdly. That the first formed virus, or what constitutes the true cow-pox pustule, invariably possesses the power I have ascribed to it, namely, that of affecting the constitution with a specific disease, is a truth that no subsequent occurrence has yet led me to doubt. But as I am now endeavouring to guard the public as much as possible against erroneous conclusions, I shall observe that when this pustule has degenerated into an ulcer (to which state it is often disposed to pass unless timely checked), I suspect that matter possessing very different properties may sooner or later be produced; and although it may have passed that stage wherein the specific properties of the matter secreted are no longer present in it, yet when applied to a sore (as in the casual way) it might dispose that sore to ulcerate, and from its irritation the system would probably become

* Thus prepared, the cow-pox virus was found perfectly active, and possessing all its specific properties, at the end of three months.

affected; and thus, by assuming some of its strongest characters, it would imitate the genuine cow-pox.

From the preceding observations on the matter of smallpox when decomposed it must, I conceive, be admitted that cow-pox matter in the state now described may produce a disease, the effects of which may be felt both locally and generally, yet that the disease thus induced may not be effectual in obviating the future effects of variolous contagion. In the case of Mary Miller, related by Mr. Kite in the volume above alluded to, it appears that the inflammation and suppuration of the inoculated arm were more than usually severe, although the system underwent no specific change from the action of the virus; which appears from the patient's sickening seven weeks afterwards with the natural smallpox, which went through its course. Some of the cases communicated by Mr. Earle tend further to confirm this fact, as the matter there manifestly produced ulceration on the inoculated part to a considerable extent.

Fourthly. Whether the cow-pox is a spontaneous disease in the cow, or is to be attributed to matter conveyed to the animal, as I have conceived, from the horse, is a question which, though I shall not attempt now fully to discuss, yet I shall digress so far as to adduce some further observations, and to give my reasons more at large for taking up an opinion that to some had appeared fanciful. The aggregate of these observations, though not amounting to positive proof, forms presumptive evidence of so forcible a kind that I imagine it might, on any other person, have made the same impression it did on me, without fixing the imputation of credulity.

First: I conceived this was the source, from observing that where the cow-pox had appeared among the dairies here (unless it could be traced to the introduction of an infected cow or servant) it had been preceded at the farm by a horse diseased in the manner already described, which horse had been attended by some of the milkers.

Secondly: From its being a popular opinion throughout this great dairy country, and from its being insisted on by those who here attend sick cattle.

Thirdly: From the total absence of the disease in Ireland and Scotland, where the men-servants are not employed in the dairies.*

Fourthly: From having observed that morbid matter generated by the horse frequently communicates, in a casual way, a disease to the human subject so like the cow-pox that, in many cases, it would be difficult to make the distinction between one and the other.†

Fifthly: From being induced to suppose, from experiments, that some of those who had been thus affected from the horse resisted the smallpox.

Sixthly: From the progress and general appearance of the pustule on the arm of the boy whom I inoculated with matter taken from the hand of a man infected by a horse; and from the similarity to the cow-pox of general constitutional symptoms which followed.‡

I fear it would be trespassing too far to adduce the general testimony of our farmers in support of this opinion; yet I beg leave to introduce an extract of a letter on this subject from the Rev. Mr. Moore, of Chalford Hill, in this county:

"In the month of November, 1797, my horse had diseased heels, which was certainly what is termed the grease; and at a short subsequent period my cow was also affected with what a neighbouring farmer (who was conversant with the complaints of cattle) pronounced to be the cow-pox, which he at the same time observed my servant would be infected with: and this proved to be the case; for he had eruptions on his hands, face, and many parts of the body, the pustules appearing large, and not much like the smallpox, for which he had been inoculated a year and a half before, and

---

* This information was communicated to me from the first authority.

† The sound skin does not appear to be susceptible of this virus when inserted into it, but, when previously diseased from little accidents, its effects are often conspicuous.

‡ This case (on which I laid no inconsiderable stress in my late treatise, as presumptive evidence of the fact adduced) seems to have been either mistaken or overlooked by those who have commented upon it. (See Case XVIII, p. 36.) The boy, unfortunately, died of a fever at a parish workhouse before I had an opportunity of observing what effects would have been produced by the matter of smallpox.

had then a very heavy burthen.   The pustules on the face might arise from contact with his hands, as he had a habit of rubbing his forehead, where the sores were the largest and the thickest.

"The boy associated with the farmer's sons during the continuance of the disease, neither of whom had had the smallpox, but they felt no ill effects whatever.   He was not much indisposed, as the disease did not prevent him from following his occupations as usual.   No other person attended the horse or milked the cow but the lad above mentioned.   I am firmly of opinion that the disease in the heels of the horse, which was a virulent grease, was the origin of the servant's and the cow's malady."

But to return to the more immediate object of this proposition.

From the similarity of symptoms, both constitutional and local, between the cow-pox and the disease received from morbid matter generated by a horse, the common people in this neighbourhood, when infected with this disease, through a strange perversion of terms, frequently call it the cow-pox.   Let us suppose, then, such a malady to appear among some of the servants at a farm, and at the same time that the cow-pox were to break out among the cattle; and let us suppose, too, that some of the servants were infected in this way, and that others received the infection from the cows.   It would be recorded at the farm, and among the servants themselves wherever they might afterwards be dispersed, that they had all had the cow-pox.   But it is clear that an individual thus infected from the horse would neither be for a certainty secure himself, nor would he impart security to others were they inoculated by virus thus generated.   He still would be in danger of taking the smallpox. Yet were this to happen before the nature of the cow-pox be more maturely considered by the public my evidence on the subject might be depreciated unjustly.   For an exemplification of what is here advanced relative to the nature of the infection when received directly from the horse see Inquiry into the Causes and Effects of the Variolæ Vaccinæ, pp. 27, 28, 29, 30, and p. 35; and by way of further example, I beg leave to subjoin the following intelligence received from Mr. Fewster, Surgeon, of Thornbury, in this county, a gentleman perfectly well acquainted with the appearances of the cow-pox on the human subject:

"William Morris, aged thirty-two, servant to Mr. Cox of Almondsbury, in this county, applied to me the 2d of April, 1798. He told me that, four days before, he found a stiffness and swelling in both his hands, which were so painful it was with difficulty he continued his work; that he had been seized with pain in his head, small of the back, and limbs, and with frequent chilly fits succeeded by fever. On examination I found him still affected with these symptoms, and that there was a great prostration of strength. Many parts of his hands on the inside were chapped, and on the middle joint of the thumb of the right hand there was a small phagedenic ulcer, about the size of a large pea, discharging an ichorous fluid. On the middle finger of the same hand there was another ulcer of a similar kind. These sores were of a *circular* form, and he described their first appearance as being somewhat like blisters arising from a burn. He complained of excessive pain, which extended up his arm into the axilla. These symptoms and apperances of the sores were so exactly like the cow-pox that I pronounced he had taken the distemper from milking cows. He assured me he had not milked a cow for more than half a year, and that his master's cows had nothing the matter with them. I then asked him if his master had a *greasy* horse, which he answered in the affirmative, and further said that he had constantly dressed him twice a day for the last three weeks or more, and remarkad that the smell of his hands was much like that of the horses's heels. On the 5th of April I again saw him, and found him still complaining of pain in both hands, nor were his febrile symptoms at all relieved. The ulcers had now spread to the size of a seven-shilling gold coin, and another ulcer, which I had not noticed before, appeared on the first joint of the forefinger of the left hand, equally painful with that on the right. I ordered him to bathe his hands in warm bran and water, applied escharotics to the ulcers, and wrapped his hands up in a soft cataplasm. The next day he was much relieved, and in something more than a fortnight got well. He lost his nails from the thumb and fingers that were ulcerated."

The sudden disappearance of the symptoms in this case after the application of the escharotics to the sores is worthy of observation; it seems to show that they were kept up by the irritation of the ulcers.

The general symptoms which I have already described of the cow-pox, when communicated in a casual way to any great extent, will, I am convinced, from the many cases I have seen, be found accurate; but from the very slight indisposition which ensues in cases of inoculation, where the pustule, after affecting the constitution, quickly runs into a scab spontaneously, or is artificially suppressed by some proper application, I am induced to believe that the violence of the symptoms may be ascribed to the inflammation and irritation of the ulcers (when ulceration takes place to any extent, as in the casual cow-pox), and that the constitutional symptoms which appear during the presence of the sore, while it assumes the character of a pustule only, are felt but in a very trifling degree. This mild affection of the system happens when the disease makes but a slight local impression on those who have been accidentally infected by cows; and, as far as I have seen, it has uniformly happened among those who have been inoculated, when a pustule only and no great degree of inflammation or any ulceration has taken place from the inoculation. The following cases will strengthen this opinion.

The cow-pox appeared at a farm in the village of Stonehouse, in this county, about Michaelmas last, and continued gradually to pass from one cow to another till the end of November. On the twenty-sixth of that month some ichorous matter was taken from a cow and dried upon a quill. On the 2d of December some of it was inserted into a scratch, made so superficial that no blood appeared, on the arm of Susan Phipps, a child seven years old. The common inflammatory appearances took place in consequence, and advanced till the fifth day, when they had so much subsided that I did not conceive any thing further would ensue.

6th: Appearances stationary.

7th: The inflammation began to advance.

8th: A vesication, perceptible on the edges, forming, as in the inoculated smallpox, an appearance not unlike a grain of wheat, with the cleft or indentation in the centre.

9th: Pain in the axilla.

10th: A little headache; pulse, 110; tongue not discoloured; countenance in health.

11th, 12th: No perceptible illness; pulse about 100.

13th: The pustule was now surrounded by an efflorescence, interspersed with very minute confluent pustules to the extent of about an inch. Some of these pustules advanced in size and maturated. So exact was the resemblance of the arm at this stage to the general appearance of the inoculated smallpox that Mr. D, a neighbouring surgeon, who took some matter from it, and who had never seen the cow-pox before, declared he could not perceive any difference.* The child's arm now shewed a disposition to scab, and remained nearly stationary for two or three days, when it began to run into an ulcerous state, and *then* commenced a febrile indisposition accompanied with an increase of axillary tumour. The ulcer continued spreading near a week, during which time the child continued ill, when it increased to a size nearly as large as a shilling. It began now to discharge pus; granulations sprang up, and it healed. This child had before been of a remarkably sickly constitution, but is now in very high health.

Mary Hearn, twelve years of age, was inoculated with matter taken from the arm of Susan Phipps.

6th day: A pustule beginning to appear, slight pain in the axilla.

7th: A distinct vesicle formed.

8th: The vesicle increasing; edges very red; no deviation in its appearance at this time from the inoculated smallpox.

---

* That the cow-pox was a supposed guardian of the constitution from the action of the smallpox has been a prevalent idea for a long time past; but the similarity in the constitutional effects between one disease and the other could never have been so accurately observed had not the inoculation of the cow-pox placed it in a new and stronger point of view. This practice, too, has shewn us, what before lay concealed, the rise and progress of the pustule formed by the insertion of the virus, which places in a most conspicuous light its striking resemblance to the pustule formed from the inoculated smallpox.

9th: No indisposition; pustule advancing.

10th: The patient felt this evening a slight febrile attack.

11th: Free from indisposition.

12th, 13th: The same.

14th: An efflorescence of a faint red colour extending several inches round the arm. The pustule, beginning to shew a disposition to spread, was dressed with an ointment composed of *hydrarg. nit. rub. and ung. ceræ.* The efflorescence itself was covered with a plaster of *ung. hydr. fort.* In six hours it was examined, when is was found that the efflorescence had totally disappeared.

The application of the ointment with the *hydr. nit. rub.* was made use of for three days, when, the state of the pustule remaining stationary, it was exchanged for the *ung. hydr. nit.* This appeared to have a more active effect than the former, and in two or three days the virus seemed to be subdued, when a simple dressing was made use of; but the sore again shewing a disposition to inflame, the *ung. hydr. nit.* was again applied, and soon answered the intended purpose effectually. The girl, after the tenth day, when, as has been observed, she became a little ill, shewed not the least symptom of indisposition. She was afterwards exposed to the action of variolous matter, and completely resisted it. Susan Phipps also went through a similar trial. Conceiving these cases to be important, I have given them in detail: first, to urge the precaution of using such means as may stop the progress of the pustule; and, secondly, to point out (what appears to be the fact) that the most material indisposition, or at least that which is felt most sensibly, *does not arise primarily from the first action of the virus on the constitution, but that it often comes on, if the pustule is left to chance, as a secondary disease.* This leads me to conjecture, what experiment must finally determine, that they who have had the smallpox are not afterwards susceptible of the primary action of the cow-pox virus; for seeing that the simple virus itself, when it has not passed beyond the boundary of a vesicle, excites in the system so little commotion, is it not probable the trifling illness thus induced may be lost in that which so quickly, and oftentimes so severely, follows in the casual cow-pox from the presence of corroding ulcers? This consideration induces me to suppose that I may have been mistaken in my former observation on this subject.

In this respect, as well as many others, a parallel may be drawn between this disease and the smallpox. In the latter, the patient first feels the effect of what is called the absorption of the virus. The symptoms then often nearly retire, when a fresh attack commences, different from the first, and the illness keeps pace with the progress of the pustules through their different stages of maturation, ulceration, etc.

Although the application I have mentioned in the case of Mary Hearn proved sufficient to check the progress of ulceration and prevent any secondary symptoms, yet, after the pustule has duly exerted its influence, I should prefer the destroying it quickly and effectually to any other mode. The term caustic to a tender ear (and I conceive none feel more interested in this inquiry than the anxious guardians of a nursery) may sound harsh and unpleasing, but every solicitude that may arise on this account will no longer exist when it is understood that the pustule, in a state fit to be acted upon, is then quite superficial, and that it does not occupy the space of a silver penny.*

As a proof of the efficacy of this practice, even before the virus has fully exerted itself on the system, I shall lay before my reader the following history:

By a reference to the treatise on the Variolæ Vaccinæ it will be seen that, in the month of April, 1798, four children were inoculated with the matter of cow-pox, and that in two of these cases the virus on the arm was destroyed soon after it had produced a perceptible sickening. Mary James, aged seven years, one of the children alluded to, was inoculated in the month of December following with fresh variolous matter, and at the same time was exposed to the effluvia of a patient affected with the smallpox. The appearance and progress of the infected arm was, in every respect,

---

* I mention escharotics for stopping the progress of the pustule because I am acquainted with their efficacy; probably more simple means might answer the purpose quite as well, such as might be found among the mineral and vegetable astringents.

similar to that which we generally observe when variolous matter has been inserted into the skin of a person who has not previously undergone either the cow-pox or the smallpox. On the eighth day, conceiving there was infection in it, she was removed from her residence among those had not had the smallpox. I was now anxiously waiting the result, conceiving, from the state of the girl's arm, she would fall sick about this time. On visiting her on the evening of the following day (the ninth) all I could learn from the woman who attended her was that she felt somewhat hotter than usual during the night, but was not restless; and that in the morning there was the faint appearance of a rash about her wrists. This went off in a few hours, and was not at all perceptible to me on my visit in the evening. Not a single eruption appeared, the skin having been repeatedly and carefully examined. The inoculated arm continued to make the usual progress to the end, through all the stages of inflammation, maturation, and scabbing.

On the eighth day matter was taken from the arm of this girl (Mary James) and inserted into the arms of her mother and brother (neither of whom had had either the smallpox or the cow-pox), the former about fifty years of age, the latter six.

On the eighth day after the insertion the boy felt indisposed, and continued unwell two days, when a measles-like rash appeared on his hands and wrists, and was thinly scattered over his arms. The day following his body was marbled over with an appearance somewhat similar, but he did not complain, nor did he appear indisposed. A few pustules now appeared, the greater part of which went away without maturating.

On the ninth day the mother began to complain. She was a little chilly and had a headache for two days, but *no pustule appeared on the skin*, nor had she any appearance of a rash.

The family was attended by an elderly woman as a nurse, who in her infancy had been exposed to the contagion of the smallpox, but had resisted it. This woman was now infected, but had the disease in the slightest manner, a very few eruptions appearing, two or three of which only maturated.

From a solitary instance like that adduced of Mary James,

whose constitution appears to have resisted the action of the variolous virus, after the influence of the cow-pox virus had been so soon arrested in its progress, no positive conclusion can be fairly drawn; nor from the history of the three other patients who were subsequently infected, but, nevertheless, the facts collectively may be deemed interesting.

That one mild variety of the smallpox has appeared I have already plainly shewn*; and by the means now mentioned we probably have it in our power to produce at will another.

At the time when the pustule was destroyed in the arm of Mary James I was informed she had been indisposed about twelve hours; but I am now assured by those who were with her that the space of time was much less. Be that as it may, in cases of cow-pox inoculation I would not recommend any application to subdue the action of the pustule until convincing proofs had appeared of the patient's having felt its effects at least twelve hours. No harm, indeed, could ensue were a longer period to elapse before the application was made use of. In short, it should be suffered to have as full an effect as it could, consistently with the state of the arm.

As the cases of inoculation multiply, I am more and more convinced of the extreme mildness of the symptoms arising merely from the primary action of the virus on the constitution, and that those symptoms which, as in the accidental cow-pox, affect the patient with severity, are entirely secondary, excited by the irritating processes of inflammation and ulceration; and it appears to me that this singular virus possesses an irritating quality of a peculiar kind, but as a single cow-pox pustule is all that is necessary to render the variolous virus ineffectual, and as we possess the means of allaying the irritation, should any arise, it becomes of little or no consequence.

It appears then, as far as an inference can be drawn from the present progress of cow-pox inoculation, that it is an accidental circumstance only which can render this a violent disease, and a circumstance of that nature which, fortunately, it is in the power of

* See Inquiry into the Causes and Effects of the Variolæ Vaccinæ, p. 54 (of original article).

almost every one to avoid. I allude to the communication of the disease from cows. In this case, should the hands of the milker be affected with little accidental sores to any extent, every sore would become the nidus of infection and feel the influence of the virus; and the degree of violence in the constitutional symptoms would be in proportion to the number and to the state of these local affections. Hence it follows that a person, either by accident or design, might be so filled with these wounds from contact with the virus that the constitution might sink under the pressure.

Seeing that we possess the means of rendering the action of the sores mild, which, when left to chance, are capable of producing violent effects; and seeing, too, that these sores bear a resemblance to the smallpox, especially the confluent, should it not encourage the hope that some topical application might be used with advantage to counteract the fatal tendency of that disease, when it appears in this terrific form? At what stage or stages of the disease this may be done with the most promising expectation of success I will not pretend now to determine. I only throw out this idea as the basis of further reasoning and experiment.

I have often been foiled in my endeavours to communicate the cow-pox by inoculation. An inflammation will sometimes succeed the scratch or puncture, and in a few days disappear without producing any further effect. Sometimes it will even produce an ichorous fluid, and yet the system will not be affected. The same thing we know happens with the smallpox virus.

Four or five servants were inoculated at a farm contiguous to this place, last summer, with matter just taken from an infected cow. A little inflammation appeared on all their arms, but died away without producing a pustule; yet all these servants caught the disease within a month afterwards from milking the infected cows, and some of them had it severely. At present no other mode than that commonly practiced for inoculating the smallpox has been used for giving the cow-pox; but it is probable this might be varied with advantage. We should imitate the casual communication more clearly were the first, by making the smallest superficial incision or puncture on the skin, to produce a little scab, and then, removing it, to touch the abraded part with the virus. A small portion of a thread imbrued in the virus (as in the old method of inoculating the smallpox) and laid upon the slightly incised skin might probably prove a successful way of giving the disease; or the cutis might be exposed in a minute point by an atom of blistering plaster, and the virus brought in contact with it. In the cases just alluded to, where I did not succeed in giving the disease constitutionally, the experiment was made with matter taken in a purulent state from a pustule on the nipple of a cow.

Is *pure pus*, though contained in a smallpox pustule, ever capable of producing the smallpox perfectly? I suspect it is not. Let us consider that it is always preceded by the limpid fluid, which, in constitutions susceptible of variolous contagion, is always infectious; and though, on opening a pustule, its contents may appear perfectly purulent, yet a given quantity of the limpid fluid may, at the same time, be blended with it, though it would be imperceptible to the only test of our senses, the eye. The presence, then, of this fluid, or its mechanical diffusion through pus, may at all times render active what is apparently *mere pus*, while its total absence (as in stale pustules) may be attended with the imperfect effects we have seen.

It would be digressing too widely to go far into the doctrine of secretion, but as it will not be quite extraneous, I shall just observe that I consider both the pus and the limpid fluid of the pustule as secretions, but that the organs established by nature to perform the office of secreting these fluids may differ essentially in their mechanical structure. What but a difference in the organization of glandular bodies constitutes the difference in the qualities of the fluids secreted? From some peculiar derangement in the structure or, in other words, some deviation in the natural action of a gland destined to create a mild, innoxious fluid, a poison of the most deadly nature may be created; for example: That gland, which in its sound state secretes pure saliva, may, from being thrown into diseased action, produce a poison of the most destructive quality. Nature appears to have no more difficulty in forming minute glands among the vascular parts of the body than she has in forming blood vessels, and millions of these can be called into existence, when inflammation is excited, in a few hours.*

In the present early stage of the inquiry (for early it certainly must be deemed), before we know for an absolute certainty how soon the virus of the cow-pox may suffer a change in its specific properties, after it has quitted the limpid state it possesses when forming a pustule, it would be prudent for those who have been inoculated with it to submit to variolous inoculation. No injury or inconvenience can accrue from this; and were the same method practiced among those who, from inoculation, have felt the small-pox in an unsatisfactory manner at any period of their lives, it might appear that I had not been too officious in offering a cautionary hint in recommending a second inoculation with matter in its most perfect state.

And here let me suppose, for argument's sake (not from conviction), that one person in an hundred after having had the cow-pox should be found susceptible of the smallpox, would this invalidate the utility of the practice? For, waiving all other considerations, who will deny that the inoculated smallpox, although abstractedly it may be considered as harmless, does not involve in itself something that in numberless instances proves baneful to the human frame.

That in delicate constitutions it sometimes excites scrofula is a fact that must generally be subscribed to, as it is so obvious to common observation. This consideration is important.

As the effects of the smallpox inoculation on those who have had the cow-pox will be watched with the most scrupulous eye by those who prosecute this inquiry, it may be proper to bring to their recollection some facts relative to the smallpox, which I must consider here as of consequence, but which hitherto seem not to have made a due impression.

It should be remembered that the constitution cannot, by previous infection, be rendered totally unsusceptible of the variolous poison; neither the casual nor the inoculated smallpox, whether

---

* Mr. Home, in his excellent dissertation on pus and mucus, justifies this assertion.

it produces the disease in a mild or in a violent way, can perfectly extinguish the susceptibility. The skin, we know, is ever ready to exhibit, though often in a very limited degree, the effects of the poison when inserted there; and how frequently do we see, among nurses, when much exposed to the contagion, eruptions, and these sometimes preceded by sensible illness! yet should any thing like an eruption appear, or the smallest degree of indisposition, upon the insertion of the variolous matter on those who have gone through the cow-pox, my assertions respecting the peculiarities of the disease might be unjustly discredited.

I know a gentleman who, many years ago, was inoculated for the smallpox, but having no pustules, or scarcely any constitutional affection that was perceptible, he was dissatisfied, and has since been repeatedly inoculated. A vesicle has always been produced in the arm in consequence, with axillary swelling and a slight indisposition; this is by no means a rare occurrence. It is probable that a fluid thus excited upon the skin would always produce the smallpox.

On the arm of a person who had gone through the cow-pox many years before I once produced a vesication by the insertion of variolous matter, and, with a little of the fluid, inoculated a young woman who had a mild, but very efficacious, smallpox in consequence, although no constitutional effect was produced on the patient from whom the matter was taken. The following communication from Mr. Fewster affords a still clearer elucidation of this fact. Mr. Fewster says: "On the 3d of April, 1797, I inoculated Master H——, aged fourteen months, for the smallpox. At the usual time he sickened, had a plentiful eruption, particularly on his face, and got well. His nursemaid, aged twenty-four, had many years before gone through the smallpox, in the natural way, which was evident from her being much pitted with it. She had used the child to sleep on her left arm, with her left cheek in contact with his face, and during his inoculation he had mostly slept in that manner. About a week after the child got well she (the nurse) desired me to look at her face, which she said was very painful. There was a plentiful eruption on the left cheek, *but not on any other part of the body*, which went on to maturation.

"On enquiry I found that three days before the appearance of the eruption she was taken with slight chilly fits, pain in her head and limbs, and some fever. On the appearance of the eruption these pains went off, and now, the second day of the eruption, she complains of a little sore throat. Whether the above symptoms are the effects of the smallpox or a recent cold I do not know. On the fifth day of the eruption I charged a lancet from two of the pustules, and on the next day I inoculated two children, one two years, the other four months, old, with the matter. At the same time I inoculated the mother and eldest sister with variolous matter taken from Master H——. On the fifth day of their inoculation *all* their arms were inflamed alike; and on the eighth day the eldest of those inoculated from the nurse sickened, and the youngest on the eleventh. They had both a plentiful eruption, from which I inoculated several others, who had the disease very favourably. The mother and the other child sickened about the same time, and likewise had a plentiful eruption.

"Soon after, a man in the village sickened with the smallpox and had a confluent kind. To be convinced that the children had had the disease effectually I took them to his house and inoculated them in both arms with matter taken from him, but without effect."

These are not brought forward as uncommon occurrences, but as exemplifications of the human system's susceptibility of the variolous contagion, although it has been previously sensible of its action.

Happy is it for mankind that the appearance of the smallpox a second time on the same person, beyond a trivial extent, is so extremely rare that it is looked upon as a phœnomenon! Indeed, since the publication of Dr. Heberden's paper on the *Varicellæ*, or chicken-pox, the idea of such an occurrence, in deference to authority so truly respectable, has been generally relinquished. This I conceive has been without just reason; for after we have seen, among many others, so strong a case as that recorded by Mr. Edward Withers, Surgeon, of Newbury, Berks, in the fourth volume of the Memoirs of the Medical Society of London (from which I take the following extracts), no one, I think, will again doubt the fact.

"Mr. Richard Langford, a farmer of West Shefford, in this county (Berks), about fifty years of age, when about a month old had the smallpox at a time when three others of the family had the same disease, one of whom, a servant man, died of it. Mr. Langford's countenance was strongly indicative of the malignity of the distemper, his face being so remarkably pitted and seamed as to attract the notice of all who saw him, so that no one could entertain a doubt of his having had that disease in a most inveterate manner." Mr. Withers proceeds to state that Mr. Langford was seized a second time, had a bad confluent smallpox, and died on the twenty-first day from the seizure; and that four of the family, as also a sister of the patient's, to whom the disease was conveyed by her son's visiting his uncle, falling down with the smallpox, fully satisfied the country with regard to the nature of the disease, which nothing short of this would have done; the sister died.

"This case was thought so extraordinary a one as to induce the rector of the parish to record the particulars in the parish register."

It is singular that in most cases of this kind the disease in the first instance has been confluent; so that the extent of the ulceration on the skin (as in the cow-pox) is not the process in nature which affords security to the constitution.

As the subject of the smallpox is so interwoven with that which is the more immediate object of my present concern, it must plead my excuse for so often introducing it. At present it must be considered as a distemper not well understood. The inquiry I have instituted into the nature of the cow-pox will probably promote its more perfect investigation.

The inquiry of Dr. Pearson into the history of the cow-pox having produced so great a number of attestations in favour of my assertion that it proves a protection to the human body from the smallpox, I have not been assiduous in seeking for more; but as some of my friends have been so good as to communicate the following, I shall conclude these observations with their insertion.

Extract of a letter from Mr. Drake, Surgeon, at Stroud, in this county, and late Surgeon to the North Gloucester Regiment of Militia:

"In the spring of the year 1796 I inoculated men, women, and children to the amount of about seventy. Many of the men did not receive the infection, although inoculated at least three times and kept in the same room with those who actually underwent the disease during the whole time occupied by them in passing through it. Being anxious they should, in future, be secure against it, I was very particular in my inquiries to find out whether they ever had previously had it, or at any time been in the neighbourhood of people labouring under it. But, after all, the only satisfactory information I could obtain was that they had had the cow-pox. As I was then ignorant of such a disease affecting the human subject, I flattered myself what they imagined to be the cow-pox was in reality the smallpox in a very slight degree. I mentioned the circumstance in the presence of the officers, at the time expressing my doubts if it were not smallpox, and was not a little surprised when I was told by the Colonel that he had frequently heard you mention the cow-pox as a disease endemial to Gloucestershire, and that if a person were ever affected by it, you supposed him afterwards secure from the smallpox. This excited my curiosity, and when I visited Gloucestershire I was very inquisitive concerning the subject, and from the information I have since received, both from your publication and from conversation with medical men of the greatest accuracy in their observations, I am fully convinced that what the men supposed to be cow-pox was actually so, and I can safely affirm that they effectually resisted the smallpox."

Mr. Fry, Surgeon, at Dursley in this county, favours me with the following communication:

"During the spring of the year 1797 I inoculated fourteen hundred and seventy-five patients, of all ages, from a fortnight old to seventy years; amongst whom there were many who had previously gone through the cow-pox. The exact number I cannot state; but if I say there were nearly thirty, I am certainly within the number. There was not a single instance of the variolous matter producing any constitutional effect on these people, nor any greater degree of local inflammation than it would have done in the arm of a person who had before gone through the smallpox, notwithstanding it was invariably inserted four, five, and sometimes six different times, to satisfy the minds of the patients. In the common course of inoculation previous to the general one scarcely a year passed without my meeting with one or two instances of persons who had gone through the cow-pox, resisting the action of the variolous contagion. I may fairly say that the number of people I have seen inoculated with the smallpox who, at former periods, had gone through the cow-pox, are not less than forty; and in no one instance have I known a patient receive the small-pox, notwithstanding they invariably continued to associate with other inoculated patients during the progress of the disease, and many of them purposely exposed themselves to the contagion of the natural smallpox; whence I am fully convinced that a person who had *fairly* had the cow-pox is no longer capable of being acted upon by the variolous matter.

"I also inoculated a very considerable number of those who had had a disease which ran through the neighbourhood a few years ago, and was called by the common people the *swine-pox*, not one of whom received the smallpox.*

"There were about half a dozen instances of people who never had either the cow- or swine-pox, yet did not receive the smallpox, the system not being in the least deranged, or the arms inflamed, although they were repeatedly inoculated, and associated with others who were labouring under the disease; one of them was the son of a farrier."

Mr. Tierny, Assistant Surgeon of the South Gloucester Regiment of Militia, has obliged me with the following information:

"That in the summer of the year 1798 he inoculated a great number of the men belonging to the regiment, and that among

---

* This was that mild variety of the smallpox which I have noticed in the late Treatise on the Cow-Pox, p. 54 (of original article).

them he found eleven who, from having lived in dairies, had gone through the cow-pox. That all of them resisted the smallpox except one, but that on making the most rigid and scrupulous enquiry at the farm in Gloucestershire, where the man said he lived when he had the disease, and among those with whom, at the same time, he declared he had associated, and particularly of a person in the parish, whom he said had dressed his fingers, it most clearly appeared that he aimed at an imposition, and that he never had been affected with the cow-pox.* Mr. Tierny remarks that the arms of many who were inoculated after having had the cow-pox inflamed very quickly, and that in several a little ichorous fluid was formed."

Mr. Cline, who in July last was so obliging at my request as to try the efficacy of the cow-pox virus, was kind enough to give me a letter on the result of it, from which the following is an extract:

"MY DEAR SIR:

"The cow-pox experiment has succeeded admirably. The child sickened on the seventh day, and the fever, which was moderate, subsided on the eleventh. The inflammation arising from the insertion of the virus extended to about four inches in diameter, and then gradually subsided, without having been attended with pain or other inconvenience. There were no eruptions.

"I have since inoculated him with smallpox matter in three places, which were slightly inflamed on the third day, and then subsided.

"Dr. Lister, who was formerly physician to the Smallpox Hospital, attended the child with me, and he is convinced that it is not possible to give him the smallpox. I think the substituting the cow-pox poison for the smallpox promises to be one of the greatest improvements that has ever been made in medicine; and the more I think on the subject, the more I am impressed with its importance.

"With great esteem

"I am, etc.,

"HENRY CLINE.

"*Lincoln's Inn Fields*, August 2, 1798."

* The public cannot be too much upon their guard respecting persons of this description.

From communications, with which I have been favoured from Dr. Pearson, who has occasionally reported to me the result of his private practice with the vaccine virus in London, and from Dr. Woodville, who also has favoured me with an account of his more extensive inoculation with the same virus at the Smallpox Hospital, it appears that many of their patients have been affected with eruptions, and that these eruptions have maturated in a manner very similar to the variolous. The matter they made use of was taken in the first instance from a cow belonging to one of the great milk farms in London. Having never seen maturated pustules produced either in my own practice among those who were casually infected by cows, or those to whom the disease had been communicated by inoculation, I was desirous of seeing the effect of the matter generated in London, on subjects living in the country. A thread imbrued in some of this matter was sent to me, and with it two children were inoculated, whose cases I shall transcribe from my notes.

Stephen Jenner, three years and a half old.

3d day: The arm shewed a proper and decisive inflammation.

6th: A vesicle arising.

7th: The pustule of a cherry colour.

8th: Increasing in elevation. A few spots now appear on each arm near the insertion of the inferior tendons of the biceps muscles. They are very small and of a vivid red colour. The pulse natural; tongue of its natural hue; no loss of appetite or any symptom of indisposition.

9th: The inoculated pustule on the arm this evening began to inflame, and gave the child uneasiness; he cried and pointed to the seat of it, and was immediately afterwards affected with febrile symptoms. At the expiration of two hours after the seizure a plaster of *ung. hydrarg. fort.* was applied, and its effect was very quickly perceptible for in ten minutes he resumed his usual looks and playfulness. On examining the arm about three hours after the application of the plaster its effects in subduing the inflammation were very manifest.

10th: The spots on the arms have disappeared, but there are three visible in the face.

11th: Two spots on the face are gone; the other barely perceptible.

13th: The pustule delineated in the second plate in the Treatise on the Variolæ Vaccinæ is a correct representation of that on the child's arm as it appears at this time.

14th: Two fresh spots appear on the face. The pustule on the arm nearly converted into a scab. As long as any fluid remained in it it was limpid.

James Hill, four years old, was inoculated on the same day, and with part of the same matter which infected Stephen Jenner. It did not appear to have taken effect till the fifth day.

7th: A perceptible vesicle: this evening the patient became a little chilly; no pain or tumour discoverable in the axilla.

8th: Perfectly well.

9th: The same.

10th: The vesicle more elevated than I have been accustomed to see it, and assuming more perfectly the variolous character than is common with the cow-pox at this stage.

11th: Surrounded by an inflammatory redness, about the size of a shilling, studded over with minute vesicles. The pustule contained a limpid fluid till the fourteenth day, after which it was incrusted over in the usual manner; but this incrustation or scab being accidentally rubbed off, it was slow in healing.

These children were afterwards fully exposed to the smallpox contagion without effect.

Having been requested by my friend, Mr. Henry Hicks, of Eastington, in this county, to inoculate two of his children, and at the same time some of his servants and the people employed in his manufactory, matter was taken from the arm of this boy for the purpose. The numbers inoculated were eighteen. They all took the infection, and either on the fifth or sixth day a vesicle was perceptible on the punctured part. Some of them began to feel a little unwell on the eighth day, but the greater number on the ninth. Their illness, as in the former cases described, was of short duration, and not sufficient to interrupt, but at very short intervals, the children from their amusements, or the servants and manufacturers from following their ordinary business.

Three of the children whose employment in the manufactory was in some degree laborious had an inflammation on their arms beyond the common boundary about the eleventh or twelfth day, when the feverish symptoms, which before were nearly gone off, again returned, accompanied with increase of axillary tumor. In these cases (clearly perceiving that the symptoms were governed by the state of the arms) I applied on the inoculated pustules, and renewed the application three or four times within an hour, a pledget of lint, previously soaked in *aqua lythargyri acetati*,* and covered the hot efflorescence surrounding them with cloths dipped in cold water.

The next day I found this simple mode of treatment had succeeded perfectly. The inflammation was nearly gone off, and with it the symptoms which it had produced.

Some of these patients have since been inoculated with variolous matter, without any effect beyond a little inflammation on the part where it was inserted.

Why the arms of those inoculated with the vaccine matter in the country should be more disposed to inflame than those inoculated in London it may be difficult to determine. From comparing my own cases with some transmitted to me by Dr. Pearson and Dr. Woodville, this appears to be the fact; and what strikes me as still more extraordinary with respect to those inoculated in London is the appearance of maturating eruptions. In the two instances only which I have mentioned (the one from the inoculated, the other from the casual, cow-pox) a few red spots appeared, which quickly went off without maturating. The case of the Rev. Mr. Moore's servant may, indeed, seem like a deviation from the common appearances in the country, but the nature of these eruptions was not ascertained beyond their not possessing the property of communicating the disease by their effluvia. Perhaps the difference we perceive may be owing to some variety in the mode of action of the virus upon the skin of those who breathe the air of London and those who live in the country. That the erysipelas assumes a different form in London from what we see it put on in this country is a fact very generally acknowledged. In calling the inflammation that is excited by the cow-pox virus erysipelatous, perhaps I may not be critically exact, but it certainly approaches near to it. Now,

* Goulard's extract of Saturn.

as the diseased action going forward in the part infected with the virus may undergo different modifications according to the peculiarities of the constitution on which it is to produce its effect, may it not account for the variation which has been observed?

To this it may probably be objected that some of the patients inoculated, and who had pustules in consequence, were newly come from the country; but I conceive that the changes wrought in the human body through the medium of the lungs may be extremely rapid. Yet, after all, further experiments made in London with vaccine virus generated in the country must finally throw a light on what now certainly appears obscure and mysterious.

The principal variation perceptible to me in the action of the vaccine virus generated in London from that produced in the country was its proving more certainly infectious and giving a less disposition in the arm to inflame. There appears also a greater elevation of the pustule above the surrounding skin. In my former cases the pustule produced by the insertion of the virus was more like one of those which are so thickly spread over the body in a bad kind of confluent smallpox. This was more like a pustule of the distinct smallpox, except that I saw no instance of pus being formed in it, the matter remaining limpid till the period of scabbing.

Wishing to see the effects of the disease on an infant newly born, my nephew, Mr. Henry Jenner, at my request, inserted the vaccine virus into the arm of a child about twenty hours old. His report to me is that the child went through the disease without apparent illness, yet that it was found effectually to resist the action of variolous matter with which it was subsequently inoculated.

I have had an opportunity of trying the effects of the cow-pox matter on a boy, who, the day preceding its insertion, sickened with the measles. The eruption of the measles, attended with cough, a little pain in the chest, and the usual symptoms accompanying the disease, appeared on the third day and spread all over him. The disease went through its course without any deviation from its usual habits; and, notwithstanding this, the cow-pox virus excited its common appearances, both on the arm and on the constitution, without any febrile interruption; on the sixth day there was a vesicle.

8th: Pain in the axilla, chilly, and affected with headache.

9th: Nearly well.

12th: The pustule spread to the size of a large split-pea, but without any surrounding efflorescence. It soon afterwards scabbed, and the boy recovered his general health rapidly. But it should be observed that before it scabbed the efflorescence which had suffered a temporary suspension advanced in the usual manner.

Here we see a deviation from the ordinary habits of the small-pox, as it has been observed that the presence of the measles suspends the action of variolous matter.

The very general investigation that is now taking place, chiefly through inoculation (and I again repeat my earnest hope that it may be conducted with that calmness and moderation which should ever accompany a philosophical research), must soon place the vaccine disease in its just point of view. The result of all my trials with the virus on the human subject has been uniform. In every instance the patient who has felt its influence, has completely lost the susceptibility for the variolous contagion; and as these instances are now become numerous, I conceive that, joined to the observations in the former part of this paper, they sufficiently preclude me from the necessity of entering into controversies with those who have circulated reports adverse to my assertions, on no other evidence than what has been casually collected.

A CONTINUATION OF FACTS AND OBSERVATIONS RELATIVE TO THE VARIOLÆ VACCINÆ, OR COW-POX

By EDWARD JENNER, M.D., F.R.S., F.L.S., Etc.

PUBLISHED IN 1800

A CONTINUATION OF FACTS AND OBSERVATIONS

Since my former publications on the vaccine inoculation I have had the satisfaction of seeing it extend very widely. Not only in this country is the subject pursued with ardour, but from my correspondence with many respectable medical gentlemen on the Continent (among whom are Dr. De Carro, of Vienna, and Dr. Ballhorn, of Hanover) I find it is as warmly adopted abroad, where it has afforded the greatest satisfaction. I have the pleasure, too, of seeing that the feeble efforts of a few individuals to depreciate the new practice are sinking fast into contempt beneath the immense mass of evidence which has arisen up in support of it.

Upwards of six thousand persons have now been inoculated with the virus of cow-pox, and the far greater part of them have since been inoculated with that of smallpox, and exposed to its infection in every rational way that could be devised, without effect.

It was very improbable that the investigation of a disease so analogous to the smallpox should go forward without engaging the attention of the physician of the Smallpox Hospital in London.

Accordingly, Dr. Woodville, who fills that department with so much respectability, took an early opportunity of instituting an inquiry into the nature of the cow-pox. This inquiry was begun in the early part of the present year, and in May Dr. Woodville published the result, which differs essentially from mine in a point of much importance. It appears that three-fifths of the patients inoculated were affected with eruptions, for the most part so perfectly resembling the smallpox as not to be distinguished from them. On this subject it is necessary that I should make some comments.

When I consider that out of the great number of cases of casual inoculation immediately from cows which from time to time presented themselves to my observation, and the many similar instances which have been communicated to me by medical gentlemen in this neighbourhood; when I consider, too, that the matter with which my inoculations were conducted in the years 1797, '98, and '99, was taken from some different cows, and that in no instance anything like a variolous pustule appeared, I cannot feel disposed to imagine that eruptions, similar to those described by Dr. Woodville, have ever been produced by the *pure uncontaminated cow pock virus;* on the contrary, I do suppose that those which the doctor speaks of originated in the action of variolous matter which crept into the constitution with the vaccine. And this I presume happened from the inoculation of a great number of the patients with variolous matter (some on the third, others on the fifth, day) after the vaccine had been applied; and it should be observed that the matter thus propagated became the source of future inoculations in the hands of many medical gentlemen who appeared to have been previously unacquainted with the nature of the cow-pox.

Another circumstance strongly, in my opinion, supporting this supposition is the following: The cow-pox has been known among our dairies time immemorial. If pustules, then, like the variolous, were to follow the communication of it from the cow to the milker, would not such a fact have been known and recorded at our farms? Yet neither our farmers nor the medical people of the neighbourhood have noticed such an occurrence.

A few scattered pimples I have sometimes, though very rarely, seen, the greater part of which have generally disappeared quickly, but some have remained long enough to suppurate at their apex. That local cuticular inflammation, whether springing up spontaneously or arising from the application of acrid substances, such, for instance, as *cantharides, pix Burgundica, antimonium tartarizatum,* etc., will often produce cutaneous affections, not only near the seat of the inflammation, but on some parts of the skin far beyond its boundary, is a well-known fact. It is, doubtless, on this principle that the inoculated cow-pock pustule and its concomitant efflorescence may, in very irritable constitutions, produce this affection. The eruption I allude to has commonly appeared some time in the third week after inoculation. But this appearance is too trivial to excite the least regard.

The change which took place in the general appearance during the progress of the vaccine inoculation at the Smallpox Hospital should likewise be considered.

Although at first it took on so much of the variolous character as to produce pustules in three cases out of five, yet in Dr. Woodville's last report, published in June, he says: "Since the publication of my reports of inoculations for the cow-pox, upwards of three hundred cases have been under my care; and out of this number only thirty-nine had pustules that suppurated; viz., out of the first hundred, nineteen had pustules; out of the second, thirteen; and out of the last hundred and ten, only seven had pustules. Thus it appears that the disease has become considerably milder; which I am inclined to attribute to a greater caution used in the choice of the matter, with which the infection was communicated; for, lately, that which has been employed for this purpose has been taken only from those patients in whom the cow-pox proved very mild and well characterised."*

The inference I am induced to draw from these premises is very different. The decline, and, finally, the total extinction nearly, of these pustules, in my opinion, are more fairly attributable to the cow-pox virus, assimilating the variolous,† the former probably being the original, the latter the same disease under a peculiar, and at present an inexplicable, modification.

One experiment tending to elucidate the point under discussion

---

*In a few weeks after the cow-pox inoculation was introduced at the Smallpox Hospital I was favoured with some virus from this stock. In the first instance it produced a few pustules, which did not maturate; but in the subsequent cases none appeared.—E. J.

† In my first publication on this subject I expressed an opinion that the smallpox and the cow-pox were the same diseases under different modifications. In this opinion Dr. Woodville has concurred. The axiom of the immortal Hauter, that *two diseased actions cannot take place at the same time in one and the same part*, will not be injured by the admission of this theory.

I had myself an opportunity of instituting. On the supposition of its being possible that the cow which ranges over the fertile meadows in the vale of Gloucester might generate a virus differing in some respects in its qualities from that produced by the animal artificially pampered for the production of milk for the metropolis, I procured, during my residence there in the spring, some cow pock virus from a cow at one of the London milk-farms.* It was immediately conveyed into Gloucestershire to Dr. Marshall, who was then extensively engaged in the inoculation of the cow-pox, the general result of which, and of the inoculation in particular with this matter, I shall lay before my readers in the following communication from the doctor:

"DEAR SIR:

"My neighbour, Mr. Hicks, having mentioned your wish to be informed of the progress of the inoculation here for the cow-pox, and he also having taken the trouble to transmit to you my minutes of the cases which have fallen under my care, I hope you will pardon the further trouble I now give you in stating the observations I have made upon the subject. When first informed of it, having two children who had not had the smallpox, I determined to inoculate them for the cow-pox whenever I should be so fortunate as to procure matter proper for the purpose. I was, therefore, particularly happy when I was informed that I could procure matter from some of those whom you had inoculated. In the first instance I had no intention of extending the disease further than my own family, but the very extensive influence which the conviction of its efficacy in resisting the smallpox has had upon the minds of the people in general has rendered that intention nugatory, as you will perceive, by the continuation of my cases enclosed in this letter,† by which it will appear that since the 22d of March I have inoculated an hundred and seven persons; which, considering the

---

* It was taken by Mr. Tanner, then a student at the Veterinary College, from a cow at Mr. Clark's farm at Kentish Town.

† Doctor Marshall has detailed these cases with great accuracy, but their publication would now be deemed superfluous.—E. J.

retired situation I resided in, is a very great number. There are also other considerations which, besides that of its influence in resisting the smallpox, appear to have had their weight; the peculiar mildness of the disease, the known safety of it, and its not having in any instance prevented the patient from following his ordinary business. In all the cases under my care there have only occurred two or three which required any application, owing to erysipelatous inflammation on the arm, and they immediately yielded to it. In the remainder the constitutional illness has been slight but sufficiently marked, and considerably less than I ever observed in the same number inoculated with the smallpox. In only one or two of the cases have any other eruptions appeared than those around the spot where the matter was inserted, and those near the infected part. Neither does there appear in the cow-pox to be the least exciting cause to any other disease, which in the smallpox has been frequently observed, the constitution remaining in as full health and vigour after the termination of the disease as before the infection. Another important consideration appears to be the impossibility of the disease being communicated except by the actual contact of the matter of the pustule, and consequently the perfect safety of the remaining part of the family, supposing only one or two should wish to be inoculated at the same time.

"Upon the whole, it appears evident to me that the cow-pox is a pleasanter, shorter, and infinitely more safe disease than the inoculated smallpox when conducted in the most careful and approved manner; neither is the local affection of the inoculated part, or the constitutional illness, near so violent. I speak with confidence on the subject, having had an opportunity of observing its effects upon a variety of constitutions, from three months old to sixty years; and to which I have paid particular attention. In the cases alluded to here you will observe that the removal from the original source of the matter had made no alteration or change in the nature or appearance of the disease, and that it may be continued, *ad infinitum* (I imagine), from one person to another (if care be observed in taking the matter at a proper period) without any necessity of recurring to the original matter of the cow.

"I should be happy if any endeavours of mine could tend further to elucidate the subject, and shall be much gratified in sending you any further observations I may be enabled to make.

"I have the pleasure to subscribe myself,

"Dear sir, etc.,

"JOSEPH H. MARSHALL.

"EASTINGTON, GLOUCESTERSHIRE, April 26, 1799."

The gentleman who favoured me with the above account has continued to prosecute his inquiries with unremitting industry, and has communicated the result in another letter, which at his request I lay before the public without abbreviation.

Dr. Marshall's second letter:

"DEAR SIR:

"Since the date of my former letter I have continued to inoculate with the cow-pox virus. Including the cases before enumerated, the number now amounts to four hundred and twenty-three. It would be tedious and useless to detail the progress of the disease in each individual—it is sufficient to observe that I noticed no deviation in any respect from the cases I formerly adduced. The general appearances of the arm exactly corresponded with the account given in your first publication. When they were disposed to become troublesome by erysipelatous inflammation, an application of equal parts of vinegar and water always answered the desired intention. I must not omit to inform you that when the disease had duly acted upon the constitution I have frequently used the vitriolic acid. A portion of a drop applied with the head of a probe or any convenient utensil upon the pustule, suffered to remain about forty seconds, and afterwards washed off with sponge and water, never failed to stop its progress and expedite the formation of a scab.

"I have already subjected two hundred and eleven of my patients to the action of variolous matter, *but every one resisted it.*

"The result of my experiments (which were made with every requisite caution) has fully convinced me that the *true cow-pox* is a safe and infallible preventive from the smallpox; that in no case which has fallen under my observation has it been in any considerable degree troublesome, much less have I seen any thing like danger; for in no instance were the patients prevented from following their ordinary employments.

"In Dr. Woodville's publication on the cow-pox I notice an extraordinary fact. He says that the generality of his patients had pustules. It certainly appears extremely extraordinary that in all my cases there never was but one pustule, which appeared on a patient's elbow on the inoculated arm, and maturated. It appeared exactly like that on the incised part.

"The whole of my observations, founded as it appears on an extensive experience, leads me to these obvious conclusions; that those cases which have been or may be adduced against the preventive powers of the cow-pox could not have been those of the true kind, since it must appear to be absolutely impossible that I should have succeeded in such a number of cases without a single exception if such a preventive power did not exist. I cannot entertain a doubt that the inoculated cow-pox must quickly supersede that of the smallpox. If the many important advantages which must result from the new practice are duly considered, we may reasonably infer that public benefit, the sure test of the real merit of discoveries, will render it generally extensive.

"To you, Sir, as the discoverer of this highly beneficial practice, mankind are under the highest obligations. As a private individual I participate in the general feeling; more particularly as you have afforded me an opportunity of noticing the effects of a singular disease, and of viewing the progress of the most curious experiment that ever was recorded in the history of physiology.

"I remain, dear sir, etc.,

"JOSEPH H. MARSHALL."

"P. S. I should have observed that, of the patients I inoculated and enumerated in my letter, one hundred and twenty-seven were infected with the matter you sent me from the London cow. I discovered no dissimilarity of symptoms in these cases from those which I inoculated from matter procured in this country. No pustules have occurred, except in one or two cases, where a single one appeared on the inoculated arm. No difference was apparent in the local inflammation. There was no suspension of ordinary employment among the labouring people, nor was any medicine required.

"I have frequently inoculated one or two in a family, and the remaining part of it some weeks afterwards. The uninfected have slept with the infected during the whole course of the disease without being affected; so that I am fully convinced that the disease cannot be taken but by actual contact with the matter.

"A curious fact has lately fallen under my observation, on which I leave you to comment.

"I visited a patient with the confluent smallpox and charged a lancet with some of the matter. Two days afterwards I was desired to inoculate a woman and four children with the cow-pox, and I inadvertently took the vaccine matter on the same lancet which was before charged with that of smallpox. In three days I discovered the mistake, and fully expected that my five patients would be infected with smallpox; but I was agreeably surprised to find the disease to be genuine cow-pox, which proceeded without deviating in any particular from my former cases. I afterwards inoculated these patients with variolous matter, but all of them resisted its action.

"I omitted mentioning another great advantage that now occurs to me in the inoculated cow-pox; I mean the safety with which pregnant women may have the disease communicated to them. I have inoculated a great number of females in that situation, and never observed their cases to differ in any respect from those of my other patients. Indeed, the disease is so mild that it seems as if it might at all times be communicated with the most perfect safety."

I shall here take the opportunity of thanking Dr. Marshall and those other gentlemen who have obligingly presented me with the result of their inoculations; but, as they all agree in the same point as that given in the above communication, namely, the security of the patient from the effects of the smallpox after the cow-pox, their perusal, I presume, would afford us no satisfaction that has not been amply given already. Particular occurrences I shall, of course, detail. Some of my correspondents have mentioned the appearance of smallpox-like eruptions at the commencement of their inoculations; but in these cases the matter was derived from the original stock at the Smallpox Hospital.

I have myself inoculated a very considerable number from the matter produced by Dr. Marshall's patients, originating in the London cow, without observing pustules of any kind, and have dispersed it among others who have used it with a similar effect. From this source Mr. H. Jenner informs me he has inoculated above an hundred patients without observing eruptions. Whether the nature of the virus will undergo any change from being farther removed from its original source in passing successively from one person to another time alone can determine. That which I am now employing has been in use near eight months, and not the least change is perceptible in its mode of action either locally or constitutionally. There is, therefore, every reason to expect that its effects will remain unaltered and that we shall not be under the necessity of seeking fresh supplies from the cow.

The following observations were obligingly sent me by Mr. Tierny, Assistant Surgeon to the South Gloucester Regiment of Militia, to whom I am indebted for a former report on this subject.

"I inoculated with the cow-pox matter from the eleventh to the latter part of April, twenty-five persons, including women and children. Some on the eleventh were inoculated with the matter Mr. Shrapnell (surgeon to the regiment) had from you, the others with matter taken from these. The progress of the puncture was accurately observed, and its appearance seemed to differ from the smallpox in having less inflammation around its basis on the first days—that is, from the third to the seventh; but after this the inflammation increased, extending on the tenth or eleventh day to a circle of an inch and a half from its centre, and threatening very sore arms; but this I am happy to say was not the case; for, by applying mercurial ointment to the inflamed part, which was repeated daily until the inflammation went off, the arm got well without any further application or trouble. The constitutional symptoms which appeared on the eighth or ninth day after inoculation scarcely deserved the name of disease, as they were so slight as to be scarcely perceptible, except that I could connect a slight headache and |languor, with a stiffness and rather painful sensation in the axilla. This latter symptom was the most striking—it remained from twelve to forty-eight hours. In no case did I observe the smallest pustule, or even discolouration of the skin, like an incipient pustule, except about the part where the virus has been applied.

"After all these symptoms had subsided and the arms were well, I inoculated four of this number with variolous matter, taken from a patient in another regiment. In each of these it was inserted several times under the cuticle, producing slight inflammation on the second or third day, and always disappearing before the fifth or sixth, except in one who had the cow-pox in Gloucestershire before he joined us, and who also received it at this time by inoculation. In this man the puncture inflamed and his arm was much sorer than from the insertion of the cow-pox virus; but there was no pain in the axilla, nor could any constitutional affection be observed.

"I have only to add that I am now fully satisfied of the efficacy of the cow-pox in preventing the appearance of the smallpox, and that it is a most happy and salutary substitute for it.

"I remain, etc.,

"M. J. TIERNY."

Although the susceptibility of the virus of the cow-pox is, for the most part, lost in those who have had the smallpox, yet in some constitutions it is only partially destroyed, and in others it does not appear to be in the least diminished.

By far the greater number on whom trials were made resisted it entirely; yet I found some on whose arm the pustule from inoculation was formed completely, but without producing the common efflorescent blush around it, or any constitutional illness, while others have had the disease in the most perfect manner. A case of the latter kind having been presented to me by Mr. Fewster, Surgeon, of Thornbury, I shall insert it:

"Three children were inoculated with the vaccine matter you obligingly sent me. On calling to look at their arms three days after I was told that John Hodges, one of the three, had been inoculated with the smallpox when a year old, and that he had a full burthen, of which his face produced plentiful marks, a circumstance I was not before made acquainted with. On the sixth day the arm of the boy appeared as if inoculated with variolous matter, but the pustule was rather more elevated. On the ninth day he complained of violent pain in his head and back, accompanied with vomiting and much fever. The next day he was very well and went to work as usual. The punctured part began to spread, and there was the areola around the inoculated part to a considerable extent.

"As this is contrary to an assertion made in the Medical and Physical Journal, No. 8, I thought it right to give you this information, and remain,

"Dear sir, etc.,

"J. Fewster."

It appears, then, that the animal economy with regard to the action of this virus is under the same laws as it is with respect to the variolous virus, after previously feeling its influence, as far as comparisons can be made between the two diseases.

Some striking instances of the power of the cow pox in suspending the progress of the smallpox after the patients had been several days casually exposed to the infection have been laid before me by Mr. Lyford, Surgeon, of Winchester, and my nephew, the Rev. G. C. Jenner. Mr. Lyford, after giving an account of his extensive and successful practice in the vaccine inoculation in Hampshire, writes as follows:

"The following case occurred to me a short time since, and may probably be worth your notice. I was sent for to a patient with the smallpox, and on inquiry found that five days previous to my seeing him the eruption began to appear. During the whole of this time two children who had not had the smallpox, were constantly in the room with their father, and frequently on the bed with him.

The mother consulted me on the propriety of inoculating them, but objected to my taking the matter from their father, as he was subject to erysipelas. I advised her by all means to have them inoculated at that time, as I could not procure any variolous matter elsewhere. However, they were inoculated with vaccine matter, but I cannot say I flattered myself with its proving successful, as they had previously been so long and still continued to be exposed to the variolous infection. Notwithstanding this I was agreeably surprised to find the vaccine disease advance and go through its regular course; and, if I may be allowed the expression, to the total extinction of the smallpox."

Mr. Jenner's cases were not less satisfactory. He writes as follows:

"A son of Thomas Stinchcomb, of Woodford, near Berkeley, was infected with the natural smallpox at Bristol, and came home to his father's cottage. Four days after the eruptions had appeared upon the boy, the family (none of which had ever had the smallpox), consisting of the father, mother, and five children, was inoculated with vaccine virus. On the arm of the mother it failed to produce the least effect, and she, of course, had the smallpox,* but the rest of the family had the cow-pox in the usual way, and were not affected with the smallpox, although they were in the same room, and the children slept in the same bed with their brother who was confined to it with the natural smallpox; and subsequently with their mother.

"I attended this family with my brother, Mr. H. Jenner."

The following cases are of too singular a nature to remain unnoticed.

Miss R——, a young lady about five years old, was seized on the evening of the eighth day after inoculation with vaccine virus, with such symptoms as commonly denote the accession of violent fever. Her throat was also a little sore, and there were some uneasy sensations about the muscles of the neck. The day following a rash

* Under similar circumstances I think it would be advisable to insert the matter into each arm, which would be more likely to insure the success of the operation.— E. J.

was perceptible on her face and neck, so much resembling the efflorescence of the *scarlatina anginosa* that I was induced to ask whether Miss R—— had been exposed to the contagion of that disease. An answer in the affirmative, and the rapid spreading of the redness over the skin, at once relieved me from much anxiety respecting the nature of the malady, which went through its course in the ordinary way, but not without symptoms which were alarming both to myself and Mr. Lyford, who attended with me. There was no apparent deviation in the ordinary progress of the pustule to a state of maturity from what we see in general; yet there was a total suspension of the *areola* or florid discolouration around it, until the *scarlatina* had retired from the constitution. As soon as the patient was freed from this disease this appearance advanced in the usual way.*

The case of Miss H—— R—— is not less interesting than that of her sister, above related. She was exposed to the contagion of the *scarlatina* at the same time, and sickened almost at the same hour. The symptoms continued severe about twelve hours, when the scarlatina-rash shewed itself faintly upon her face, and partly upon her neck. After remaining two or three hours it suddenly disappeared, and she became perfectly free from every complaint. My surprise at this sudden transition from extreme sickness to health in great measure ceased when I observed that the inoculated pustule had occasioned, in this case, the common efflorescent appearance around it, and that as it approached the centre it was nearly in an erysipelatous state. But the most remarkable part of this history is that, on the fourth day afterwards, so soon as the efflorescence began to die away upon the arm and the pustule to dry up, the *scarlatina* again appeared, her throat became sore, the rash spread all over her. She went fairly through the disease with its common symptoms.

That these were actually cases of *scarlatina* was rendered certain by two servants in the family falling ill at the same time with the distemper, who had been exposed to the infection with the young ladies.

Some there are who suppose the security from the smallpox

---

* I witnessed a similar fact in a case of measles. (See page 55 of original article.) The pustule from the cow pock virus advanced to maturity, while the measles existed in the constitution, but no *efflorescence* appeared around it until the measles had ceased to exert its influence.

obtained through the cow-pox will be of a temporary nature only. This supposition is refuted not only by analogy with respect to the habits of diseases of a similar nature, but by incontrovertible facts, which appear in great numbers against it. To those already adduced in the former part of my first treatise* many more might be adduced were it deemed necessary; but among the cases I refer to, one will be found of a person who had the cow-pox fifty-three years before the effect of the smallpox was tried upon him. As he completely resisted it, the intervening period I conceive must necessarily satisfy any reasonable mind. Should further evidence be thought necessary, I shall observe that, among the cases presented to me by Mr. Fry, Mr. Darke, Mr. Tierny, Mr. H. Jenner, and others, there were many whom they inoculated ineffectually with variolous matter, who had gone through the cow-pox many years before this trial was made.

It has been imagined that the cow-pox is capable of being communicated from one person to another by effluvia without the intervention of inoculation. My experiments, made with the design of ascertaining this important point, all tend to establish my original position, that it is not infectious except by contact. I have never hesitated to suffer those on whose arms there were pustules exhaling the effluvia from associating or even sleeping with others who never had experienced either the cow-pox or the smallpox. And, further, I have repeatedly, among children, caused the uninfected to breathe over the inoculated vaccine pustules during their whole progress, yet these experiments were tried without the least effect. However, to submit a matter so important to a still further scrutiny, I desired Mr. H. Jenner to make any further experiments which might strike him as most likely to establish or refute what had been advanced on this subject. He has since informed me "that he inoculated children at the breast, whose mothers had not gone through either the smallpox or the cow-pox; that he had inoculated mothers whose sucking infants had never undergone either of these diseases; that the effluvia from the inoculated pustules, in either case, had been inhaled from day to day during the whole progress of their maturation, and that

* See pages 9, 11, 12, 13, 14, 20, etc., of original article.

there was not the least perceptible effect from these exposures. One woman he inoculated about a week previous to her *accouchement*, that her infant might be the more fully and conveniently exposed to the pustule; but, as in the former instances, no infection was given, although the child frequently slept on the arm of its mother with its nostrils and mouth exposed to the pustule in the fullest state of maturity. In a word, is it not impossible for the cow-pox, whose *only* manifestation appears to consist in the pustules *created by contact*, to produce *itself* by effluvia?

In the course of a late inoculation I observed an appearance which it may be proper here to relate. The punctured part on a boy's arm (who was inoculated with fresh limpid virus) on the sixth day, instead of shewing a beginning vesicle, which is usual in the cow-pox at that period, was encrusted over with a rugged, amber-coloured scab. The scab continued to spread and increase in thickness for some days, when, at its edges, a vesicated ring appeared, and the disease went through its ordinary course, the boy having had soreness in the axilla and some slight indisposition. With the fluid matter taken from his arm five persons were inoculated. In one it took no effect. In another it produced a perfect pustule without any deviation from the common appearance; but in the other three the progress of the inflammation was exactly similar to the instance which afforded the virus for their inoculation; there was a creeping scab of a loose texture, and subsequently the formation of limpid fluid at its edges. As these people were all employed in laborious exercises, it is possible that these anomalous appearances might owe their origin to the friction of the clothes on the newly-inflamed part of the arm. I have not yet had an opportunity of exposing them to the smallpox.

In the early part of this inquiry I felt far more anxious respecting the inflammation of the inoculated arm than at present; yet that this affection will go on to a greater extent than could be wished is a circumstance sometimes to be expected. As this can be checked, or even entirely subdued, by very simple means, I see no reason why the patient should feel an uneasy hour because an application may not be absolutely necessary. About the tenth or eleventh day, if the pustule has proceeded regularly, the appearance of the arm will almost to a certainty indicate whether this is to be expected or not.　Should it happen, nothing more need be done than to apply a single drop of the *aqua lythargyri acetati** upon the pustule, and, having suffered it to remain two or three minutes, to cover the efflorescence surrounding the pustule with a piece of linen dipped in the *aqua lythargyri compos.*†　The former may be repeated twice or thrice during the day, the latter as often as it may feel agreeable to the patient.

When the scab is prematurely rubbed off (a circumstance not unfrequent among children and working people), the application of a little *aqua lythargyri acet.* to the part immediately coagulates the surface, which supplies its place, and prevents a sore.

In my former treatises on this subject I have remarked that the human constitution frequently retains its susceptibility to the smallpox contagion (both from effluvia and contact) after previously feeling its influence.　In further corroboration of this declaration many facts have been communicated to me by various correspondents.　I shall select one of them.

"DEAR SIR:

"Society at large must, I think, feel much indebted to you for your Inquiries and Observations on the Nature and Effects of the Variolæ Vaccinæ, etc., etc.　As I conceive what I am now about to communicate to be of some importance, I imagine it cannot be uninteresting to you, especially as it will serve to corroborate your assertion of the susceptibility of the human system of the variolous contagion, although it has previously been made sensible of its action.　In November, 1793, I was desired to inoculate a person with the smallpox.　I took the variolous matter from a child under the disease in the natural way, who had a large burthen of distinct pustules.　The mother of the child being desirous of seeing my method of communicating the disease by inoculation, after

---

* Extract of Saturn.

† Goulard water.　For further information on this subject see the first Treatise on the Var. Vac., Dr. Marshall's letters, etc.

having opened a pustule, I introduced the point of my lancet in the usual way on the back part of my own hand, and thought no more of it until I felt a sensation in the part which reminded me of the transaction. This happened upon the third day; on the fourth there were all the appearances common to inoculation, at which I was not at all surprised, nor did I feel myself uneasy upon perceiving the inflammation continue to increase to the sixth and seventh day, accompanied with a very small quantity of fluid, repeated experiments having taught me it might happen so with persons who had undergone the disease, and yet would escape any constitutional affection; but I was not so fortunate; for on the eighth day I was seized with all the symptoms of the eruptive fever, but in a much more violent degree than when I was before inoculated, which was about eighteen years previous to this, when I had a considerable number of pustules. I must confess I was now greatly alarmed, although I had been much engaged in the smallpox, having at different times inoculated not less than two thousand persons. I was convinced my present indisposition proceeded from the insertion of the variolous matter, and, therefore, anxiously looked for an eruption. On the tenth day I felt a very unpleasant sensation of stillness and heat on each side of my face near my ear, and the fever began to decline. The affection in my face soon terminated in three or four pustules attended with inflammation, but which did not maturate, and I was presently well.

"I remain, dear sir, etc.,

"THOMAS MILES."

This inquiry is not now so much in its infancy as to restrain me from speaking more positively than formerly on the important point of scrophula as connected with the smallpox.

Every practitioner in medicine who has extensively inoculated with the smallpox, or has attended many of those who have had the distemper in the natural way, must acknowledge that he has frequently seen scrophulous affections, in some form or another, sometimes rather quickly shewing themselves after the recovery of the patients. Conceiving this fact to be admitted, as I presume it must be by all who have carefully attended to the subject, may I not ask whether it does not appear probable that the general introduction of the smallpox into Europe has not been among the most conductive means in exciting that formidable foe to health? Having attentively watched the effects of the cow-pox in this respect, I am happy in being able to declare that the disease does not appear to have the least tendency to produce this destructive malady.

The scepticism that appeared, even among the most enlightened of medical men when my sentiments on the important subject of the cow-pox were first promulgated, was highly laudable. To have admitted the truth of a doctrine, at once so novel and so unlike any thing that ever had appeared in the annals of medicine, without the test of the most rigid scrutiny, would have bordered upon temerity; but now, when that scrutiny has taken place, not only among ourselves, but in the first professional circles in Europe, and when it has been uniformly found in such abundant instances that the human frame, when once it has felt the influence of the genuine cow-pox in the way that has been described, is never afterwards at any period of its existence assailable by the smallpox, may I not with perfect confidence congratulate my country and society at large on their beholding, in the mild form of the cow-pox, an antidote that is capable of extirpating from the earth a disease which is every hour devouring its victims; a disease that has ever been considered as the severest scourge of the human race!

LIST OF WRITINGS AND EDITIONS *

An Inquiry into the Causes and Effects of the Variolæ Vaccinæ, a Disease Discovered in Some of the Western Counties of England, Particularly Gloucestershire, and Known by the Name of the Cow Pox, iv, 75 pp., 4 pl., quarto, London, S. Low, 1798.

The same. iv, 75 pp., 4 pl., 1 l., quarto, London, Law and Murray and Highley, 1798.

The same. Second, vii, 182 pp., 1 l., 1 Col. pl., quarto, London, S. Low, 1800.

The same. Third, viii, 182 pp., 3 Col. pl., quarto, London, D. N. Shury, 1801, with portrait of Jenner inserted.

The same. From second Lond. edition, iv, 116 pp., 3 pl., 16mo, Springfield, Ashley and Brewer, 1802.

* From various sources.

The same. Untersuchungen über die Ursachen und Wirkungen der Kuhpock-
en. . . . aus dem Englischen übersetzt—von G. Fr. Ballhorn, x pp.,
4 l., 52 pp., 1 pl., octavo, Hannover, Gebr. Hahn, 1799.

The same. Disquisitio de Causis et effectibus variolarum vaccinarum. Ex anglico
in latinum conversa ab Aloysio Careno, vi pp., 1 p. l., 70 pp., 4 pl., quarto,
Vindobonae, Camesina, 1799.

The same. Rescherches sur les Causes et les effets de la Variolae Vaccinae
(etc.) 1 p. l., 60 pp., octavo, Lyon, Reymann et Cie., 1800.

The same. Indagação sobre as Causas, e effeitos das bexigas de Vacca, Molestia
des Coberta em alguns dos condados occidentaes da Inglaterra, Partic-
ularmente Na Comarca de Gloucester, e Conhecida pelo Nome de Vaccina.
Second Ed. Traduzione do original inglez por J. A. M., 137 pp., 6 l., 1 tab.,
4 pl., octavo Lisboa, 1803.

The same. Ricerche sulle Cause e Sugli effetti del Vajuolo delle Vacche Traduzione dall'inglese Corredata d'aggiunte e d'una relazione del Vajuolo Che
affetta le vacche in Lombardia del Dottor Luigi Careno. Seconda edizione
Corretta ed accresciuta di un'appendici e d'una proposta di Massime Generali
raccomandate ai Governi onde radicalmente estirpare il Contagio, Arabo
del dottor Gio Michele Goldoni, xviii, 144 pp., 12mo, Modena tip. di
Antonio ed Angelo Cappelli, 1853. 1st ed. 1800 Pavia.

Further observations on the Variolæ Vaccinæ, or Cow Pox, 1 p. l., 64 pp., quarto,
London, S. Low, 1799. Bound with his: Inquiry into the Causes and
Effects of the Variolæ Vaccinæ, quarto, London, 1798.

Lithograph of postscript to a letter from Edward Jenner to Thos. Jefferson,
and also lithograph letter from Thos. Jefferson to Benjamin Waterhouse,
1801.

Vaccination. (Letter respecting the "Varieties and Modifications of the Vaccine
Pustule, Occasioned by an Herpetic and Other Eruptive States of the Skin"),
MS., 2 l. quarto (1804?). Bound with his: An inquiry into the Causes
and Effects of the Variolæ Vaccinæ, quarto, London, 1798.

Letter to William Dillwyn, Esq., On the Effects of Vaccination in Preserving from
the Small Pox, to which are added Sundry Documents Relating to Vaccination, referred to and accompanying the letter, 20 pp., octavo, Philadelphia,
published by the Philadelphia Vaccine Society, 1818.

A letter to Charles Henry Parry, M.D., etc., on the Influence of Artificial Eruption
in Certain Diseases Incident to the Human Body. With an inquiry respecting the probable Advantages to be derived from further experiments,
67 pp., quarto, London, Baldwin, Craddock and Joy, 1822.

Facts for the Most Part Unobserved, or not duly Noticed, Respecting Variolous
Contagion, 17 pp., quarto, London, S. Gosnell, 1808.

On the Varieties and Modifications of the Vaccine Pustule, occasioned by an
Herpetic State of the Skin, 13 pp., quarto, Cheltenham, H. Ruff, 1806;
reprinted by J. Roberts, Gloucester, 1819; reprinted from Med. and Phys.
J., London, 1804, xii.

Some Observations on the Migration of Birds, 36 pp., quarto, London, W. Nicol
1824.

On the Origin of the Vaccine Inoculation, 1 p. l., 8 pp., quarto, London, D. N. Shury, 1801; reprinted London, G. Glück, 1863.

An Inquiry, etc. (see above . . . . cow pox), printed for the author, London, 1798, 36 pp., 12mo. London, Cassell and Co., 1896.

The same. Onderzoek naar de oorzaaken, etc. In het Nederduitsoh Vertaald en met een bijvoegsel Ver Meerderd Door, L. Davids, 52 pp.; 48 pp., 4 Col. pl., octavo, Haarlem, H. Loosjes, 1801.

Signs of Rain. Forty Reasons for not accepting the Invitation of a Friend, 5 pp., octavo, London, I. Clifford.

On the Natural History of the Cuckoo. Philosophical Transactions, London, 1788.

A Process for Preparing pure Emetic Tartar, by Re-Crystallization. Transactions of a Society for the Improvement of Medical and Chirurgical Knowledge, vol. i, p. 30, London, 1793.

Inquiry into the Cause and Effects of the Variolae Vaccine, London, 1798, 4to.

A Continuation of Facts and Observations, relative to the Variolae Vaccinae, London, 1800, 4to.

A Complete Statement of Facts and Observations relative to the Cow-pock, London, 1800, 4to.

Observations on the Distemper in Dogs. Transactions of the Medico-Chirurgical Society, vol. i, p. 263, London, 1809.

Two Cases of Small-pox Infection, communicated to the Foetus in Utero, under peculiar circumstances, with additional remarks. Ibid., p. 269.

Anesthesia

WILLIAM THOMAS GREEN MORTON
1819-1868

Morton was born August 19, 1819, on a farm in the neighborhood of Charlton, a small New England town. His early years
were spent in work on the farm, his education being obtained from
the district school, and later from one of the larger academies.
At seventeen, his father having failed, he removed to Boston to take
a position in a bookshop, but shortly afterward returned to his home
to assist his father in a small store which the latter had opened
in the nearby town. At this time his education was carried on as
his business would allow. He seems to have entertained early the
desire to study medicine, but opportunity to gratify this wish
not presenting itself, he caught at what he considered the next
best—dentistry. The American Society of Dental Surgery was
just being established when Morton came of age (1840) and the
Baltimore College of Dental Surgery had been opened recently
under the auspices of this Society. At this school Morton gradu-
ated in dentistry in 1842, being twenty-three years of age. Immediately upon graduation he began to practice in Boston in partnership with Horace Wells (also a dentist), whose name figures in the
famous controversy over the ether discovery. For financial
reasons this partnership was dissolved within a year of its formation,
the two parting on amicable terms. During this association the
partners had given much attention to the manufacture of artificial
teeth. The method employed at that time in the preparation of the
old teeth and for attaching the plate they considered "stupid and
barbarous," consequently they devised a superior one, which,
however, necessitated the removal of *all* the old fangs. Though
they offered many inducements to persons to avail themselves
of the new method, few were willing to submit to the pain of

having so many teeth drawn. This demand for a pain-deadener by which his method might be more universally adopted may be considered the impulse that originally started Morton on his investigation, which ultimately resulted in his great discovery.

The earlier experiments were with such agents as brandy and champagne to the point of intoxication; laudanum in doses of 100 to 300 drops; opium in mass of 10 to 12 grains. The following extract from his case-book is of interest:

"Mrs. S.—to have * * * teeth of both jaws extracted. Commenced giving opiates about noon. Gave * * * 150 drops of laudanum. Twenty minutes later gave 150 more. Waited ten minutes and gave 100 drops more. Gave 100 drops more with intervals of five minutes. Whole amount given 500 drops in forty-five minutes. At expiration of this time she was sleepy but able to walk to chair. Immediately on extraction of the first tooth she vomited. She continued in this way for one hour, during which time the rest of the teeth were extracted. She was conscious but insensible to a considerable degree. On returning home she continued to vomit at intervals during the afternoon. Entirely recovered in a week."

As he proceeded with his investigations he realized that a greater knowledge of medicine was essential to his success. In March, 1844, at Boston, he therefore entered as a student of medicine the office of Dr. Charles T. Jackson, whose name appears also in the ether controversy. The following autumn (being in his twenty-fifth year) he matriculated in the Harvard Medical School. During the summer prior to beginning his medical studies he continued to practise dentistry and to search for an agent with which to deaden pain. Morton was engaged at this time in a very lucrative practice. His account-books show among his patients persons of distinction and from distant points. A month's income (May, 1844) foots up $1,126.50, and for the same month in the two succeeding years twice this sum for each year. It will thus be seen that it was with some financial sacrifice that he pursued his studies in medicine.

During this summer of 1844 among the agents which he made trial of was *sulphuric ether*, suggested to him by Dr. C. T. Jackson. This he applied locally in one case, and finding that it acted satisfactorily, he tried it upon birds and other animals, but with indifferent success. For the next eighteen months his investigations were almost exclusively with this agent, which he employed in extracting teeth and on animals. Though his results were very variable it was evident that he was within reach of a great discovery, and in obtaining information, which he did from every available source, the records show that he maintained a cautious secrecy. It was, however, his perseverance in face of repeated failures and his boldness in employing what was declared to be a deadly poison which led all fair-minded judges, in spite of this secrecy which many condemned, to award to Morton the honor of being the discoverer. He and Wells had experimented with nitrous oxide, and, from ignorance of the proper way to administer it, Wells had failed (in a public demonstration) to prove its value as an anæsthetic agent in extracting teeth. Wells's claim was not that he had discovered the power of ether but that of nitrous oxide, and so had been first in giving the world an anæsthetic agent for capital operations—not that he had discovered an agent, but a principle—anæsthesia. Morton never disputed Wells's claim to having pointed out the powers of nitrous oxide, but maintained that it was not suitable for capital operations, and therefore was in the same class as many other inefficient agents already known. Moreover, he showed that in 1799 Sir Humphry Davy had experimented with nitrous oxide, had published his results, and had suggested its use in minor operations. Subsequent investigation has proven all this to be correct.

By the summer of 1846 Morton was so much occupied with his research that his dental business was carried on almost entirely by assistants. From among these he selected two volunteers, after having offered, unsuccessfully, money rewards to longshoremen and others of that class as inducement to subject themselves to experiment. The result of the trials upon the assistants was with partial success only. He was convinced that the fault lay in the quality of his agent, and in order to investigate this, he extended his inquiry into the chemistry of ether. From Dr. Charles T. Jackson, his preceptor and a noted chemist and physicist, Morton learned much regarding the chemistry, the most important information being that in order to get proper effects the ether should be *pure*. From the moment he used the pure preparation his failures were explained and success began to come. To Jackson Morton unhesitatingly attributes this information, and even offered him a percentage interest in the patent benefits, which offer *he accepted*. It is evident that, though Jackson was in possession of facts regarding the inhalation of ether, he did not investigate by experiment these effects, probably because he considered (according to his written and spoken statements) its administration fraught with great danger to life.

Morton now experimented upon himself. The following extract from his memoir to the Academy of Arts and Sciences at Paris gives the result of this experiment: "* * * * I shut myself up in my room; seated myself in the operating chair and commenced inhaling. * * * * It partially suffocated me but produced no decided effect. I then saturated my handkerchief and inhaled it from that. I looked at my watch and soon lost consciousness. As I recovered I felt a numbness in my limbs with a sensation like a nightmare and would have given the world for some one to come and arouse me. I thought for a moment I should die. * * * * At length I felt a slight tingling of the blood in the end of my third finger and made an effort to touch it with my thumb, but without success. At a second effort I touched it, but there seemed to be no sensation. * * * * I pinched my thigh, but * * * sensation was imperfect. * * * * I immediately looked at my watch. * * * I had been insensible between seven and eight minutes. * * * *"

This was in his dental establishment in Boston, September 30, 1846. Morton waited through the day for a suitable case to appear upon whom he could make a fuller trial. About 9 o'clock that evening the man Frost, whose affidavit appears in all the Congressional and other investigations, expressed his willingness to have a

Horace Wells

painful tooth extracted under the influence of the agent.   Between this date and October 16th several experiments were made, a report of which appears in the articles reprinted below.   About October 5th Morton called upon Dr. John C. Warren, senior surgeon to the Massachusetts General Hospital, and applied for permission to employ his method in a capital operation.   He was at this time twenty-seven years old, and as a medical student was attending clinics at this hospital.   On October 14th he received the following letter:

Dear Sir:
    I write at the request of Dr. J. C. Warren to invite you to be present on Friday morning at 10 o'clock, at the hospital, to administer to a patient who is then to be operated upon the preparation which you have invented to diminish the sensibility to pain.
                         Yours respectfully,
                             C. F. HEYWOOD,
                                 House Surgeon to the General Hospital.
Dr. Morton, Tremont Row.   October 14th, 1846.

Morton was at this time under the impression that a special apparatus was necessary for the proper administration of ether. He obtained from several of the most prominent instrument-makers suggestions in this matter.   The experiment upon himself, above recorded, revealed to him that a handkerchief was all the apparatus necessary, but he did not make use of this information until much later.   Between the receipt of the letter just given and October 16th Morton was engaged in perfecting this apparatus, failure to complete which caused the delay in his appearance referred to in the following extract from the records of the Massachusetts General Hospital:

Extract from Records of Massachusetts General Hospital for October 16th, 1846:
    "This case is remarkable in the annals of surgery.   It was the first surgical operation performed under the influence of ether. Dr. Warren had been applied to by Dr. Morton, a dentist, with the request that he would try the inhalation of a fluid * * * * effectual in preventing pain during operations on the teeth.   Dr.

Warren, * * * satisfied * * * that the breathing of the fluid would be harmless, agreed to employ it. * * * * * Some time was lost in waiting for Dr. Morton, and ultimately it was thought he would not appear; at length he arrived and explained his detention by informing Dr. Warren that he had been occupied in preparing his apparatus, which consisted of a tube connected with a glass globe. * * * "

The remainder of this record appears among the reports reprinted below. On the following day a second operation was performed under ether, but from the 16th of October to the 6th of November Morton was not again called to the hospital, for reasons to be given presently. During this month of October Morton applied to the United States Government for a patent. For this he has been much censured and many motives were attributed to his action. On November 12, 1846, his patent was granted. From this source he never benefited financially, as it was impossible to bring suit for infringement when such was merely the use of an agent already well known. Had his apparatus been an essential to etherization, he might have protected that by patent, but he had himself proved this not to be the case. He could patent the suggestion but he could protect nothing. While, therefore, his action regarding the patent seemed to bring him only opprobrium and distress, it was probably this very patent which aroused the Congressional interest and led to the drastic investigations before that body and fixed, as public opinion never could have, the right to Morton of the honor of being the discoverer.

He soon learned the cause of his not being called again to the hospital after two successful demonstrations of his method. The administrators of the Massachusetts General Hospital were ignorant of the nature of the agent they were employing, and they therefore informed Morton that "the surgeons of the hospital think it their duty to decline the use of the preparation until informed what it is." To this Morton sent the following reply to Dr. Warren:

Boston, Nov. 5th, 1846.

Dear Sir:

As it may sometimes be desirable that surgical operations should be performed at the Massachusetts General Hospital under the influence of the preparation employed by me for producing temporary insensibility to pain, you will allow me through you to offer to the hospital the free use of it for all the hospital operations. I should be pleased to give to the surgeons of the hospital any information, in addition to what they now possess, which they may think desirable in order to employ it with confidence. I will also instruct such persons as they may select, connected with the hospital, in the mode of employing it. This information, I must request, should be regarded as confidential, as I wish for ample time to make such modifications as experience may suggest in its exhibition. It is also my intention to have persons suitably instructed who will go wherever desired, for a reasonable compensation and administer it for private operations: thus enabling any surgeon to employ it in his private practice whenever he may have occasion. I think you will agree with me that this will be wiser until its merits are fuller established, than to put it into the hands of everybody, thereby bringing discredit upon the preparation by its injudicious employment. Should you wish me to administer at any of the operations to-morrow, I shall do so with pleasure; and should the above proposition be deemed worthy of being entertained, I shall be ready to make the arrangement as soon as informed of your wishes.

W. T. G. MORTON

Dr. Warren

In reply he received the following:

Dear Sir:

I beg leave to acknowledge the reception of your polite letter. I shall lose no time in laying it before the surgeons of the hospital.

I remain respectfully yours,

J. C. WARREN.

Park Street, Nov. 6th.

This reply was received on a day set for operations and Morton waited impatiently at his office. While thus waiting, Dr. Henry J. Bigelow, who had followed with interest Morton's demonstrations and who had given him every encouragement, called upon him and took him to the hospital. On arrival at the hospital Dr. Bigelow left Morton in the reception room and himself went to the operating room. There Morton's letter, quoted above, was read aloud by Dr. Warren, whereupon it was decided to allow Morton to employ his method at that operation. Dr. Bigelow at once fetched Dr. Morton, who, on entering the amphitheatre, announced that in order to remove any hesitation on the part of the surgeons he would state his agent to be *sulphuric ether*. From this date many operations in the Massachusetts General Hospital were performed under etherization without further opposition. These details are all here given because they are of historic interest to-day; the indorsement of the Massachusetts General Hospital and the taking out of the patent, which, it will be observed, was applied for between the dates of the first and second operations (October 16th and November 6th) were the most important factors in fixing honor where it was due. It may be said that between October 16, 1846, when the first capital operation under ether was performed, and November 12th of the same year, when the patent was granted, occurred the most important events in the history of the discovery of anæsthesia. Shortly after the last date the controversy regarding the discovery of anæsthesia began. A long, and, in some respects, unpleasant exposition of the manner in which such questions are treated. There is a striking similarity between the accounts of the vaccination and circulation of the blood discovery and that of anæsthesia, in that the same incredulity first arose, which was followed by a brief period of awe, to be followed again by many "jump up behinders," and finally by almost wilful maltreatment of the discoverer. Harvey, Jenner, and Morton suffered financially and in their practice, and the two latter, in consequence of these sufferings, together with disappointment at the manner in which their work was received, experienced personal distress, the full extent of which the world may never know. Happily we have examples of a different spirit in our day in the honor accorded men like Carrol, Lazear, Manson, Reed and Ross. With regard to Morton's and Jackson's position, the former has well expressed it in the following: "I am ready to acknowledge my indebtedness to men and books for all my information upon this subject. I have got here a little and there a little. I learned from Dr. Jackson in 1844 the effect of ether applied to a sensitive tooth and proved by experiment that it would gradually render the nerve insensible. I learned from Dr. Jackson, also in 1844, the effect of ether when inhaled by students at college, which was corroborated by Spear's account and by what I read. I further acknowledge that I was subsequently indebted to Dr. Jackson for valuable information as to the kinds and preparations of ether, and for the recommendations of the highly rectified from Burnett's as the most safe and efficient. But my obligation to him hath this extent, no further."*

The question regarding the discoverer became a national one, probably because the United States Government as well as the English Government had granted patent rights. The House of Representatives appointed a committee to investigate. Thus every fact, letter and statement was examined as sworn testimony, and this not once, but three times, over a period of eight years. There has never before been, and probably never again will be, such a thorough trial of a scientific subject by a legislative body.

In this connection the following extract of a letter of Daniel Webster's is of interest:

Washington, December 20, 1851.

DR. W. T. G. MORTON.

Dear Sir: * * * * I then formed the opinion, which I have since seen no reason to change, that the merit of that great discovery belonged to you, and I had supposed that the reports of the trustees of the hospital (Massachusetts General) and of the Committee of the House of Representatives of the United States were conclusive on this point. * * * *

The Committee of the House were I believe unanimous in awarding to you the merit of having made the first practical application of ether, and a majority by their report awarded to you the entire credit. * * * *

Very respectfully your obedient servant,
DANIEL WEBSTER.

* *Note:* "Trials of a Public Benefactor," by Nathan P. Rice, M.D., 1859, Pudney & Russel, N. Y.

Morton, however, was receiving no pecuniary benefit from his patent, nor was he able or willing to press suit for infringement. It was therefore proposed in Congress to award him $100,000. As example of like action an award to Jenner of £10,000 (Pettigrew) by Parliament, also an award of money to Beaumont by Congress for his investigations on gastric function, were quoted. For eight years Morton pursued this proposal before three sittings of Congress, and was finally told that his only hope lay in bringing suit against the United States Government (which was freely employing etherization in its army and navy hospitals) for infringement upon his patent. This was a formality, but the other claimants could not be brought into such an action, and it was the advocates of Jackson and Wells who, on former occasions, had blocked the award. By now, however (1854), Morton was reduced to worse than poverty; his property was heavily mortgaged. A subscription was raised which was liberally answered, and, what is a bright spot in all this unpleasant account, the most generous response was from the profession. It was a national tribute.

The mills of the gods had been grinding slowly but exceeding small, and it was undoubtedly this which enabled posterity to fix beyond dispute the honor upon Morton. When considering Morton's efforts to profit financially by taking out a patent and by proceeding with secrecy, it must be remembered that he was a comparatively young man (twenty-seven years) when he found himself in possession of one of the greatest discoveries known to mankind. He was not, however, conscious of the full significance of his find, and having been brought up in business methods, he looked for financial benefits first and honor last. His chief opponent, Dr. Jackson, was a scientist of international reputation, while he was but a dentist. When Dr. Jackson's sealed claim to the discovery was read at the Academy in Paris, it was accepted as coming from a very worthy source. When Morton, *the dentist*, disputed this claim, the Academicians were inclined to smile, and finally, on receiving additional evidence in support of Morton's claim, they awarded equal honor to both claimants, which Morton refused to accept.

Though Morton partially re-established his shattered health and fortune before his death, July 15, 1868, he never had the honor which is now fully accorded him, and which is attested by the monument erected in Boston on the fiftieth anniversary of the discovery of anæsthesia.

The word "anæsthesia" has become so familiar that one forgets that it had a beginning. Not so with "Letheon," which is practically forgotten. The following letter is of interest in this connection:

Boston, Nov. 21st, 1846.

My dear Sir:

Everybody wants to have a hand in a great discovery. All I will do is to give you a hint or two, as to names or the name to be applied to the state produced and the agent.

The state should, I think, be called "Anæsthesia." This signifies insensibility, more particularly (as used by Linnæus and Cullen) to objects of touch. (See Good, Nosology, p. 259.) The adjective will be "Anæsthetic." Thus we might say, the state of anæsthesia or the anæsthetic state. The means employed would be properly called anti-æsthetic agent. Perhaps it might be allowable to say anæsthetic agent, but this admits question.

The words antineuric, neuro-leptic, neuro-lepsic, neuro-etasis, etc., seem too anatomical; whereas the change is a physiological one. I throw them out for consideration.

I would have a name pretty soon, and consult some accomplished scholar, such as President Everett or Dr. Bigelow, senior, before fixing upon the terms, which will be repeated by the tongues of every civilized race of mankind. You could mention these words which I suggest for their consideration; but there may be others more appropriate and agreeable.

Yours respectfully,

O. W. HOLMES.

Rice, in "The Trials of a Public Benefactor," gives the following: "The term 'Letheon' given to the ether immediately after the American patent was secured, and by which it was at first generally known, was adopted simply 'to avoid circumlocution,' and was brought about in this wise. Drs. H. J. Bigelow, Holmes, and Morton, having met at the house of Dr. A. A. Gould, the latter read aloud a list of names which he had prepared. Dr. Morton, in catching the word 'Letheon'—the same that Dr. Gould had also put on his list—exclaimed, 'That is the name the discovery shall be christened.' Returning to his office soon after, where the writer was then sitting, he said, 'I have found a name for the discovery, and am going to call it Letheon.'"

1847

REMARKS ON THE PROPER MODE OF ADMIN-
ISTERING SULPHURIC ETHER BY
INHALATION

———

Boston
DUTTON AND WENTWORTH, PRINTERS
1847

TO THE

Surgeons of the Mass. Gen. Hospital,

THIS LITTLE WORK IS RESPECTFULLY DEDICATED,
AS AN EVIDENCE
THAT THEIR EARLY AND CONTINUED INTEREST IN THE
ADMINISTRATION OF SULPHURIC ETHER IS
GRATEFULLY APPRECIATED
BY THEIR
OBT. SERVT.,
WM. T. G. MORTON

REMARKS

Although various publications have appeared since the new application of sulphuric ether was discovered which have made it evident that it can be used, both safely and effectually, for the relief of much of the suffering to which the human race is liable, I believe that a manual, containing an account of the mode of administering it, the effect which it produces, the symptoms of insensibility, the difficulties and dangers attending its use, and the best means of obviating and removing these, as far as possible, is still a desideratum. This is particularly the case with those who have not had an opportunity to witness its administration, but who may wish to make use of it in their own practice. To supply this want, and to avoid the necessity of replying to the letters frequently addressed to me for information upon these subjects, the following pages have been written. To those who have used the ether, many of the directions may appear tediously minute; but to those who have not, they will afford desirable information.

In the first place, it is of the utmost consequence that the ether which is used should be not only free from all impurities, but as highly concentrated as possible; as some of these impurities would prove injurious if taken into the system, and as, of course, the stronger the ether, the sooner the patient comes under its influence. Unrectified sulphuric ether contains, as impurities, alcohol, water, sulphurous acid, and oil of wine; and is unfit for use internally.

In order to make it fit for inhalation unrectified sulphuric ether must be redistilled and washed, and then dried with chloride of calcium. This will free it from the impurities above mentioned, and render it more concentrated than the original article.

To explain the process of preparing pure sulphuric ether is not, however, the object of these remarks, but, rather, to state how it may be best used after it has been prepared. I shall, therefore, dismiss this part of my subject with the assurance that, if any one wishes to attain success in the administration of ether, he must, in the first place, provide himself with that which is not only freest from impurities, but also most highly concentrated. And, as I believe that establishments which manufacture a large quantity of ether can not only produce a better article, but can also afford it at a less price than it would cost individuals to prepare small quantities for themselves, I think any one wishing to use it will find it for his advantage to purchase it of those druggists who have it purified expressly for inhalation.

The next point I have to treat of is the best mode of administering ether. The earliest experiments were mostly made by pouring ether upon cloths and inhaling it from them. The results obtained in this way were somewhat uncertain and not always satisfactory, and this mode of administering it was, before long, exchanged for that by means of an apparatus, which rendered the experiments more uniformly successful. Some alterations and improvements were afterward made in this apparatus, but, substantially, it remained the same as long as it continued in use; and, as many persons may read these pages who have never seen the apparatus, or one like it, a few words by way of description will not, perhaps, be unacceptable.

The apparatus first used consisted of a glass vessel about six inches square, with rounded corners; one opening, two inches in diameter, was left on the top, through which a sponge was inserted and the ether poured, and another, an inch and a half in diameter, on one side for the admission of external air. On the side opposite the last-named opening was a glass tube, two inches in diameter and an inch in length, terminating in a metal mouth-piece three inches long,* and of the same calibre as the glass tube. This mouth-piece was provided with two valves, one covering a circular opening, three-quarters of an inch in diameter, on the top, and the other ex-

---

* In the early administration of ether I sometimes made use of a flexible tube, about four inches long, with a mouth-piece at its end; but I soon discontinued the use of this, as patients were not so soon brought under the influence of the ether when at this distance from the apparatus.

tending across it. These valves were so arranged that, when the patient filled his lungs, the upper valve shut down, closing the aperture in the top of the mouth-piece, while the one across the mouth-piece opened and allowed the ethereal vapor, mixed with atmospheric air, to pass into the lungs; and, when he emptied his lungs, the pressure of the expired air closed the valve across the tube, while the same pressure opened the upper valve and allowed the vapor, which had been once breathed, to pass into the room instead of returning into the reservoir. Thus, at each inspiration, the patient had a fresh supply of air thoroughly charged with the vapor of ether, which vapor was continually given off by the sponge which was placed in the reservoir and thoroughly saturated with ether.

This apparatus answered the desired purpose, and, with some unimportant alterations, was the one used by me in my own practice, by the surgeons of the Massachusetts General Hospital, and others who administered ether in this country until the early part of April last, when it was found that, if a sponge well saturated with ether was placed over the nose and mouth of a patient, so that all the air which he breathes must necessarily pass through it, he was brought as completely under the influence of the ether, and in about as short a time, as if he breathed it from the apparatus. Further experience having fully established this fact, and, as that which will produce a desired effect in the simplest and cheapest manner is always to be preferred, the sponge will, probably, before long, be in general use, in preference to any "inhalers," however ingeniously contrived.

Although it may excite some surprise that I thus unceremoniously dispose of instruments, many of which evince much care and ingenuity, a little consideration of the facts of the case will show that there is good ground for my assertions. The vapor of sulphuric ether, as is well known, will not support life in its pure and unmixed state, being destitute of oxygen; and fears were entertained, when it was first applied to its present use, that, unless extreme care was taken to supply the patient with a large amount of atmospheric air, not enough oxygen would enter the lungs to decarbonize the blood and change if from venous to arterial; venous blood would then be sent to the brain, and the patient die from asphyxia, in the same manner as when deprived of oxygen by immersion in water, or from any other cause. Attention was immediately turned to this point, and, in all the inhalers which have been constructed, apertures of greater or less size have been left for the admission of external air. There is, however, one fact which renders it a matter of extreme difficulty so to arrange the apertures that a sufficient supply of atmospheric air shall, in every case, be afforded to the patient. This is, that a given amount of ether will not, under all circumstances, afford the same quantity of ethereal vapor; the amount produced by evaporation of the ether being much greater in warm weather than in cold. Thus, an apparatus, the aperture of which is amply sufficient for the admission of external air when the thermometer stands at 65°, and which may be used with perfect safety at that temperature, becomes positively dangerous with the thermometer at 90°, although the same aperture is left open and the same quantity of ether used. This danger is completely obviated by using the sponge; for, however high the temperature may be, and however great the consequent evaporation of ether, the patient has always a full allowance of atmospheric air; as the ethereal vapor, instead of being confined in the reservoir of the apparatus with no outlet but the air-hole and the mouth-piece, escapes freely into the room, and the patient breathes but little, if any, more of it than under ordinary circumstances. The sponge, too, has another advantage which, practically speaking, is of no small importance. This is, that, when the ether is given by a sponge, there is much less disposition to cough on the part of the patient than when it is given by the apparatus. This is owing to two circumstances: one, that ether inhaled from a sponge reaches the lungs mixed with a larger portion of atmospheric air than when it is inhaled from the apparatus; the other, that the sponge can be, at first, held at a little distance from the patient's mouth, and the ether thus entering the throat and lungs largely diluted with atmospheric air, the parts become gradually accustomed to the irritation which it produces, there is much less disposition to cough on the part of the patient, and less danger of producing spasm of the glottis, by which the wind-pipe might be closed. It can, too, be given more easily from the sponge than the apparatus where the patient is unwilling, or unable, to assist in the process, as in the case of operations on young children, and on the inferior animals in veterinary surgery. The simple sponge can also be easily cleansed, while that which remains in the apparatus must be frequently removed at the expense of considerable trouble, or there is danger of its becoming musty and offensive.

Inhaling ether from a sponge, therefore, may be considered as the most convenient, safest, and best method of taking it. The sponges best suited to this purpose are whole Turkey sponges, of a conical or bell shape, tapering from the base, which should be from four to six inches in diameter, up toward the apex. The lower surface, or mouth of the bell, should be sufficiently concave to avoid bringing the sponge in direct contact with the lips.

Before going on to speak of the mode of administering ether, and to describe the effects produced by it, it is proper to state that it is not necessary for patients who take it for different purposes to be at all put in precisely the same condition. That is, it is not necessary that all who take it should be brought equally under the influence of the ether, but that different degrees of etherization should be produced, according to the end proposed to be effected in different classes of cases. For instance, most surgical operations occupy a longer time than does the extraction of teeth, and the pain is, necessarily, of longer duration; of course, then, a patient must be brought more completely under the influence of ether to render him insensible to pain which is to last a number of minutes, than it is necessary to prevent him from feeling that which lasts only a few seconds. There are some conditions, too, usually attending operations in dentistry, which do not belong to most operations in surgery. Teeth are usually extracted at the house of the dentist, and the patient expects, as soon as the tooth is out, to be able to leave the room and go about his ordinary avocations. Now this may be done in a large majority of the cases where teeth are extracted while the patient is under the influence of ether, provided only enough has been given to render him insensible to the short, and comparatively slight, pain caused by the extraction of a tooth, and not as much as is required to prevent him from feeling a severe surgical operation. Many dentists have, no doubt, been prevented from using ether from a fear that its effects, after the tooth was extracted, would prove annoying both to themselves and their patients; which fear arose, I think, from an erroneous belief that a patient must be brought as much under the influence of ether to have a tooth extracted, as to undergo the amputation of a limb. That some cases have occurred where nausea and vomiting have followed the use of ether I have neither the wish, nor the intention, to deny; but they are by no means frequent, and have never, to my knowledge, been followed by any permanent ill effects. Ought we, then, to be deterred from using ether,—which we know to be an antidote to a positive evil, pain,—from the fear of consequences which but rarely follow its use, and which, when they do occur, seem to be of little moment?

Having made the necessary previous examination, decided upon the operation to be performed, and arranged the instruments near at hand, so as to lose no time when the ether takes effect, proceed as follows: Place your patient in the position which he is to occupy during the operation (which position should be made as comfortable as possible), and direct him to close his eyes and remain perfectly still. Direct, also, any one who may be present to say nothing to the patient, as talking materially retards the process. Where a tooth is to be extracted, or any operation performed upon the mouth, the patient should be directed to inhale the ether with his mouth open; for, if he commences this process with his mouth closed, he will sometimes keep it firmly shut after he is under the influence of the ether. Should the patient, at any time, close his teeth in this way, the operator must press the palm of his left hand firmly upon the patient's forehead, so as to fix the head steadily against the head-piece of the chair; then, placing his right hand upon the chin, overcome the resistance of the muscles by a sudden, but firm, downward pressure. Having made these preparations, pour upon the inside of such a bell-shaped sponge as I have above described two ounces of pure sulphuric ether; then bring the hollow part of the sponge to within an inch of the patient's mouth, and allow him to take four or five inspirations with it in this position. If no cough is produced, the sponge may then be applied so as to cover the nose and mouth of the patient, so that all the air he breathes must pass through it. If any cough is produced by the first breathing of the ether, the sponge should not be applied so as to cover the mouth and both nostrils, but should be inclined a little to one side, so that one nostril may remain open for the air to pass through until the patient becomes so accustomed to the ether that it does not produce coughing. Any forced or irregular breathing should be discouraged, and the patient told to breathe in a steady, regular, and natural manner.

Inhalation should be thus persevered in for three minutes, without anything being said to the patient, unless there is reason to believe, before that time, that he is under the influence of the ether; this can only be known by carefully observing the symptoms of etherization. These are*: redness of the countenance, dilatation of the pupils, which are also sometimes fixed or turned up, increased action of the heart, so that the pulse is quicker, and usually fuller, relaxation of the muscles generally (sometimes accompanied by a flow of saliva from the corners of the mouth), and, finally, loss of consciousness and slowness of the pulse. It is not necessary, nor is it desirable, that, in every case where ether is inhaled, the patient should exhibit all these symptoms. When, therefore, a dentist is giving ether to a patient for the purpose of extracting a tooth, if, at the end of a minute from the time when the sponge is placed at the patient's lips, he perceives that the countenance is flushed, the pulse quickened, and, particularly, if there is any relaxation of the muscular system (which, I think, first manifests itself in a heavy drooping of the eyelids, similar to that which precedes natural sleep), he should be told to open his eyes. If the patient opens his eyes quickly, and if, when he does so, the pupils appear clear, bright, and natural, he should be directed to close them again, and nothing

---

* This is the usual appearance, although the countenance is sometimes pale; but this can easily be distinguished from the purple or livid appearance which too long a use of the ether produces.

more should be said to him until another minute has elapsed, when the same process should be repeated. If, on the contrary, when the patient is directed to open his eyes, he either neglects doing so entirely, or else partially raises the lids in a heavy, languid manner, disclosing dilated pupils, with a dull, lack-lustre expression, he should be asked whether he will have his tooth extracted; if he makes no reply, or drawls out a slow, hesitating assent, the instrument should be applied, and the tooth extracted immediately. This may surprise those dentists who are not in the habit of using ether; but I assure them that patients frequently retain sufficient consciousness to comprehend what is said to them, and even to express their willingness to have a tooth extracted, although, when it is done, they feel no pain. Sometimes, when in this state, they know when the instrument is applied, and know that a tooth is extracted, but regard it as belonging to some one else; or, if they are aware that it is their own, declare that it causes them no pain. Sometimes a patient will scream when a tooth is extracted, and very frequently will raise his hand to his head when the instrument is applied to it; but these must not be considered as indications that he is conscious of suffering, for I have very often had patients do so, and yet declare, when they fully recovered, that they had felt no pain.* As patients, however, sometimes seize the hand or instrument of the operator, and thus prevent the extraction of the tooth, it is well to have an assistant near, who can hold the hands of the patient if necessary; and those persons who appear to be uneasy and restless while inhaling ether, should be directed to grasp firmly the hands of an assistant, as this frequently tranquillizes and quiets them.

By carefully following the above directions, dentists may be assured that they will rarely fail to render their patients insensible to the extraction of teeth, and will usually be able to do this in from one to three minutes. If the ether does not take effect in three minutes, they will please to follow the directions given below

---

* Sometimes, where it has been necessary to extract several teeth, when I have removed one, I have had the patient say to me, "Be quick! Be quick!" and yet declare positively, when he recovered, that he had felt no pain.

for administering it in surgical operations; excepting that a dentist need not wait until the patient does not open his eyes when directed to do so, but may proceed to extract the tooth if the patient opens his eyes in the heavy, languid manner, or speaks in the slow, drawling tone before described.

I should mention here that it has been proposed, and practised, to allow patients to inhale ether with the eyes open, in order to observe the effect which it produces upon the pupils, and judge of the time for extracting the tooth by the appearance which they present. I have tried this method, but, on the whole, prefer the one which I have mentioned above as being more certain.

When a surgical operation is to be performed, the inhalation should be steadily continued for three minutes without speaking to the patient. If, at the end of this time, the pulse is quickened and the muscles relaxed, so that the head has a tendency to fall on one side, the patient should be told, in a loud, distinct tone, to open his eyes; and, if he does *not* do so, the operation should be immediately commenced. If he does open his eyes, even in a slow and languid manner, he should be directed to close them, and the inhalation should be continued two minutes longer, when the same question may be repeated; and it will usually be found that, by this time, the patient is unconscious. Should this not occur, however, the surgeon should place his hand over about one-half of the sponge, so as to prevent loss of ether by evaporation, and continue the inhalation until ten minutes have elapsed from the time when the patient first began to breathe it, calling upon him to open his eyes at intervals of about one minute each.* If, at the end of ten minutes, he still continues to open his eyes when directed to do so, the inhalation should be discontinued, and not resumed again for at *least* five minutes. At the end of that time two ounces more of ether should be poured upon the sponge, and the inhaling resumed as before; but if, after inhaling a second time for ten minutes, it does not produce its effect, an *interval* of *ten* minutes must be allowed

* Throughout the whole of the inhalation the operator should bear constantly in mind the symptoms indicating danger, which I have given below, and remove the sponge from the patient's mouth as soon as any of them appear.

to the patient, and then, the ether having been again renewed, the inhaling may be resumed once more. If, at the end of the third trial of inhaling ether, the patient still remains unaffected by it, the operation had better be deferred until another day; but I can hardly suppose that this will ever happen where the ether is pure and highly concentrated, and has been administered in the manner above described.

In the course of inhaling it, frequently more ether is required than has been at first poured upon the sponge. No certain rule can be given as to the amount to be added in these cases, as the evaporation, and, of course, the waste of ether, is so much greater in warm weather than cold. If, however, the operator perceives that the sponge has lost its moist and cold feeling, and does not give off the ethereal vapor as freely as before, he should pour upon the upper part of the sponge, without removing it from the patient's mouth, from half an ounce to an ounce of ether.* In long operations it is frequently necessary to repeat the inhalation, after the patient has once become insensible, for fear that he should recover this consciousness before the operation is concluded. If, then, the patient should appear, from his motions or groans, to be recovering his consciousness before the operation is finished, the sponge should be re-applied to the mouth as it is, if it appears to be tolerably moist; and, if it is dry, half an ounce of ether, poured upon the inside of it, will enable the patient, by four or five inspirations, to resume his state of entire unconsciousness.

Before leaving this part of the subject I wish all who make use of ether distinctly to understand that I by no means consider it necessary that patients should, in every instance, inhale it for so long a time as ten minutes. Some patients have remained insensible to the pain of severe surgical operations, after an inhalation of only three minutes, many after one of five minutes, and most require but eight minutes. I wish, therefore, ten minutes to be considered as

---

* The ether produces the most powerful effect when poured upon the inside of the sponge, as at first directed; but as, after the sponge has been once applied, this occasions some loss of time, it is found most convenient to pour it on the top of the sponge, without removing it from the mouth.

the *longest* time that the inhalation should last, without removing the sponge from the patient's mouth; and I feel satisfied that, if it be administered according to the directions, very few cases will occur which will render it necessary to continue the inhalation so long as ten minutes.

The next class of cases differ, in one important particular, from those before mentioned. This is that, in those cases of which I have already spoken, ether is given to patients before they are subjected to pain, in order to render them insensible to it when it does come; but, in those of which I am about to speak, it is given to relieve them of pain which they already suffer. The cessation of pain, then, in these cases, is the best indication for suspending the use of ether.

First in importance among this class are the pains of child-birth. When the use to which sulphuric ether is now principally applied was first made known, it was not at once perceived that it exerted its influence over the voluntary muscles alone. Before long this fact was noticed, and it was then proposed to administer it in cases of midwifery, the expulsion of the child depending chiefly upon the involuntary contractions of the womb. It was at first supposed that ether would be mostly used in cases of preternatural labor, where it was necessary to turn the child, or where instruments were to be used. It was, however, soon after administered in cases of natural labor, and was found to save the mother from suffering without injuring the child or retarding its progress into the world. As soon as this fact was known, many physicians eagerly availed themselves of this means of relieving those sufferings, which they had before been compelled to witness, without the power of mitigating. The cases of midwifery in which ether has been employed, although not numerous when compared with those in which it has been used for other purposes, are still many;*

* To say nothing of the experience of other physicians in the use of ether for cases of midwifery, Professor Simpson, of Edinburgh, had, up to March 22d "used etherization some forty or fifty times, with the most perfect safety and success" (British and Foreign Med. Review, No. 46, p. 568). Since this date I believe that Dr. Simpson has added largely to his number of cases, but I have not seen any report of them.

and the very fact that no fatal or even injurious consequences have been made public, as having been caused by its use, at a time when the medical profession is everywhere so much interested upon this subject, and so desirous of adding to the common stock of information, affords good ground for belief that it never has produced such consequences.

Having decided upon giving ether in a case of labor, the first point to be settled is, at what time shall its administration be commenced. Most cases of labor begin, as is well known, by wandering pains, extending from the loins and back across the abdomen to the pubes; but these are not at first severe, and, being followed by intervals of ease, during which the patient can frequently sleep, not hard to bear. The pains which follow these, and which attend the dilatation of the orifice of the womb, are of a cutting, grinding character, and frequently cause extreme suffering. Is it, then, advisable to administer ether at this time? In those cases where these pains are not very severe, and, particularly, in cases of first children, when a somewhat long labor is usually to be expected, it will perhaps be well to avoid giving ether; as, after a woman has once taken it and experienced the relief which it affords to her sufferings, she is unwilling afterward to bear a single pain without it, and we may thus be compelled to give more than we wish to. If, however, the patient undergoes the severe distress which frequently accompanies these cutting, grinding pains, we should be cruel to deprive her of a remedy which we actually hold in our hands, and which we have known to be administered freely, in many instances, without having ever known of a single evil result which could justly be attributed to it. Patients should, therefore, be encouraged to bear the less severe pains with fortitude, while the worst ones should be relieved by ether. When the orifice of the womb is well dilated and the head of the child pressing down with steady, regular, well-sustained, expulsive pains, there can be no doubt of the propriety of administering ether; and it may be continued, for most of the severe pains, until the child is born. If the accoucheur has any doubt whether the pains advance the child as much with the ether as without it, he should allow the patient to go through two or three pains without ether, until he has satisfied himself on this point. In most cases he will find, owing to the relaxing power which the ether exerts upon the muscles, thus diminishing the resistance to the child's head, that the labor advances rather more rapidly, when a patient is under its influence, than when she is not. When the accoucheur administers it the first time, the patient had better sit up in bed; he will thus be able to observe exactly the time which the ether takes to produce its effect, for the patient not only ceases to complain, but sinks quietly back on the pillow as soon as the pain is relieved. The ether is to be administered in the manner before described, one ounce of it only being poured upon the inside of the sponge; but, as in this instance, the cessation of pain is the indication to cease using the sponge, it is seldom necessary to apply it longer than from one to three minutes. After a patient has been once brought under the influence of ether, a few inspirations will usually relieve her of the subsequent pains; and this, too, often from the sponge used before, without adding to it any more ether, or only one or two teaspoonfuls. As a patient usually drops her hand, if it be elevated, when she has inhaled enough ether to be insensible to pain, it is best, in most cases in this stage of labor, to allow her to hold the sponge herself, and apply it to her mouth when she feels a pain coming on. An assistant should, however, in this case, be stationed at the bedside, with directions to remove the sponge from her mouth as soon as she is insensible, if she does not do it herself. When the head of the child is about to pass through the external organs, it is best, after allowing the patient to inhale ether till she is insensible to the pain, to entrust the sponge to the care of the assistant, with directions to allow the patient to take a few inspirations from it if she seems about to recover her consciousness before she is delivered.

In those cases of midwifery where it is necessary to apply the instruments, or to turn the child, the ether should be given in the same manner as where a surgical operation is to be performed.

The mode of administering ether in cases of colic, cramp, or the passage of renal calculi along the ureters is similar to that which I have described as applicable to cases of midwifery, the cessation of pain being the principal indication for suspending its use.   Still, it must not be forgotten in these cases, as well as in those of midwifery, that there are other symptoms, besides the cessation of pain, which indicate that the use of ether should be immediately suspended.

When ether is given to assist the surgeon in returning a strangulated hernia, reducing a dislocation, or adjusting the bones in a bad case of fracture, it is to be administered in the manner described as appropriate to surgical operations, and persevered in until complete muscular relaxation ensues, unless the symptoms indicating danger should occur.   An inhalation of from three to five minutes will usually be found sufficient in these cases.

Without going minutely into the effect produced on the brain and nervous system by inhaling sulphuric ether, it is sufficient to say that it is a kind of intoxication which is complete while it lasts, which usually comes on and passes off with equal rapidity, and without leaving the ill effects of ordinary intoxication.   This seems to be owing to the mode it is administered, that is, by inhalation, and not by being taken into the stomach.   For when the lungs are filled with the ethereal vapor, it is necessarily brought in contact with the innumerable blood-vessels which ramify through every part of them; the vapor is taken into the circulation by direct absorption, and, being sent to the brain, produces immediate intoxication. The recovery is equally rapid, because, when the effect of the vapor first inhaled passes away, and the sponge is removed from the mouth, there being no more vapor to be taken into the circulation, the patient necessarily recovers.   An intoxicating liquor, on the contrary, when taken into the stomach, is slower in producing its effects, as it must get into the circulation by the ordinary process; and the effects last longer, because intoxication continues while any of it remains in the stomach to be absorbed.   It has been long known that a person in a state of complete intoxication is insensible to the pain of a surgical operation;* and it is probable that patients

---

* In January last a patient was brought to the Massachusetts General Hospital in a state of complete intoxication, whose leg was so badly crushed as to require amputation; this was performed soon after he entered without his being at all aware of it.

would have been intoxicated in the ordinary manner before performing operations upon them, had it not been thought that the amount of spirituous liquor necessary to produce perfect intoxication would injure the health of the patient, and so retard his recovery. The inhalation of sulphuric ether answers perfectly the desired end, as it intoxicates speedily and completely, and, when the inhalation is discontinued, its effects rapidly pass away.

As, then, the effects produced by inhaling ether are similar to those caused by taking alcoholic drinks into the stomach, so the results of too long an inhalation of ether, as shown in experiments on the inferior animals, seem to resemble those produced by an excessive use of alcohol. When a person has taken alcohol to intoxication, temporary insensibility, as is well known, usually ensues; and a similar condition is induced when ether is fully inhaled, although it does not last so long. If a person takes an excessive amount of alcohol into the stomach, the blood vessels of the brain may become permanently congested, or even ruptured, or the blood may be so overcharged with alcohol as to exert a poisonous influence on the brain and nervous system, and prostration, coma, and death ensue. It would, doubtless, be possible to give ether long enough to produce the same result; but with an agent the effect of which is so quickly manifested, passes away so rapidly, and is thus so completely under our control as sulphuric ether, any fatal result in administering it to the human race can hardly be anticipated if proper precautions are taken. And I am confident that any one who wishes to make use of it, if he will administer it exactly according to the directions given above, and will pay attention to the symptoms of danger which I am now about to detail, may give it without endangering the safety of his patients.

If, then, at any time during the administration of sulphuric ether (even if the patient has but just begun to inhale it), the countenance should become of a livid, purplish hue; the breathing labored and stertorous or snoring; if the pulse, in an adult, fall to sixty-five, or, in a child above ten years of age, to seventy, or, under ten, to eighty, the inhalation must be *immediately* discontinued. It is of no consequence whether the inhalation has rendered the patient insensible or not; if any of these symptoms appear, the sponge must be immediately removed from the mouth; and if the pulse does not rise, the color come back to the face, and the breathing become natural, cold water must be dashed into the face, strong aqua ammonia (which should be always kept at hand) applied to the nostrils, and ten drops of it in a wine-glass of water given internally. If this does not arouse the patient, he should be taken up, if possible, and walked about the room, with a person supporting him under each arm, while the affusion of cold water, application of aqua ammonia to the nostrils, and administering it internally still go on. It has been suggested to employ electro-magnetism for the recovery of patients from the effects of ether. I have never used it myself, but should advise its trial where other means have failed, as it has been found by M. Ducros to arouse chickens and pigeons immediately from the stupor which the inhalation produced. A current of positive electricity passed into them when they were upon the isolating stool roused them in about thirty seconds; but the negative electricity prolonged the insensibility instead of abridging it.*

But these remarks must be understood to apply to extreme cases, which can hardly be supposed to occur if proper caution is used. Ether, like alcohol, may be taken to a dangerous extent; but if the abuse of a thing is to be regarded as an argument against its careful and judicious use, many articles of almost daily domestic consumption might be immediately discarded.

Some caution ought to be observed as to the state of the health of patients before administering ether to them. It will be proper to ascertain whether they have ever had hæmorrhage from the lungs, epilepsy, disease of the heart, or a tendency to apoplexy, and, in

---

* See London Medical Gazette, May, p. 829. The London Lancet, July 24th, p. 101, states that M. Ducros has rendered patients insensible to the extraction of teeth by the electro-magnetic current. In order to try these experiments I applied the wires of an electro-magnetic apparatus of considerable power to the thigh of a chicken, from which the feathers had previously been removed, and allowed the electric current to pass through it for five minutes; I then cut through the thigh to the bone without any evidence of pain being given at the part of the animal, although, when the other leg was slightly pricked, it quickly withdrew it. Similar experiments were tried, with the same results, upon a frog and a squirrel.

such cases, the operator should decline giving ether.* In persons of great nervous excitability also, particularly females, it should not be given for slight causes.

The age of a patient was at first thought worthy of consideration in administering ether, and I at first declined, in most instances, giving it to young children. More extended observation has convinced me that it may be done with perfect safety; and a severe operation has, within a few weeks, been performed at the Massachusetts General Hospital, on an infant, three months old, whose sufferings were very much mitigated by the use of ether.

As to the effect ether produces on persons in the habit of freely using ardent spirits, I should say, judging from the cases where patients acknowledged this to be the case (which are not frequent), that the specific effects of ether may always be produced upon them, but not in so short a time as in other cases.

When the present use of ether first attracted attention, it was feared that its vapor, mingling with the atmosphere of the room, would form a dangerous explosive mixture, which would ignite when exposed to the flame of a candle. To obviate this danger it was proposed that Sir H. Davy's safety-lamp should be used whenever ether was to be inhaled at night. To satisfy myself upon this point, I placed an ounce of ether upon a shovel, fastened to a pole eight feet long; I then placed the shovel under a lighted gas lamp, so that the ethereal vapor was exposed to its blaze; and, finding that it did not ignite, I inhaled if for a minute or two, and found that I could breathe directly against the flame of a lamp without any danger. I afterward held a lighted paper over a saucer of ether, and found that, at the distance of two inches, no effect was produced, but, that when the flame was brought within half an inch of the ether, it immediately ignited. From these experiments I conclude that the evil results to be dreaded from this

---

* I think it, however, proper to state that, since September last, I have made daily use of it, both in my own practice and in that of others, and, in many cases, without knowing the state of the patient's health in these respects, and I have never had any case where the patient, to my knowledge, experienced any permanent ill effects from its use.

source have been very much overrated, but that it will be proper to avoid bringing a lighted lamp very near to the patient, or the bottle of ether, when using it at night.

Having now finished the various subjects upon which I proposed to speak, I will conclude by expressing my firm belief that, if any one will make use of ether in the manner I have described, he will find that he can thereby greatly increase the comfort and relieve the sufferings of his patients, without endangering their safety.

1846

MORTON'S LETHEON*

CONSISTING OF LETTERS, ARTICLES, AND COMMUNICA-
TIONS, THE MOST IMPORTANT OF THESE BEING THAT
OF DR. JOHN C. WARREN, WHO PERFORMED THE
FIRST SURGICAL OPERATION ON A PATIENT
UNDER THE INFLUENCE OF ETHER

* *Note.*—Term used in obtaining patent. See p. 311.—(C. N. B. C.)

"Dear Sir:

"You are supposed to take sufficient interest in the subject of which this circular treats to admit of an apology for taking the liberty of transmitting the following extracts from the communication of Dr. H. J. Bigelow, one of the surgeons of the Massachusetts General Hospital, in this city, read before the Boston Society of Medical Improvement November 9, 1846, and before the American Academy of Arts and Sciences on the third of the same month.

"You will observe that the experiments referred to by Dr. B. were among the earliest to which spectators were admitted; and, although striking and conclusive in themselves, they are, if possible, more than equalled by the numerous operations daily made, under the use of the discovery, in this city, as well as in other places where I have granted licenses for the employment of it.

"It has long been an important problem in medical science to devise some method of mitigating the pain of surgical operations. An efficient agent for this purpose has at length been discovered. A patient has been rendered completely insensible during an amputation of the thigh, regaining consciousness after a short interval. Other severe operations have been performed without the knowledge of the patients. So remarkable an occurrence will, it is believed, render the following details relating to the history and character of the process not uninteresting.

"On the sixteenth of October, 1846, an operation was performed at the hospital upon a patient who had inhaled a preparation administered by Dr. Morton, a dentist of this city, with the alleged intention of producing insensibility to pain. Dr. Morton was understood to have extracted teeth under similar circumstances, without the knowledge of the patient. The present operation was performed by Dr. Warren, and though comparatively slight, involved an incision near the lower jaw of some inches in extent. During the

335

operation the patient muttered, as in a semi-conscious state, and afterwards stated that the pain was considerable, though mitigated; in his own words, as though the skin had been scratched with a hoe. There was, probably, in this instance, some defect in the process of inhalation, for on the following day the vapor was administered to another patient with complete success. A fatty tumor of considerable size was removed, by Dr. Hayward, from the arm of a woman, near the deltoid muscle. The operation lasted four or five minutes, during which the patient betrayed occasional marks of uneasiness; but upon subsequently regaining her consciousness professed not only to have felt no pain, but to have been insensible to surrounding objects, to have known nothing of the operation, being only uneasy about a child left at home. No doubt, I think, existed in the minds of those who saw this operation that the unconsciousness was real; nor could the imagination be accused of any share in the production of these remarkable phenomena. * * * * * * * * *

" *The Remarks of the Patients.* *—A boy of sixteen, of medium stature and strength, was seated in the chair. The first few inhalations occasioned a quick cough, which afterwards subsided; at the end of eight minutes the head fell back and the arms dropped, but, owing to some resistance in opening the mouth, the tooth could not be reached before he awoke. He again inhaled for two minutes, and slept three minutes, during which time an inferior molar was extracted. At the moment of the extraction the features assumed an expression of pain and the hand was raised. Upon coming to himself he said he had had a 'first rate dream—very quiet,' he said, 'and had dreamed of Napoleon—had not the slightest consciousness of pain—the time had seemed long,' and he left the chair, feeling no uneasiness of any kind, and evidently in a high state of admiration.

"A girl of sixteen immediately occupied the chair. After coughing a little she inhaled during three minutes and fell asleep, when a molar tooth was extracted, after which she continued to slumber tranquilly during three minutes more. At the moment when force was applied she flinched and frowned, raising her hand to her mouth, but she said she had been dreaming a pleasant dream and knew nothing of the operation.

* See page 365.

"A stout boy of twelve, at the first inspiration coughed considerably, and required a good deal of encouragement to induce him to go on. At the end of three minutes from the first fair inhalation the muscles were relaxed and the pupils dilated. During the attempt to force open his mouth he recovered consciousness, and again inhaled during two minutes, and in the ensuing one minute two teeth were extracted, the patient seeming somewhat conscious, but upon actually awakening he declared 'it was the best fun he ever saw,' avowed his attention to come there again, and insisted upon having another tooth extracted upon the spot. . . .

"The next patient was a healthy-looking, middle aged woman, who inhaled the vapor for four minutes; in the course of the next two minutes a back tooth was extracted, and the patient continued smiling in her sleep for three minutes more. Pulse 120, not affected at the moment of the operation, but smaller during sleep. Upon coming to herself she exclaimed that 'it was beautiful! she dreamed of being at home—it seeemd as if she had been gone a month.' These cases, which occurred successively in about an hour, at the room of Dr. Morton, are fair examples of the average results produced by the inhalation of the vapor, and will convey an idea of the feelings and expressions of many of the patients subjected to the process. Dr. Morton states that, in upwards of two hundred patients, similar effects have been produced. The inhalation, after the first irritation has subsided, is easy and produces a complete unconsciousness at the expiration of a period varying from two to five or six, sometimes eight, minutes; its duration varying from two to five minutes; during which the patient is completely insensible to the ordinary tests of pain. The pupils in the cases I have observed have been generally dilated; but with allowance for excitement and other disturbing influences, the pulse is not affected, at least in frequency; the patient remains in a calm and tranquil slumber, and wakes with a pleasurable feeling. . . .

"Two recent cases serve to confirm, and one I think to decide, the great utility of this process. On Saturday, the seventh of November, at the Massachusetts General Hospital, the right leg of a young girl was amputated above the knee, by Dr. Hayward, for disease of this joint.   Being made to inhale the preparation, after protesting her inability to do so from the pungency of the vapor, she became insensible in about five minutes.   The last circumstance she was able to recall was the adjustment of the mouth-piece of the apparatus, after which she was unconscious until she heard some remark at the time of securing the vessels—one of the last steps of the operation.   Of the incision she knew nothing, and was unable to say, upon my asking her, whether or not the limb had been removed.   She refused to answer several questions during the operation, and was evidently completely insensible to pain or other external influences.   This operation was followed by another, consisting of the removal of a part of the lower jaw, by Dr. Warren. The patient was insensible to the pain of the first incision, though she recovered her consciousness in the course of a few minutes.

"The character of the lethargic state which follows this inhalation is peculiar.   The patient loses his individuality and awakes after a certain period, either entirely unconscious of what has taken place, or retaining only a faint recollection of it.   Severe pain is sometimes remembered as being of a dull character; sometimes the operation is supposed by the patient to be performed on somebody else.   Certain patients whose teeth have been extracted remember the application of the extracting instruments; yet none have been conscious of any real pain. . . .

"The duration of the insensibility is another important element in the process.   When the apparatus is withdrawn at the moment of unconsciousness, it continues, upon the average, two or three minutes, and the patient then recovers completely or incompletely without subsequent ill effects.   In this sudden cessation of the symptoms this vapor in the air tubes differs in its effects from the narcotics or stimulants in the stomach, and, as far as the evidence of a few experiments of Dr. Morton's goes, from the ethereal solution of opium when breathed.   Lassitude, headache, and other symptoms lasted for several hours, when this agent was employed.

"But if the respiration of the vapor be prolonged much beyond the first period, the symptoms are more permanent in their character.   In one of the first cases, that of a young boy, the inhalation was continued during the greater part of ten minutes, and the subsequent narcotism and drowsiness lasted more than an hour. . .

"It is probable that the vapor of the new preparation ceases early to act upon the system, from the facility with which it is exhaled.

"The process is obviously adapted to operations which are brief in their duration, whatever be their severity. Of these, the two most striking are, perhaps, amputations, and the extraction of teeth. In protracted dissections the pain of the first incision alone is of sufficient importance to induce its use; and it may hereafter prove safe to administer it for a length of time, and to produce a narcotism of an hour's duration. It is not unlikely to be applicable in cases requiring a suspension of muscular motion, such as the reduction of dislocations or of strangulated hernia; and, finally, it may be employed in the alleviation of functional pain, of muscular spasm, as in cramp or colic, and as a sedative or narcotic.

"The application of the process to the performance of surgical operations is, it will be conceded, new. . . .

"It is natural to inquire with whom this invention originated. Without entering into details, I learn that the patent bears the name of Dr. Charles T. Jackson, a distinguished chemist, and of Dr. Morton, a skilful dentist, of this city, as inventors, and has been issued to the latter gentleman as proprietor. . . ."

The foregoing statements, which are only a portion of the communications of Dr. Bigelow, are alone sufficient, I presume, to enable you to form an opinion of the immediate and very great value of the invention to the afflicted or suffering, as well as to the surgical world. It is employed by, and has received, as you will perceive, the sanction of some of the most skilful and distinguished dentists and surgeons. The following are the statements of Drs. Warren and Hayward, of this city, who performed at the hospital the operations alluded to by Dr. B. and other operators, since the time mentioned by him:

INHALATION OF ETHEREAL VAPOR FOR THE PREVENTION OF PAIN IN SURGICAL OPERATIONS

By John C. Warren, M.D.

(Communicated for the Boston Medical and Surgical Journal.)

Application has been made to me by R. H. Eddy, Esq., in a letter dated November 30th, in behalf of Dr. W. T. G. Morton, to furnish an account of the operations witnessed and performed by me wherein his new discovery for preventing pain was employed. Dr. M. has also proposed to me to give him the names of such hospitals as I know of in this country, in order that he may present them with the use of his discovery. These applications, and the hope of being useful to my professional brethren, especially those concerned in the hospitals which may have the benefit of Dr. M.'s proposal, have induced me to draw up the following statement and to request that it be made public through your journal:

The discovery of a mode of preventing pain in surgical operations has been an object of strong desire among surgeons from an early period. In my surgical lectures I have almost annually alluded to it, and stated the means which I have usually adopted for the attainment of this object. I have also freely declared that, notwithstanding the use of very large doses of narcotic substances, this desideratum had never been satisfactorily obtained. The successful use of any article of the materia medica for this purpose would, therefore, be hailed by me as an important alleviation to human suffering. I have, in consequence, readily admitted the trial of plans calculated to accomplish this object whenever they were free from danger.

About five weeks since, Dr. Morton, dentist of this city, informed me that he had invented an apparatus for the inhalation of a vapor, the effect of which was to produce a state of total insensibility to pain, and that he had employed it successfully in a sufficient number of cases in his practice to justify him in a belief of its efficacy. He wished for an opportunity to test its power in surgical operations, and I agreed to give him such an opportunity as soon as practicable.

Being at that time in attendance as surgeon of the Massachusetts General Hospital, a patient presented himself in that valuable institution a few days after my conversation with Dr. Morton, who required an operation for a tumor of the neck; and, agreeably to my promise, I requested the presence of Dr. M.

On October 17th the patient being prepared for the operation, the apparatus was applied to his mouth by Dr. Morton for about three minutes, at the end of which time he sank into a state of insensibility. I immediately made an incision about three inches long through the skin of the neck, and began a dissection among important nerves and blood-vessels without any expression of pain on the part of the patient. Soon after he began to speak incoherently, and appeared to be in an agitated state during the remainder of the operation. Being asked immediately afterwards whether he had suffered much, he said he had felt as if his neck had been scratched; but subsequently, when inquired of by me, his statement was that he did not experience pain at the time, although aware that the operation was proceeding.

The effect of the gaseous inhalation in neutralizing the sentient faculty was made perfectly distinct to my mind by this experiment, although the patient, during a part of its prosecution, exhibited appearances indicative of suffering. Dr. Morton had apprized me that the influence of his application would last but a few minutes after its intermission; and as the operation was necessarily protracted, I was not disappointed that its success was only partial.

On the following day, October 18th, an operation was done by Dr. Hayward on a tumor of the arm in a female patient at the hospital. The respiration of the gas was in this case continued during the whole of the operation. There was no exhibition of pain except some occasional groans during its last stage, which she subsequently stated to have arisen from a disagreeable dream. Noticing the pulse in this patient before and after the operation, I found it to have risen from 80 to 120.

Two or three weeks after these occurrences, on meeting with Dr. Charles T. Jackson, distinguished for his philosophical spirit of inquiry, as well as for his geological and chemical science, this gentleman informed me that he first suggested to Dr. Morton the inspiration of ether as a means of preventing the pain of operations on the teeth. He did not claim the invention of the apparatus nor its practical application; for these we are indebted to Dr. Morton.

The success of this process in the prevention of pain for a certain period being quite established, I at once conceived it to be my duty to introduce the apparatus into the practice of the hospital, but was immediately arrested by learning that the proprietor intended to obtain an exclusive patent for its use. It now became a question whether, in accordance with that elevated principle long since introduced into the medical profession, which forbids its members to conceal any useful discovery, we could continue to encourage an application we were not allowed to use ourselves, and of the components of which we were ignorant. On discussing this matter with Dr. Hayward, my colleague in the hospital, we came to the conclusion that we were not justified in encouraging the further use of this new invention until we were better satisfied on these points. Dr. Hayward thereupon had a conversation with Dr. Morton, in consequence of which Dr. M. addressed to me a letter. In this he declared his willingness to make known to us the article employed, and to supply assistance to administer the inhalation whenever called upon. These stipulations he has complied with.

This being done, we thought ourselves justified in inviting Dr. Morton to continue his experiments at the hospital and elsewhere; and he, directly after, November 7th, attended at a painful and protracted operation performed by me, of the excision of a portion of the lower jaw, in which the patient's sufferings were greatly mitigated. On the same day an amputation of the thigh of a young woman was performed at the hospital by Dr. Hayward. In this case the respiration of the ethereal vapor appeared to be entirely successful in preventing the pain of the operation; the patient stating, after-wards, that she did not know that anything had been done to her.

On November 12th, an operation for the removal of a tumor from the arm of a young woman was performed by Dr. J. Mason Warren. The vapor was administered for three minutes, when the patient became unconscious; the operator then proceeded, the inspiration being continued. Standing myself on one side of the patient, while the operator was on the other, so entirely tranquil was she that I was not aware the operation was begun until it was nearly completed.

On November 21st an operation was performed by Dr. J. Mason Warren on a gentleman, for the removal of a tumor, which covered nearly the half of the front of the right thigh. The patient lying upon a bed, the vapor was administered by Dr. Morton, in the presence of Drs. Charles T. Jackson, Reynolds, J. V. C. Smith, Flagg, Gould, Shurtleff, Lawrence, Parsons, Briggs, and others. After he had breathed the vapor for three minutes his head fell and he ceased to respire it, but presently awakening, the inhalation was renewed till he again appeared insensible. The operation was then commenced. At the first stroke of the knife he clapped his hand on the wound, but I immediately seized and held it during the remainder of the operation, though not without some difficulty in consequence of his struggles. The operation was completed in two or three minutes, and the patient remained quietly on his back with his eyes closed. On examination the pupils were found to be dilated; the pulse was not materially affected. After he had lain about two minutes, I roused him with the inquiry, "How do you do to-day?" to which he replied, "Very well, I thank you." I then asked him what he had been doing. He said he believed he had been dreaming: he dreamed that he was at home and making some examination into his business. "Do you feel any pain?" "No." "How is that tumor of yours?" The patient raised himself in bed, looked at his thigh for a moment, and said, "It is gone, and I am glad of it." I then inquired if he had felt any pain during the operation, to which he replied in the negative. He soon recovered his natural state, experienced no inconvenience from the inhalation, was remarkably free from pain, and in three days went home into the country.

In all these cases there was a decided mitigation of pain; in most of them the patients, on the day after the operation, and at other times, stated that they had not been conscious of pain. All those who attended were, I think, satisfied of the efficacy of the application in preventing, or, at least, greatly diminishing, the suffering usual in such cases. The phenomena presented in these operations afforded grounds for many interesting reflections, but it being my principal intention, at this time, to give a simple statement of facts, I shall not pursue the subject further, but close with two or three remarks:

First. The breathing of the ethereal vapor appears to operate directly on the cerebral system, and the consequent insensibility is proportionate to the degree of cerebral affection.

Second. Muscular power was for the time suspended in some cases; in others its loss was partial, and in one instance was scarcely sensible. The great relaxation of muscular action produced by a full dose of the application leads to the hope that it may be employed, with advantage, in cases of spasmodic affection, both by the surgeon and by the physician.

Third. The action of the heart is remarkably accelerated in some cases, but not in all.

Fourth. The respiration is sometimes stertorous, like that of apoplexy.

All these changes soon pass off without leaving any distinct traces behind them, and the ordinary state of the function returns. This has been the course of things in the cases I have witnessed, but I think it quite probable that so powerful an agent may sometimes produce other and even alarming effects. I, therefore, would recommend that it should never be employed except under the inspection of a judicious and competent person.

Let me conclude by congratulating my professional brethren on the acquisition of a mode of mitigating human suffering which may become a valuable agent, in the hands of careful and well-instructed practitioners, even if it should not prove of such general application as the imagination of sanguine persons would lead them to anticipate.

BOSTON, December 3, 1846.

BOSTON, December 7, 1846.

DEAR SIR: In compliance with your request, I will briefly state my experience of the effects of the gas introduced into practice by Dr. Morton, and administered for the purpose of lessening the pain of surgical operations.

I have operated on four patients who had inhaled this gas: two of these cases are noticed by Dr. H. J. Bigelow in his article on the subject. In all of them the gas was administered by Dr. Morton.

The first case was the removal of the tumor from the arm of a woman; the second, the amputation of the limb of a girl, twenty years of age, above the knee; the third, the removal of the breast of a lady in private practice; and the fourth was the same operation which I did on Saturday last, at the Hospital.

In the three first cases the patients were apparently insensible and unconscious during the operation; they have since repeatedly assured me that they were so; no ill consequences followed the inhalation of the gas; they are all now nearly, if not quite, well, and their recovery has been, I think, more rapid than under ordinary circumstances, which I attribute to their having escaped the shock of the operation.

The fourth patient seemed to be conscious during the operation, answered questions, and appeared to suffer; yet she says that she did not and was not aware of what was done till it was nearly over. She has thus far been very comfortable—more so, I should say, than patients usually are in the same time after this operation.

I remain very respectfully yours,

GEO. HAYWARD.

R. H. EDDY, ESQ.

And the subjoined extracts are from a letter of Dr. Peirson, of Salem, who performed the important operations of which he speaks under the administration of the invention by Dr. Fisk, dentist of the same city, to whom I have granted the license to use it in Essex County:

"DEAR SIR: The two following cases, occurring in my practice the past week, are of interest as supporting the claims to confidence of Dr. Morton's anodyne compound:

"CASE I.—November 19th: An Irish girl, under twenty years of age, in attempting to step into the cars at Hamilton while they were in motion fell, with her arm upon the track, and had a compound, comminuted fracture at the elbow, from the wheel of the car. At about nine in the evening I amputated in the middle of the humerus. The operation lasted a little longer than if done by daylight, although it was a flap operation and quickly executed. Three vessels were tied. Dr. Fisk, dentist, of this city, accompanied me and caused the patient to inhale the vapor of the compound about three minutes before the operation commenced. By this time she appeared to have yielded entirely to its influence, and became pale, silent, and perfectly manageable, whereas she had before exhibited evidence of great physical suffering and uncontrollable grief. Before the arteries were all tied she appeared to be returning to consciousness, when, on offering the apparatus to her mouth, she seized it with avidity, respired rapidly, and soon seemed to relapse into the unconscious state. It was thus renewed four or five times before she was placed in bed. Her own statement is that she suffered no pain during the operation, that she was asleep, and when she woke she breathed again of what was offered to her and fell asleep again—that she remembers to have done this three times. She says she did not know what we were doing to her, but in her sleep she thought she had got a reaping hook in her arm, and that she heard the noise of sawing wood. She says she was not sensible of anything until she was laid in bed, when she became quite talkative and evidently somewhat excited. She slept some hours during the night. On dressing the stump on the third day, she made a violent outcry at the slightest pain. I was convinced that her statements with regard to her freedom from pain during the operation were to be believed.

"CASE II.—November 21st: An intelligent tanner, about thirty years old, with a fracture of both bones in the middle of the left leg, his ankle crushed by the cars engaged in building the Salem and Methuen Railroad. I amputated the leg just below the knee.

The patient respired the vapor under Dr. Fisk's directions. He says he was not conscious of feeling any pain, and after the operation was finished and the ligatures applied, his consciousness returned, and, with great apparent sincerity, he asked *if his limb was taken off.* He says though he felt no pain, he was conscious of the presence of those around him, and he was obedient to the directions given him. The operation was performed about 3 P.M., and the stump was dressed about 9, when, he says, the pain of a few sutures far exceeded that of the operation.

"In both these cases the pulse became somewhat accelerated after the operation, the countenance assumed a vacant expression, although in the first case there was working of the brows and the pupils were dilated. They both appear to be doing well and exhibit no symptoms worthy of note.

"Respectfully yours,

"SALEM, November 24, 1846. "A. L. PEIRSON."

(*Postscript, November 25, 1846.*) "Yesterday I made further trial of the ethereal vapor, upon a middle-aged female, from whom I removed an adipose tumor, by an incision four inches long over the clavicle and scapula; she was an unimpressible subject, and was less perfectly under the influence of the vapor than the others, but she was entirely bewildered and not able to realize the nature of what we were doing to her. She was much more quiet than patients usually are, although the dissection was somewhat protracted, by the dipping down of the tumor into the supra-spinal fossa of the clavicle, and confinement by fascia. She says she felt no pain, and did not evince any perception of the puncture of the needle in dressing the wound—a sensation which usually calls forth complaint, as it is commonly unexpected.

"From the results I have seen at the Massachusetts General Hospital and in my own practice, I am led to expect the following advantages from its exhibition:

"First: Uniformity of its effects, unlike any mode of intoxication by stimulants in the stomach or respiration of nitrous-oxide gas. My three patients were as unlike in age, temperament, and habits as could well be imagined, yet all exhibited the same appearance of passive endurance.

"Second: There was no instinctive or voluntary resistance, which is so embarrassing to an operator. This, next to its power of preventing the perception of pain, is the greatest merit claimed for it.

"Third: The securing the patient from the severity of the great shock which a capital operation inflicts on the sufferer. It was quite noticeable, in all the patients I have seen, that there was none of that extreme depression which sometimes follows a severely painful impression on the nervous system.

"Fourth: Its effects pass off rapidly, and, as far as I know, no bad results follow.

"Fifth: It can be repeated several times during the operation, except the mouth or jaws are the parts to be operated on. The repetition of the dose is always sought by the patients with avidity.

"Sixth: The last and most important of its effects is that it either wholly annuls pain or destroys the consciousness of it, so that it is not remembered; and thus the sentiment of fear is wholly obliterated. The patient appears to have been dreaming, and in the second case said that 'he was in a distinct existence' (i. e., distinct from his former experience), thus illustrating the theory of double consciousness.

"These are recommendations enough to ensure it a fair trial among the humane and enlightened members of our profession.
.   .   .

"Dr. Morton and Dr. Jackson, at least, are entitled to the hearty thanks of the profession for their discovery, and the liberal manner in which they have offered it to all the subjects of surgical operations, both in and out of the hospital.   .   .

"These gentlemen are entitled to the credit of having made it, for the first time, perfectly available to the suffering, and submitted it to the test of those competent to decide on its merits, without being content to rest its pretensions on non-professional credulity or popular notoriety.

"SALEM, November 26, 1846.   "A. L. PIERSON."

It is also gratifying for me to be able to submit the following subjoined extract from the subject from the address of the Hon. Edward Everett, LL.D., President of Harvard University, at the opening of the new Medical College of Boston, November 6, 1846:

"I am not sure that since these remarks were delivered a discovery has not been announced which fully realizes the prediction of the text: I allude to the discovery of a method of producing a state of temporary insensibility to pain by the inhalation of a prepared vapor. A full account of this discovery is given in a paper by Dr. Henry J. Bigelow in the Boston Medical and Surgical Journal for November 18, 1846. . . .

"I witnessed a very successful instance of the application of the prepared vapor on the eighteenth of November, and was informed at that time by Dr. Morton that he had employed it in several hundred cases of dentistry. It has also been made use of with entire success at the Massachusetts General Hospital, and elsewhere in Boston, in capital operations of surgery. The few cases of failure may perhaps be ascribed to irregularities in the process of inhalation, or to peculiarities of temperament or constitution on the part of the patient.

"I understand that great confidence is placed in this discovery by the most distinguished members of the medical profession of this vicinity; and that they are disposed to regard it as an effectual method of inducing complete insensibility under the most cruel operations, by means easily applied, entirely controllable, and productive of no subsequent bad consequences. It seems not easy to overrate the importance of such a discovery."

I could multiply certificates and give you accounts of cases almost without number, keeping, as I do, a record of them at my office. But it will be unnecessary, for, from the foregoing, I think you will readily conclude that the extraordinary discovery of preventing pain in dental and other surgical operations has at last been made, and the use of it secured for the benefit of the human family. It is now a matter of history that the patient can submit not only to dental operations, but the reduction of dislocations, removal of tumors, and the severest amputations, without fear, consciousness, or suffering; and that the dentist and surgeon can each perform the most arduous duty of his profession with a certainty, a facility, and satisfaction hitherto unknown. In fact, the patient escapes the great shocks to the nervous system which are incident to all other modes practiced in surgery.

The following is a circular, which I have found it necessary to issue, as a caution both to patients and those who have attempted, or may endeavour, to infringe on my legal rights.

"*Important Information for the Public at Large.—General Circular.*—The peculiar circumstances of the case requiring that the subjoined information should be fully made known at this time, the same is now published.

"*Public Caution!* Whereas letters patent of the United States have been duly granted for the new and valuable invention, whereby dental and other surgical operations may now be performed without pain or suffering, or any injurious results to the patient; and certain unprincipled persons have, in face of law and justice, without any license, instructions, or authority from me whatever, used my name and attempted to pirate said invention, endangering, from their want of skill and knowledge upon the subject, the lives of those whom they have persuaded to undergo their unwarrantable experiments:

"And whereas every person endeavoring, without such license, instructions, and authority from me, to use my name or pirate said invention, either by stealth or otherwise, and every person submitting to dental or other surgical operations under such attempts and pretenders; or directly or indirectly aiding or abetting in any infringements of my rights secured by said letters patent, thereby renders himself liable in his person and property to the certain inconvenience and expense of prosecutions and damages at law.

"Now, therefore, on the score of humanity, as well as for the protection of my own rights, I do hereby give this public notice, and warn all persons against making my apparatus or using my said invention or name, without my free license, instructions, and authority, or in any manner lending themselves to the unprincipled and illegal employment of the same, as it is alike my duty and determination to hold every such offender strictly accountable, in his person and estate, for all damages under the laws, and for every violation of my letters patent or infringement upon my property and interest in said invention. At the same time I would publicly announce that I am now prepared to dispose of licenses, or make arrangements so that every respectable dentist and surgeon, or other suitable person, can obtain for his patients the benefit of or secure himself full instructions and authority to use said invention, upon just and reasonable terms; upon such terms, indeed, as must prove altogether less expensive to the purchaser than it will probably cost him in time and money to undertake to defend himself in the courts for infringements on my rights in the premises, to say nothing of the dishonesty, dishonor, or disgrace which invariably attaches itself to every individual, who attempts to appropriate to himself, in secret or otherwise, that which is not only *not his own*, but which belongs 'in *law, equity, and in fact*,' solely to *another*, his neighbor, or fellow-citizen.

"Aware that this invention is an extraordinary one, and of very great importance, conferring, as it does, a blessing heretofore unheard of upon the human race, inasmuch as, by means of it, the afflicted or suffering may now submit, without pain or injurious results, to the severest dental and other surgical operations necessary for the preservation of health and life, I am particularly desirous that my invention should not be abused, entrusted to ignorant or improper hands, or applied to nefarious purposes.

"I therefore recommend that no individual should subject himself to the use of it under any operator unless the patient learn beforehand that such operator is really and duly licensed, instructed, and authorized to administer the same; which can be ascertained in every case by merely requesting such operator to exhibit his license; and which license every one empowered to employ my apparatus and invention possesses in *writing*, duly attested, under my own hand and seal.

"For terms and further particulars apply to 19, Tremont Row.
"W. T. G. MORTON."

BOSTON, November 26, 1846.

It was deemed advisable to proceed in a quiet way with the invention at first, in order, among other reasons, that letters patent for the discovery might be properly secured in foreign nations. But I am now fully prepared to dispose of licenses to use my invention and apparatus, in any part of the country, upon the following general terms:

TERMS FOR DENTISTS

In cities over 150,000 inhabitants,	....	$200 for seven years
" " " 50,000 and less than 150,000,	 150	" " "
" " " 40,000 " " " 50,000,	 100	" " "
" " " 30,000 " " " 40,000,	 87	" " "
" " " 20,000 " " " 30,000,	 75	" " "
" " " 10,000 " " " 20,000,	 62	" " "
" " " 5,000 " " " 10,000,	 50	" " "
" " under 5,000	 37	" " "

Surgeon's license one-half of the foregoing prices for, or those who prefer it, can have it according to the prices upon this page. Twenty-five per cent. on all charges made for performing operations wherein the discovery is used: fifteen dollars to be paid down, which will include apparatus, a bottle of the preparation, instructions, etc. The party licensed to keep a correct account of all operations, the names of the parties operated upon, and to forward the same to me; also to pay me as often as once in three months.

Apparatus, instructions, and licenses forwarded to any part of the country upon receipt of the money, which may be either forwarded to me or any person in this city, who can pay it over upon receipt of the foregoing.

Infraction of agreement to be a forfeiture of the license, at the option of the licenser.

Satisfactory security for payment of license fees to be given.

The subscriber is prepared to give and receive propositions for agencies to dispose of rights.

W. T. G. MORTON.

Establishment of Drs. N. C. Keep and W. T. G. Morton,
No. 19, Tremont Row, and 74, Boylston Street, Boston, Mass.

N. B.—As I do not wish to derive remuneration from persons in destitute circumstances, and only look for proper compensation from those able to make it, it is proper for me to add that I have given the gratuitous use of the improvement for the benefit of the poor and afflicted at the Massachusetts General Hospital, and intend to give the advantage of it to every charitable hospital for the service of the indigent and sick.

Note.—All letters addressed to me must be prepaid to ensure their being taken from the office.

(*Hospital Correspondence.*)

It has already been stated in the public prints that Dr. Morton has given the right to use the great discovery, whereby pain is prevented in surgical operations, to the public hospital. The following correspondence upon the subject, between that gentleman and the governor of the Massachusetts General Hospital, is highly creditable to all parties:

To the President and Trustees of the Massachusetts General Hospital,

GENTLEMEN: Most, if not all, of you may be aware that I have both privately and publicly declared that it is not my intention or desire to receive from benevolent infirmaries, nor from persons in destitute circumstances, any compensation for the employment of the new discovery whereby pain may be prevented or alleviated in surgical operations.

And, long convinced of the excellence of the charitable establishment over which you preside, and of its great and increasing importance in the service of humanity, I beg leave respectfully to inform you that I shall be happy to present to the Massachusetts General Hospital, if it be agreeable for the President and the Trustees to accept the same, the fullest right, under the letters patent granted me by the Government of the United States, to use the discovery above mentioned for the benefit of indigent patients—the sick or suffering poor, and other persons at the institution.

With very great respect,

I am, Gentlemen,

Your most ob't ser't,

W. T. G. MORTON.

No. 19, *Tremont Street*, Boston, December 14, 1846

23

BOSTON, December 21, 1846.

Dr. W. T. G. Morton,

SIR: At a meeting of the Trustees of the Massachusetts General Hospital, held yesterday, your letter of the fourteenth inst., presenting to the hospital the right to use your "discovery for the prevention or alleviation of pain in surgical operations," was laid before the board.

I am directed, by a vote of the Trustees, to inform you that they accept your polite offer, and to express to you their thanks for your valuable gift, and their sense of the importance of the right to use your discovery, in the institution under their control.

Your ob't ser't,

MARCUS MORTON, JR.,
Secretary Mass. General Hospital.

(*From the Boston Medical and Surgical Journal.*)

Operations without Pain.—In the leading article of this day's Journal, by Dr. H. J. Bigelow, the profession will notice that an impression exists here in Boston that a remarkable discovery has been made. Unlike the farce and trickery of mesmerism, this is based upon scientific principles, and is solely in the hands of gentlemen of high professional attainments, who make no secret of the matter or manner. To prevent it from being abused and falling into the power of low, evil-minded, irresponsible persons, we are informed that the discoverer has secured a patent, and that means were taken to have the same security in Europe even before publicity was given to it here. Without further remarks, we cheerfully publish all that has been given to us on the subject, and wait with impatience for the decision of the profession in regard to its real value.

(*From the Boston Medical and Surgical Journal.*)

The attention of the medical public has been recently fixed upon a discovery said to be capable of preventing the severe suffering of patients undergoing surgical operations. The mere announcement of such an improvement cannot fail to interest every man of common humanity, while to the operating surgeon it opens the prospect of a most gratifying triumph of his art. Every fact, well attested, is of interest in relating the history of this new expedient to relieve human suffering. The following cases having occurred in this city, and being the first operated upon under the influence of the new process, may, perhaps, be regarded of sufficient importance to deserve record.

On the twentieth ultimo, Dr. Horace Kimball, an accomplished dentist of this city, put into my hands a recent number of the Boston Medical and Surgical Journal containing an article from the pen of Dr. Bigelow on this subject. There was no room to doubt the respectability of the source from which the information was derived, and accordingly I made arrangements with Dr. Kimball to have the inhalation administered to a young lady who was to be operated on for the removal of a scirrhous tumor under the right mamma on the twenty-first ult. Owing, however, to his inability to avail himself of the use of the only apparatus for its administration at that time in New York, the lady, after having had her hopes raised, was obliged to submit to the operation without being able to participate in the benefits of the new discovery. It was successfully performed, and she has since entirely recovered.

On the fourth inst. Dr. Kimball, having become the agent of the discoverers in this city, and having provided himself with the necessary apparatus, afforded me an opportunity of making a trial of the inhalation at my office, No. 11 Carroll Place, in the presence of several professional gentlemen and medical students, in the case of a young lady from Brooklyn. The case was one of enlarged tonsils. The patient, after respiring the ethereal vapor for a few minutes, became apparently insensible, breathed heavily, had the pupils dilated and the pulse slightly accelerated, when, on attempting to open her mouth, I found the jaw closed spasmodically. This obstacle was in a minute or two overcome, and her mouth was opened, when a pleasant smile passed over her countenance. The left tonsil was excised, apparently without her notice. I laid down the instruments, intending to have the inhalation repeated before the removal of the second tonsil, but at the suggestion of Dr. Kimball that she was still under the influence of her original dose, I proceeded to the removal of the second tumor. She soon afterwards opened her eyes and smiled with returning consciousness. She declared that she had no knowledge whatever of the first operation, but remembered smiling at having her mouth "so nicely opened."

The operation in the first instance was thus perfectly successful, and in the second was partially so, and but for the time lost, quite unnecessarily, both the tonsils might have been removed during the period of her entire unconsciousness.

Another operation was performed on a boy who had been my patient in 1840, with a double hare-lip, complicated with a terrible fissure of the palate. In this case, which had been perfectly successful, the end of the nose was drawn down a little to the lip, and he had been desirous himself of trying the effect of an incision at the upper part of the lip, with the view of liberating it, and giving a better expression to these features.

He inhaled the vapor for two or three minutes and became entirely insensible. The knife, a small straight bistoury, was passed just under the ala nasi of the left side, through the upper lip, and brought out at the corresponding point at the other side, completely separating the lip from the nose, without apparently occasioning the least sensation.

It was several minutes before he recovered consciousness. On being interrogated, he declared that he was not sensible of being hurt, did not know when he was cut, and felt no pain. His appearance and expression of countenance corroborated entirely his declarations and left the fullest impression on the minds of all present of the perfect insensibility occasioned by the ethereal inhalation. As I had repeatedly inhaled the vapor of sulphuric ether as long ago as the year 1822, and as I had seen it repeatedly inhaled by others, I was desirous of trying on myself the effects of this agent, in order to satisfy myself whether I could discover any difference in its apparent effects from those of the vapor of ether.

I was thrown into a state of perfect insensibility, unaccompanied with the least pain or inconvenience, but, on the contrary, I felt, on recovering, as if I had been in a beatific vision. No headache or unpleasant sensation of any kind followed the inhalation, and I recognized precisely the sensations which I had formerly experienced from the effects of ether.

On the eighth of this month I was present, by the polite invitation of my distinguished friend, Dr. Mott, at an operation which he performed on a lady for the removal of a cluster of tumefied glands from the right axilla. After inhaling the vapor for a sufficient time to induce a state of insensibility, an incision of four or five inches in length was made parallel to the edge of the pectoralis major, and after some progress had been made in the operation, the patient was asked by Dr. Kimball how she felt. She replied, "Very comfortable." "Do you feel any pain?" "No." To the same question repeated after a short interval a similar reply was made, and after a further lapse of time, the patient partially arousing, inquired, "Have they begun the cutting?"—thus manifesting her total unconsciousness of what she had passed through up to that period. Afterwards her sense of pain appeared for some time considerably blunted, but she became gradually more and more conscious of what was done, until at last her sense of suffering seemed to be entirely natural.

In this operation, which from its position and the implication of important parts was necessarily protracted, the influence of the narcotic agent was not sufficiently permanent to prevent entirely the sense of pain; yet it was evident, both to the accomplished operator and to all spectators, as well as to the patient herself, that her sufferings were in part averted entirely, while the rest was entirely mitigated.

On the tenth inst. I accompanied a young lady to Dr. Kimball's who had a second bicuspid tooth on the left side of the upper jaw removed, under the influence of the ethereal inhalation. In this case the patient raised her hand to her mouth as if to prevent the process, but when it was accomplished, she manifested a total ignorance, not only of the pain, but of all knowledge of the operation. She declared that she knew nothing about it, and remempered only a delicious dream or vision.

No evil consequences followed in this or either of the preceding cases, and the effect of what I have seen has been on my own mind a firm conviction that the discovery of Drs. Morton and Jackson has added to the resources of the surgical art one of the most invaluable benefits of which modern times can boast. It is certainly a great boon to suffering humanity, and they deserve the unmingled gratitude of mankind. In amputations and all other surgical operations which can be performed at once with rapidity and safety this discovery furnishes a perfect immunity from pain; and in those more protracted, a great alleviation may be obtained; while that most excruciating operation, the extraction of teeth, which everybody has more or less frequently to endure, is no longer an object of dread, since, by the means of the inhalation, the patient is rendered absolutely and entirely unconscious of pain.

In reference to the *rationale* of the process, it will immediately occur to the practical surgeon that in cases of cerebral injuries where coma exists, and where operations for cutting the scalp and removing bone by trephine and saw are habitually performed without consciousness on the part of the patient, a case is presented parallel to that of insensibility from inhaling the vapor of ether. The ether is absorbed with the oxygen of the atmosphere during inspiration. Is it not natural that it should excite a certain degree of dilation of the vessels of the brain, slight and evanescent certainly, but still producing a temporary pressure on the cerebral substance, thus furnishing at once an analogy with the coma of compression, and an explanation of this most singular and interesting phenomenon of insensibility to the knife induced at will, and with an impunity as real as it is surprising?

In furnishing this record of the first cases of surgical operation performed in New York under the influence of the Boston discovery, I feel that I am contributing my humble share to the mass of testimony which my fellow-men have a right to demand on an occasion which appeals to the love of the human nature as well as to the pride and pleasure of a profession in itself most honorable, and which receives from this discovery a happy addition to its glorious and humane triumphs.

A. L. Cox.

No. 11 *Carroll Place, N. Y.*, December 18, 1846.

(*Boston Surgical Journal.*)

ARE INVENTIONS IN SURGERY AND IN CHEMISTRY LEGITIMATE SUBJECTS FOR PATENTS?

By a Correspondent who has no Property in Patent Rights.

Several correspondents of the Boston Medical and Surgical Journal, in their remarks concerning the patent granted by the general government, to Drs. Morton and Jackson, for their new and important discovery by which pain may be prevented or alleviated in surgical operations, seem to proceed upon the ground that the patent has been issued for a secret process. This is a mistake on their part; and, if they will reflect for a moment, or merely possess themselves of the ordinary law-knowledge upon the subject, they will perceive the error into which they have so inadvertently fallen.

No patent is or can be granted for a secret process. The very meaning of the word "patent" is "open," public, not private or secret; and the very first pre-requisite of a patent is that the inventor shall furnish the government with a written description of his discovery, so that any one skilled in the art or science to which it appertains may know how to make and use the same; and so, at the expiration of the term during which the law secures the exclusive right of the discovery under a patent to the inventor the public at large may be at full liberty to make and use such discovery. These are the words of the law: "But before any inventor shall receive a patent for any such new invention or discovery, he shall deliver a written description of his invention or discovery, and of the manner and process of making, constructing, using, and compounding the same, in such full, clear, and exact terms, avoiding unnecessary prolixity, as to enable any person skilled in the art or science to which it appertains, or with which it is most nearly connected, to make, construct, compound, and use the same."

The authority to grant patents is established by the Constitution of the United States, which declares that "Congress shall have power to promote the progress of science and useful arts, by securing for limited times to authors and inventors the exclusive right to their respective writings and discoveries."

The object of the framers of this clause in the Constitution was undoubtedly to sharpen the wit and ingenuity of the people, to stimulate citizens of every class in their researches and labors—to encourage them, by the prospect of an adequate remuneration, under an exclusive right for a term of years, to delve into secret recesses of nature and art, and discover, reduce to practice, and bring out to public view and use, every improvement or invention to be found, devised or thought of, for the comfort, preservation, health, or happiness of the race.

Nearly, if not all, great inventions have been patented; and were it not for the Constitution and the laws, and the decisions of the tribunals, in this behalf, very few modes, great improvements, or processes would be made—or if made at all, be promulgated to the community at large. They would be wrought in private—practised and kept in secret. * * * * * * * * * * *

1850

ON THE PHYSIOLOGICAL EFFECTS OF SULPHURIC ETHER, AND ITS SUPERIORITY TO CHLOROFORM

By WILLIAM T. G. MORTON, M.D.

BOSTON:

Printed by David Clapp, 184 Washington Street.

Medical and Surgical Journal Office.

1850.

PREFACE

As I am continually called upon, and addressed by letter, by persons unacquainted with the properties of ether, asking information concerning its safety and adaptation to their individual cases, and also why I will never, under any circumstances, willingly give chloroform, I have thought it best to draw up the following account in answer to such inquiries.

There is no work of small compass and of good authority to which I could refer the majority of popular readers for satisfactory information on these questions; and in order that I might answer, once for all, such interrogatories, I have reduced my experience of four years' practice in etherization to a convenient form in the present work.

I have compared it with the experience of the most eminent men in America and Europe, whose names will be sufficient guarantee that what is here advanced may be depended on as the present state of knowledge on these interesting subjects.

Though this is intended as a general answer to frequently repeated questions, I do not expect nor intend that it shall be thrust forward as a universal reply; I shall be, as usual, happy to give or receive any information which may tend to improve or to extend the practice of etherization.

19 *Tremont Row, Boston,*
  September, 1850.

SULPHURIC ETHER AND CHLOROFORM

It is now nearly four years since the first demonstration, by myself, that the inhalation of sulphuric ether possessed the remarkable property of annihilating pain during dental and surgical operations, and that this inhalation was attended with no risk to life. The use of this agent may now be fairly considered as an essential preliminary in all operations or conditions of the system in which pain forms an important element. After the first experiment on myself in the middle of September, 1846, I waited impatiently for some one on whom I could make a more extended trial. Towards evening a man, residing in Boston, whose certificate I have, came in, suffering great pain, and wishing to have a tooth extracted. He was afraid of the operation, and asked if he could be mesmerized. I told him I had something better, and saturating my handkerchief gave it to him to inhale. He became unconscious almost immediately. It was dark, and Dr. Hayden held the lamp, while I extracted a firmly-rooted bicuspid tooth. There was not much alteration in the pulse and no relaxation of the muscles. He recovered in a minute, and knew nothing of what had been done to him. This was on the 30th of September, 1846. This I consider to be the first demonstration of this new fact in science. As soon as the man whose tooth I had extracted left my office, I consulted Dr. Hayden as to the best mode of bringing out my discovery. We agreed it was best to announce it to the surgeons of the hospital; but as some time would elapse before an operation, I thought it best to procure some assurance which would induce my patients to take it. I therefore called upon the man who had taken it, and found him perfectly well. *I then called on Dr. Warren, who promised me an early opportunity to try the experiment.*

In the mean time I made several additional experiments in

my office with various success.   From them I select the following as examples of its varied effects.

I gave it to a lady, but it produced no other effect then drowsiness, and when breathed through the apparatus it produced suffocation. I was obliged to abandon this mode, and obtaining from Mr. Wightman a conical glass tube, I inserted a saturated sponge in the larger end, and she breathed through that.   In this way she seemed to be in an unnatural state, but continued talking and refused to have the tooth extracted.   I made her some trifling offer, to which she assented, and I drew the tooth without any indication of pain on her part, not a muscle moving.   Her pulse was at 90, her face much flushed, and after coming to, she remained a long time excessively drowsy.   From this experiment I became satisfied of what is now well proved, that consciousness will sometimes remain after sensibility to pain is removed.

I afterwards gave it to a Miss L., a lady of about twenty-five. The effect upon her was rather alarming.   She sprang up from the chair, leaped into the air, screamed, and was held down with difficulty.   When she came to she was unconscious of what had passed, but was willing to have it administered again, which I did with perfect success, extracting two molar teeth.

Agreeably to his promise, on the sixteenth of October, Dr. Warren requested my presence at the hospital to administer the ether to a patient who required an operation on the neck.   I applied the apparatus for about three minutes, when the patient sank into a state of insensibility.   An incision three inches long was made in the neck, and a difficult dissection among the important vessels and nerves of this region was commenced, without any expression of pain. Soon after he began to speak incoherently, and appeared to be in an agitated state during the remainder of the operation.   On asking him if he had felt any pain he replied in the negative; adding that he knew the operation was proceeding, and compared the knife to a blunt instrument passing roughly across his neck.

On the next day, October 17th, a tumor was removed from the arm of a female at the hospital by Dr. Hayward.   In this case I continued the application during the whole of the operation, which lasted seven minutes; there was no sign of pain, though there were occasional groans during the last stage, which she said afterwards arose from a disagreeable dream.

I continued to administer the ether in my office; the following cases, which occurred successively there, in about an hour, of which Dr. H. J. Bigelow took the following notes, are good examples of the usual results produced by the inhalation of ether, and of the feelings and expressions of patients under its influence.*

* * * * * * * * * * * * * * * * *

Having, in a previous publication,† given a sufficiently detailed account of the proper way to administer sulphuric ether, I shall not enter again into these details, but pass at once to the consideration of the comparative value of different anæsthetic agents. I need only allude to the comparatively slow progress of this discovery in America, and the immense mass of testimony from the most eminent men of Europe in favor of its almost universal applicability. To those who would be acquainted with the various attempts instigated by envy, malice, or interest, to establish priority of discovery, and deprive me of the honor of originating the idea, and the consequent experiments, I may refer to the report of the Massachusetts General Hospital, re-published with notes by R. H. Dana, Jr., to the Report of the Committee to Congress, and to the award of the Monthyon Prize by the Paris Academy of Sciences.

After the claims of ether had become fairly established, another anæsthetic agent, *chloroform*, was introduced by Professor Simpson, of Edinburgh, as a means of destroying the pains of parturition. This new agent soon created a strong impression in its favor, and has been by many substituted for ether. Its alleged advantages are its more rapid and intense action, its smaller dose, and its more agreeable taste and smell. Extensive trial, both in this country and in Europe, has, I think, proved its great dangers; several deaths have been caused by it, while there is no well-ascertained fatal result

---

* *Note.*—A summary of cases already quoted in this volume (p. 336) appears here in the original.

† On the Proper Mode of Administering Sulphuric Ether by Inhalation, Boston, 1847.

traceable to ether. For this reason many surgeons, and among others Dr. George Hayward, of this city, have denounced chloroform as dangerous, given up its use, and returned to sulphuric ether with increased confidence.

The question, then, is that of the comparative *safety* of sulphuric ether and chloroform. This question can only be settled by experience, and by comparing their effects on the system; such experience has been accumulated to a great extent, and it is the object of these pages to show that the conclusions drawn from it prove the great superiority of sulphuric ether to other anæsthetic agents. My own experience in the application of the former, which has been considerable, and probably unsurpassed by any extent in freedom from accidents, will supply abundant material for its full consideration. For the effects of chloroform I shall depend on the published accounts of the best authorities.

To make a just comparison it will be necessary to say a few words on the physiological and pathological effects of ether and chloroform.

Though the general effects of ethereal inhalation are similar in nearly all cases, yet certain idiosyncrasies, or certain conditions of the system, modify the phenomena, as they do of all other medicinal agents. Instead of quiet and sleep, you often see excitement, agitations, or even slight delirium. In some cases small doses will etherize, in others it requires a large dose to produce unconsciousness. Sometimes, while pain is annihilated, the intellect and the senses are unaffected; the circulation, respiration, muscular action, secretions, and consequent phenomena are variously modified. Besides idiosyncrasy, no doubt many of these anomalous or discordant phenomena are owing to improper quality or quantity of the ether, or some defect in the manner of administration. It is of the first consequence that the ether should be *pure* and highly concentrated. As a general rule, about two ounces * * * * * * should be used to begin with, this being sufficient for full etherization in most cases; and it is better to induce this rapidly by a large dose, than gradually by a succession of small ones. To secure a due proportion of atmospheric air to the lungs, a simple bell-shaped sponge is preferable to complex inhalers. Early experiments were attended with disagreeable results, from the supposition that it was necessary to inhale ethereal vapor alone, instead of atmospheric air charged with this vapor. The effects of ether are usually produced in from three to five minutes. On removing the sponge and allowing the introduction of pure air, recovery takes place in about the same time. That there is no danger in prolonging the state of etherization for a considerable period the records of midwifery fully prove. After recovery from this state the brain and nervous system are rarely inconvenienced by the excitement if the ether has been pure; even headache is uncommon, and nausea or vomiting, delirium, or convulsions are quite rare, unless it is inhaled soon after eating.

The symptoms indicate two distinct stages of etherization, or rather the complete and the incomplete. As the latter is all that is required for the dentist's operations, in which no important nerves or vessels are wounded, it is important to be able to recognize it. After the cessation of the slight cough which leads the patient to reject the sponge, the respiration becomes more rapid and audible; the pulse is natural or slightly accelerated; the pupils are unaffected; the muscular apparatus is somewhat excited, and the movements more or less disordered; the inspirations become deeper, till at last insensibility comes on. In this stage we meet with the most curious affection of the intellectual and sensitive functions, in which sensation is destroyed while the intellect is untouched, the pain perceived but not recollected, or the will active and the power of motion lost. These are now known to be cases of incomplete etherization. The completed stage is characterized by a perfect relaxation of the muscular system; the pulse becomes slow; the pupils often dilated; the respiration often snoring. The sign to suspend the application is the diminished force and frequency of the pulse, and even before this, the muscular relaxation.

Ether undoubtedly acts in the first place as a stimulant and finally as a narcotic. Magendie and Orfila have offered strong reasons for believing that the anæsthetic state is analogous to intoxication from alcohol. Both produce the same excitement and subsequent insensibility; both act principally on the nervous system through the medium of the circulation; both may be detected in the blood by undoubted tests. It may, then, be called an intoxication, quickly produced, and as quickly disappearing.

Much has been written by physiologists on the order in which the various parts of the nervous system are affected; and there seems to be some discrepancy of opinion at the present time. M. Flourens (in a memoir before the French Academy, in February, 1847) maintained that the action of ether on the nervous centres is in the following order: the *cerebral lobes* first are affected—in other words, the seat of the intellect; then the *cerebellum*, when *equilibrium* of motion is lost; then the *spinal marrow*, with loss of sensation and afterwards of motion; finally (if the experiment be carried to this extent), the *medulla oblongata*, cessation of respiration, and death.

My own experience leads me to adopt very nearly the conclusions of Dr. Brown, that the various parts of the nervous system are affected, in cases of complete and normal etherization, in the following order: The cerebellum first, then the cephalic ganglia, the true spinal marrow, the ganglia of special sense and the cerebro-spinal system, and lastly the cerebrum proper; though it is not probable that the cerebrum is ever fully etherized, from the occurrence of dreams; total insensibility of the cerebrum would be nearly equivalent to death or complete etherization of the medulla oblongata.

It has been a question whether ether produced its effects through the nervous or vascular systems. The first (*stimulant*) effect of ether is without question due to the conveyance of its action by the par vagum of the medulla oblongata, causing increased respiratory movements and quickened pulse; but, as far as experiments yet prove, the *narcotic* effects of ether are produced through the blood vessels. This is easily understood when we consider the great extent of the internal pulmonary surface, its vascular network, and the ease with which air is taken up; once introduced into the pulmonary blood it would be very soon sent by the heart to the cerebral organs, and produce speedy narcotism. Unlike alcohol, ether taken into the stomach does not produce its specific effects. This has been proved by the experiments of Flourens; and this we should expect from the less extent and absorbing power of the gastric surface. Whether the ingestion of *ether vapor* into the stomach would be equally ineffectual has not been proved; we know that the injection of the vapor into the rectum is speedily followed by insensibility. (See Comptes Rendus, Avril, 1847, p. 605.)

When we consider the immense number of cases in which ether has been administered, and the exceedingly few and trifling accidents consequent on its use, we may fairly say that its inhalation is unattended with danger. I have administered it in thousands of cases without a single alarming result, to persons of every age, temperament, and condition of bodily health. The experience of Dr. George Hayward, of this city, is to the same effect. He says (Boston Medical and Surgical Journal, April 10, 1850): "I have administered it to persons of all ages, of every variety of constitution, and in almost every state of the system, and I have never known in a single instance a fatal or alarming result. I have given it to infants of seven weeks old and to individuals of seventy-five years with entire success. There is reason to doubt whether death has in a single instance been produced by it when it has been properly administered."

Its advantages as an anæsthetic agent are its perfect safety, the ease with which it is administered, and the absence of ill consequences. Nausea, vomiting, and irritation of the air-passages rarely occur unless the ether be impure or be improperly administered; excessive narcotism may be remedied by cold water externally and stimulants internally, which will soon excite the respiration to free the lungs from the ethereal vapor. The pungent and disagreeable odor of ether is a trifling objection compared with its advantages over chloroform in point of safety. I may again quote Dr. Hayward in this connection, who says: "I should give it the preference over every other article with which I am acquainted that is used for the purpose of producing insensibility."

I leave it to surgeons and physicians to speak the praises of ether in the various surgical, medical, and obstetrical operations in which it is now universally used, whenever the relief of pain is an object of importance; I shall only allude further to a few results of my own experience in dentistry, which may not be uninteresting to the profession. I will here introduce a table showing these results for a short period of my practice, which will enable me to show the nature of the operations, the quantity of ether required, the time for producing and the duration of unconsciousness, with the general effects on patients of different ages and temperaments. [In the original a table is here given which is summarized by the author in the following paragraph.]

From these cases, forty-four in number, we see that both sexes are affected in the same manner; that ether may be given at all ages; that for ordinary operations the quantity required varies from one half to two ounces; that insensibility is produced in from one to four minutes; that recovery takes place in less time, proportioned to the severity of the operation; that it is well borne by every variety of temperament; that the pulse, when affected at all, is generally slightly quickened, rarely slower than natural; and that, for the most part, those under its influence remain perfectly quiet and undisturbed by nausea or vomiting.

Chloroform, or the perchloride of formyle, which was at first extensively employed as a substitute for ether, till numerous fatal accidents led to its more limited use, was first brought into notice as an anæsthetic agent by Dr. Simpson, of Edinburgh, who is entitled to the greatest praise for his scientific endeavors to improve our knowledge of anæsthetic agents. He says it possesses over sulphuric ether the following advantages: it is more powerful, 120 drops being sufficient to produce insensibility; he has seen it produced "by six or seven inspirations of thirty drops of the liquid"; its action is more rapid and complete, and generally more persistent; it is more agreeable to the taste and smell. He might have added, if experiments then had allowed, that it is also *very much more dangerous*, and its very danger consists in its so-called advantages. We have reason to believe that the chloroform used by Dr. Simpson is a purer and superior article to that commonly used here; this may account for the favor with which he views it. To counterbalance its agreeable taste and odor, chloroform is of an acrid, caustic nature, and is apt to excoriate the skin. According to Dr. Hayward, its administration is generally followed by headache and vomiting, which continue for hours, with restlessness and want of sleep. Several cases came to his notice where it was taken in small quantity for dental operations, in which the brain and nervous system were affected to an alarming extent. Convulsions have frequently attended its use, as detailed by Dr. J. C. Warren (On Chloroform, Boston, 1848).

The physiological effects of chloroform are of the same nature as those of ether, only greater in degree, more rapidly produced, less to be calculated on, and therefore more dangerous. That the partizans of chloroform were too hasty in maintaining that it always produces a calm sleep, without agitation or excitement (which was one of its alleged advantages), we may quote the distinguished surgeon Roux, who (Comptes Rendus, December, 1847) gives details of operations under its influence performed by himself, in which the involuntary movements (in a state of complete insensibility) were so violent that they were with difficulty managed; in another case the patient's recovery was attended with the same excitement, disordered intelligence, and loquacity which have been set down as peculiar to ethereal inhalation.

Velpeau, though allowing the rapidity and certainty of its action, says that the duration of the insensibility is such as to render it dangerous in unskilful hands. A woman, who had inhaled it for only two minutes, remained for eighteen minutes without giving the least sign of sensibility. Its strength is such that an animal dies under its influence in two minutes, that would require the influence of *ether* for twelve minutes. As a general rule, *a drachm of chloroform* is considered equal to an *ounce of ether*. The very fact of its quick and certain action renders it formidable if prolonged carelessly; it is impossible to know exactly when to stop, and the fatal blow may be given before we are aware of the danger.

M. Dumas, the eminent chemist, considering the extreme power of this substance (see authority last quoted) and its liability to abuse, remarked that chloroform ought to be classed among the *poisons* whose sale is forbidden *by law* unless on the prescription of a physician, and recommended the police to attend to the subject.

These, and many other authorities which might be quoted, sufficiently attest the great danger of chloroform; and, unfortunately, there are many cases of *death* which can only be attributed to this powerful agent, though administered with care to healthy persons, in very small quantities, and by cautious practitioners. Even the death of a *single* individual should open the eyes of its advocates to the dangers of its use; but when upwards of *twenty* fatal cases can be clearly traced to the action of chloroform, it seems unjustifiable practice to submit a patient to its dangers, especially when we have in sulphuric ether an agent equally *effectual* and perfectly *safe*.

Malgaigne, in his Report to the French Academy, says that chloroform possesses a poisonous action peculiar to itself, which action, by being too much prolonged, may cause instant death; we can never be certain of being able to control it within the bounds which produce mere *insensibility*, when the passage from this to *death* is so sudden and so near.

Dr. Hayward, alluding to the undoubted fatal cases from the use of chloroform, says: "I know not how a conscientious man, knowing this fact, can willingly take the responsibility and expose his patient to this fearful result."

To show the danger of chloroform, its power, suddenness of action, symptoms, and morbid appearances, the table in Dr. Warren's work (above quoted) containing ten fatal cases may be consulted with advantage. Of these ten cases, three were for operation connected with dentistry, viz., extraction of stumps, toothache, etc.; two had never used any anæsthetic agent before; while the third had used chloroform frequently without bad effects, yet she died instantly at last while under its influence—showing that previous use with impunity is no security against a final fatal result. The time of inhalation in most of the cases was about *one* minute, from a sponge, handkerchief, or apparatus; the quantity varied from twenty drops to half an ounce; death ensued in two cases instantly, in the other in from one to ten minutes—showing the fatal issue cannot depend on the quantity inhaled nor on the manner or duration of the inhalation, but on an instantaneous poisoning of the nervous centres. The symptoms in most of the cases were paleness of the face, discoloration of the lips, disordered respiration, extremely feeble pulse with relaxation of the limbs, preceded in some by rigidity or slight convulsions; in two cases, in which the heart and liver were enlarged, the face is described as of a livid hue. The morbid appearances varied according to the quantity used and the duration of its influence in most of the cases, though in some the poisonous action was so quick that the appearances could not be attributed to the influence on the blood; thus, congestion of the brain, heart, and lungs was found in some who had inhaled but a small quantity for a short period; while in others, under the opposite conditions, these organs were natural. A remarkable fluidity of the blood was a constant phenomenon. It is very evident that the cause of death is not asphyxia, but sudden poisoning of the nervous system or an instantaneous paralysis of the heart's action.

In the same journal (for September 30, 1849) may be found an interesting account, by M. Robert, of the Hospital Beaujon, Paris, of four cases in which the administration of chloroform was followed by extreme agitation, in two of the cases ending fatally, as he believed, from pulmonary emphysema produced by this excitement.

Chloroform, injected into the arteries, causes in the muscles supplied by such vessels an increased amount of contractility, which may justly be called a partial and uninterrupted *tetanus;* and this it does by a special action on the muscle fibre, and not by any direct action on the blood or on the nerves. Experiments going to prove this may be found in the Comptes Rendus for April, 1849.

As to the relative safety of sulphuric ether and chloroform we may justly conclude, from the numerous data now existing in the annals of medicine and surgery:

1. That there is an immense preponderance of testimony in favor of sulphuric ether, both during and after its application.

2. While there is but one case, and that not well ascertained, in which ether has been accused of producing fatal results, there are not

less than twenty, and probably many more, in which the fatal result is clearly traceable to chloroform.

3. Chloroform has caused death in the young and the old, the strong and the weak, the healthy and the diseased; and cannot be said to be safe in any condition of the system.

4. Chloroform is much stronger and more prompt in its action than ether, and less volatile, which renders it impossible to calculate its effects, and difficult to avert danger in season to save life. The anæsthetic effects of ether gradually subside when its use is stopped; but the less volatility of chloroform often causes an aggravation of the symptoms after the inhalation has ceased.

5. Chloroform may kill directly by its action on the nervous system and the blood, or indirectly by asphyxia.

6. There are certain idiosyncrasies which cannot be known in advance in which a very minute quantity of chloroform has produced, and will again produce, death.

7. In females and children, in whom there is generally a greater susceptibility of the nervous system, the action of chloroform is quicker, more complete, and therefore more dangerous.

8. Chloroform has produced instant death from syncope, or cessation of the action of the heart; it is, therefore, extremely dangerous in cases where the heart's action is enfeebled by lingering disease, by fear, by valvular or aneurismal disease, by old age, by sudden or large losses of blood, or any other cause of weakness.

9. There is no reason for diminution of confidence in the *efficacy* and perfect *safety* of sulphuric ether; while there is an unanswerable reason why chloroform should be abandoned, as its use involves the risk of a *fatal result*, which can neither be foreseen nor prevented, from the immediate suspension of the powers of life during its administration, or consequent changes in the nervous and vascular systems.

10. That while sulphuric ether will produce *safely* all necessary results expected of anæsthetic agents, no one is justified in submitting his patient to the risk of his life by using chloroform, simply because it is more agreeable, more powerful, cheaper, or more portable.

The above conclusions will apply to chloric ether as well as to chloroform, with a due modification for the inferior strength of the former, and for the fact that as yet no fatal effects have followed its use, as far as I know. Many surgeons speak highly of it as an anæsthetic agent, and are satisfied of its safety. But as *chloric ether* is a tincture of *chloroform*, or a mixture in variable proportions of the latter with alcohol, it must obtain its anæsthetic effects from chloroform. Alcohol cannot diminish the danger in idiosyncrasy or in conditions where chloroform has proved fatal. Though its odor is more agreeable, the quantity required to produce insensibility is as great as that of sulphuric ether, and the same time is required in both; it also irritates the skin, is more apt to produce nausea and vomiting and greater disturbance of the nervous system. Says Dr. Hayward: "I cannot divest myself of the belief that chloric ether is an unsafe anæsthetic agent. . . . I fear that if it be used with the same freedom that sulphuric ether is, we shall soon have to record some very different results. . . . We cannot be by any means certain that death, when not looked for, may not follow its exhibition."

19 *Tremont Row, Boston,*
September 3, 1850.

LIST OF WRITINGS*

Remarks on the Proper Mode of Administering Sulphuric Ether by Inhalation, 12mo, Dutton and Wentworth, Boston, 1847.

On the Physiological Effects of Sulphuric Ether and its Superiority to Chloroform, octavo, D. Clapp, Boston, 1850.

Mémoire sur la de'couverte du Nouvel emploi de l'éther sulfurique. Suivi des pièces Justificatives, 60 pp., octavo, Paris, E. Bautrache, 1847.

*As they appear in the Surgeon General's Library, Index Catalogue (Washington).

1848

ACCOUNT OF A NEW ANÆSTHETIC AGENT, AS A SUBSTITUTE FOR SULPHURIC ETHER IN SURGERY AND MIDWIFERY*

By J. Y. SIMPSON, M.D., F.R.S.E.,

PROFESSOR OF MIDWIFERY IN THE UNIVERSITY OF EDINBURGH; PHYSICIAN-ACCOUCHEUR TO THE QUEEN IN SCOTLAND, ETC.

I esteem it the office of the physician, not only to restore health, but to mitigate pain and dolors.—BACON.

Communicated to the Medico-Chirurgical Society of Edinburgh at their Meeting on 10th November, 1847

NEW YORK:

REPUBLISHED BY RUSHTON, CLARKE AND CO., CHEMISTS AND DRUGGISTS, 110 BROADWAY, AND 10 ASTOR HOUSE,

1848

THIS REPRINT IS DEDICATED,

WITH RESPECT,

TO

THE MEDICAL FACULTY OF THE UNITED STATES

BY THEIR OBEDIENT SERVANTS,

RUSHTON, CLARKE AND CO.

*This article is introduced for its historic interest. It contains no epoch-making observations.—C. N. B. C.

PREFACE TO THE AMERICAN EDITION

The subscribers have been induced to republish this pamphlet in consequence of the deep interest felt, at the present time, in everything relating to the newly discovered method of relieving and preventing pain during surgical and all other painful operations.

During the short time which has elapsed since the successful experiments with ETHER were made known to the medical world, scientific and medical men have investigated the subject with great attention, and every arrival from Europe brings accounts of new series of successful experiments, proving the value of the discovery.

As DR. SIMPSON speaks so confidently of the superiority of chloroform to ether, as being more uniform in its effects, and also more safe and agreeable, and the few extracts from his pamphlet which have appeared in our medical journals and newspapers being so incomplete, we have thought the republication of it would meet with the approval of the public generally.

RUSHTON, CLARKE & CO.

(late Rushton & Co.)

NEW YORK, January 1, 1848.

INSCRIBED

TO

M. J. DUMAS

MEMBER OF THE INSTITUTE, DEAN OF THE FACULTY OF SCIENCES, PARIS, ETC.

ON CHLOROFORM

From the time at which I first saw ether-inhalation successfully practised, in January last, I have had the conviction impressed upon my mind that we would ultimately find that other therapeutic agents were capable of being introduced with equal rapidity and success into the system, through the same extensive and powerful channel of pulmonary absorption. In some observations, which I wrote and published in February last, relative to the inhalation of sulphuric ether in midwifery, I stated that, in several obstetric cases, I had used ergot of rye in this way along with ether. (See *Monthly Journal of Medical Science*, pp. 724 and 795, Case of Successful Inhalation of Opium to Arrest the Vomiting of Pregnancy.)

With various professional friends, more conversant with chemistry than I am, I have, since that time, taken opportunities of talking over the idea which I entertained of the probable existence or discovery of new therapeutic agents capable of being introduced into the system by respiration, and the possibility of producing for inhalation vaporizable or volatile preparations of some of our more active and old-established medicines; and I have had, during the summer and autumn, ethereal tinctures, etc., of several potent drugs, manufactured for me for experiment by Messrs. Duncan, Flockhart and Co., the excellent chemists and druggists of this city.

Latterly, in order to avoid, if possible, some of the inconveniences and objections pertaining to sulphuric ether (particularly its disagreeable and very persistent smell, its occasional tendency to irritation of the bronchi during its first inspirations, and the large quantity of it occasionally required to be used, more especially in protracted cases of labor), I have tried upon myself and others the inhalation of different other volatile fluids, with the hope that some one of them might be found to possess the advantages of ether, without its disadvantages. For this purpose I selected for experiment and have inhaled several chemical liquids of a more fragrant or agreeable odor, such as the chloride of hydro-carbon (or Dutch liquid), acetone, nitrate or oxide of ethyle (nitric ether), benzoin, the vapor of iodoform, etc.*

I have found, however, one infinitely more efficacious than any of the others, viz., chloroform, or the perchloride of formyle, and I am enabled to speak most confidently of its superior anæsthetic properties, having now tried it upon upwards of thirty individuals. The liquid I have used has been manufactured for me by Mr. Hunter, in the laboratory of Messrs. Duncan, Flockhart and Co.

Chloroform was first discovered and described at nearly the same time by Soubeiran (1831) and Liebig (1832); its composition was first accurately ascertained by the distinguished French chemist, Dumas, in 1835. (See the *Annales de Chimie et de Physique*, vols. xlviii, xlix, and lviii.) It has been used by some practitioners internally. Guillot prescribed it as an anti-spasmodic in asthma, exhibiting it in small doses, and diluted 100 times. (See Bouchardat's *Annuaire Therapeutique* for 1844, p. 35.) But no person, so far as I am aware, has used it by inhalation, or discovered its remarkable anæsthetic properties till the date of my own experiments.

It is a dense, limpid, colorless liquid, readily evaporating and possessing an agreeable, fragrant, fruit-like odor, and a saccharine, pleasant taste.

As an inhaled anæsthetic agent it possesses over sulphuric ether the following advantages:

1. A greatly less quantity of chloroform than of ether is requisite to produce the anæsthetic effect: usually from a hundred to a hun-

---

* In talking over with different chemists what fluids might be sufficiently volatile to be respirable, and hence deserving of being experimented upon, Mr. Waldie first named to me the Perchloride of Formyle as worthy, among others, of a trial; Dr. Gregory suggested a trial of the chloride of hydrocarbon, etc. I have been deeply indebted to Dr. Gregory and Dr. Anderson, for their kindness in furnishing me with the requisite chemical agents for these experiments: and also to my assistants, Dr. Keith and Dr. Duncan, for the great and hearty zeal with which they have constantly aided me in conducting the inquiry.

dred and twenty drops of chloroform only being sufficient; and with some patients much less. I have seen a strong person rendered completely insensible by six or seven inspirations of thirty drops of the liquid.

2. Its action is much more rapid and complete, and generally more persistent. I have almost always seen from ten to twenty full inspirations suffice. Hence the time of the surgeon is saved; and that preliminary stage of excitement, which pertains to all narcotizing agents, being curtailed, or indeed practically abolished, the patient has not the same degree of tendency to exhilaration and talking.*

3. Most of those who know from previous experience the sensations produced by ether inhalàtion, and who have subsequently

---

* In practice I have found that any such tendency, even with ether, is avoided by, first, giving the patient from the first a large and overwhelming dose of the vapor, and, secondly, by keeping him perfectly quiet and still and preventing all noise and talking around him. I have elsewhere insisted on the importance of these points. (See the numbers of the *Monthly Journal of Medical Science* for March, 1847, p. 726, and for September, p. 154.) In the paper last referred to I took occasion, when discussing the conditions requisite for insuring successful etherization, to observe: "*First*, The patient ought to be left, as far as possible, in a state of absolute quietude and freedom from mental excitement, both during the induction of etherization and during his recovery from it. All talking and all questioning should be strictly prohibited. In this way any tendency to excitement is eschewed, and the proper effect of the ether inhalation more speedily and certainly induced. And, *secondly*, with the same view, the primary stage of exhilaration should be entirely avoided, or at least reduced to the shortest possible limit, by impregnating the respired air as fully with the ether vapor as the patient can bear, and by allowing it to pass into the lungs both by the mouth and the nostrils, so as rapidly and at once to superinduce its complete and anæsthetic effect; . . . a very common but certainly a very unpardonable error being to exhibit an imperfect and exciting, instead of a perfect and nacotizing, dose of the vapor. Many of the alleged failures and misadventures are doubtless entirely attributable to the neglect of this simple rule—not the principle of etherization, but the mode of putting it in practice being altogether to blame. But, *thirdly*, whatever means or mode of etherization is adopted, the most important of the conditions required for procuring a satisfactory and successful result from its employment in surgery consists in obstinately determining to avoid the commencement of the operation itself, and never venturing to apply the knife *until* the patient is under the full influence of the ether vapor, *and thoroughly and indubitably soporized by it.*" In fulfilling all these indications the employment of chloroform evidently offers great and decided advantages, in facility and efficiency, over the employment of ether.

breathed the chloroform, have strongly declared the inhalation and influence of chloroform to be far more agreeable and pleasant than those of ether.

4. I believe that, considering the small quantity requisite, as compared with ether, the use of chloroform will be less expensive than that of ether; more especially as there is every prospect that the means of forming it may be simplified and cheapened.

5. Its perfume is not unpleasant, but the reverse; and the odor of it does not remain for any length of time obstinately attached to the clothes of the attendant, or exhaling in a disagreeable form from the lungs of the patient, as so generally happens with sulphuric ether.

6. Being required in much less quantity, it is much more portable and transmissible than sulphuric ether.

7. No special kind of inhaler or instrument is necessary for its exhibition. A little of the liquid diffused upon the interior of a hollow-shaped sponge, or a pocket handkerchief, or a piece of linen or paper, and held over the mouth and nostrils, so as to be fully inhaled, generally suffices in about a minute or two to produce the desired effect.*

I have not yet had an opportunity of using chloroform in any capital surgical operation, but have exhibited it with perfect success in tooth-drawing,† opening abscesses, for annulling the pain of

---

* When used for surgical purposes, perhaps it will be found to be most easily given upon a handkerchief, gathered up into a cup-like form in the hand of the exhibitor, and with the open end of the cup placed over the nose and mouth of the patient. For the first inspiration or two it should be held at a distance of a half an inch or so from the face, and then more and more closely applied to it. To insure a rapid and perfect anæsthetic effect—more especially where the operation is to be severe—one or two teaspoonfuls of the chloroform should be at once placed upon the hollow of the handkerchief, and immediately held to the face of the patient. Generally, a snoring sleep speedily supervenes; and when it does so, it is a perfect test of the superinduction of complete insensibility. But a patient may be quite anæsthetic without this symptom supervening.

† A young dentist who has himself had two teeth extracted lately, one under the influence of ether and the other under the influence of chloroform, writes me the following statement of the results: "About six months ago I had an upper molar tooth extracted whilst under the influence of ether by Mr. Imlach. The inhalation was continued for several minutes before I presented the usual appearances of

dysmenorrhœa and of neuralgia, and in two or three cases where I was using deep, and otherwise very painful, galvano-puncture for the treatment of ovarian dropsy, etc. I have employed it also in obstetric practice with entire success. The lady to whom it was first exhibited during parturition, had been previously delivered in the country by perforation of the head of the infant, after a labor of three days' duration. In this, her second confinement, pains supervened a fortnight before full time. Three hours and a half after they commenced, and, ere the first stage of the labor was completed, I placed her under the influence of the chloroform, by moistening, with a teaspoonful of the liquid, a pocket handkerchief, rolled up into a funnel shape, and with the broad or open end of the funnel placed over her mouth and nostrils. In consequence of the evaporation of the fluid it was once more renewed in about ten or twelve minutes. The child was expelled in about twenty-five minutes after the inhalation was begun. The mother subsequently remained longer soporose than commonly happens after ether. The squalling of the child did not, as usual, rouse her; and some minutes elapsed before the placenta was expelled, and after the child was removed into another room by the nurse, before the patient awoke. She then turned round and observed to me that she had "enjoyed a very comfortable sleep, and indeed required it, as she was so tired,* but would now be more able for the work before her." I evaded entering into discussion with her, believing, as I have already stated, that the most complete possible quietude forms

complete etherization; the tooth was then extracted; and, although I did not feel the least pain, yet I was conscious of the operation being performed and was quite aware when the crash took place. Some days ago I required another molar extracted on account of toothache, and this operation was again performed by the same gentleman. I inhaled the vapor of chloroform, half a drachm being poured upon a handkerchief for that purpose, and held to my nose and mouth. Insensibility took place in a few seconds; but I was so completely *dead* this time that I was not in the very slightest degree aware of anything that took place. The subsequent stupefying effects of the chloroform went off more rapidly than those of the ether; and I was perfectly well and able again for my work in a few minutes."

* In consequence of extreme anxiety at the unfortunate result of her previous confinement she had slept little or none for one or two nights preceding the commencement of her present accouchement.

one of the principal secrets for the successful employment of either ether or chloroform. In a little time she again remarked that she was afraid her "sleep had stopped the pains." Shortly afterwards her infant was brought in by the nurse from the adjoining room, and it was a matter of no small difficulty to convince the astonished mother that the labor was entirely over, and that the child presented to her was really her "own living baby."

Perhaps I may be excused from adding that since publishing on the subject of Ether Inhalation in Midwifery, seven or eight months ago,* and then for the first time directing the attention of the medical profession to its great use and importance in natural and morbid parturition, I have employed it, with few and rare exceptions, in every case of labor that I have attended; and with the most delightful results. And I have no doubt whatever that some years hence the practice will be general. Obstetricians may oppose it, but I believe our patients themselves will force the use of it upon the profession.† I have never had the pleasure of watching over a series of better and more rapid recoveries; nor once witnessed any disagreeable result follow to either mother or child; whilst I have now seen an immense amount of maternal pain and agony saved by its employment. And I most conscientiously believe that the proud mission of the physician is distinctly twofold—namely, to alleviate human suffering, as well as preserve human life.

CHEMICAL CONSTITUTION OF CHLOROFORM

Formyle is the hypothetical radical of formic acid. In the red ant (*Formica rufa*) formic acid was first discovered, and hence its name. Gehlen pointed it out as a peculiar acid; and it was afterwards first artificially prepared by Doebereiner. Chemists have now devised a variety of processes by which formic acid may be

---

* See Monthly Journal of Medical Science for February, p. 639; for March, pp. 718 and 721; and April, p. 794, etc.

† I am told that the London physicians, with two or three exceptions only, have never yet employed ether-inhalation in their midwifery practice. Three weeks ago I was informed, in a letter from Professor Montgomery, of Dublin, that he believed that in that city, up to that date, it had not been used in a single case of labor.

obtained from starch, sugar, and, indeed, most other vegetable substances.

A series of chlorides of formyle are produced when chlorine and the hypochlorites are brought to act on the chloride, oxide, and hydrated oxide of methyle (pyroxylic or wood spirit). In the same way as formic acid may be artificially procured from substances which do not contain formyle ready formed, so also are the chlorides of this radical capable of being procured from substances which do not originally contain it.

Chloroform, chloroformyle, or the perchloride of formyle may be made and obtained artificially by various processes,—as by making milk of lime, or an aqueous solution of caustic alkali act upon chloral,—by distilling alcohol, pyroxylic spirit, or acetone, with chloride of lime,—by leading a stream of chlorine gas into a solution of caustic potass in spirit of wine, etc. The preparation which I have employed was made according to the following formula of Dumas:

"R. Chloride of lime in powder.........................lb. iv.
Water...lb. xii.
Rectified spirit...................................f$\mathfrak{Z}$ xii.

"Mix in a capacious retort or still, and distill as long as a dense liquid, which sinks in the water with which it comes over, is produced."—(Gray's *Supplement to the Pharmacopœia*, 1846, p. 633.)

The resulting perchloride of formyle consists of two atoms of carbon, one of hydrogen, and three of chlorine. Its specific gravity is much greater than that of water, being as high as 1.480. It boils at 141.° The density of its vapor is 4.2. It is not inflammable, nor changed by distillation with potassium, potash, sulphuric, or other acids.— (See Turner's *Elements of Chemistry*, eighth edition, p. 1009; Gregory's *Outlines of Chemistry*, part ii, p. 401; Fownes' *Manual of Elementary Chemistry*, p. 419; Thompson's *Chemistry of Organic Bodies*, p. 312; Loewig's *Organische Chemie*, vol. i, p. 498.)

It is now well ascertained that three compound chemical bodies possess, when inhaled into the lungs, the power of superinducing a state of anæsthesia, or insensibility to pain, in surgical operations, etc., namely, nitrous oxide, sulphuric ether, and perchloride of formyle. The following tabular view shows that these agents are entirely different from each other in their chemical constitution, and hence that their elementary composition affords no apparent clue to the explanation of their anæsthetic properties:

	Proportion of Nitrogen.	Proportion of Oxygen.	Proportion of Carbon.	Proportion of Hydrogen.	Proportion of Chlorine.
Nitrous oxide.........	1 atom	1 atom	——	——	——
Sulphuric ether......	——	1 atom	4 atoms	5 atoms	——
Chloroform..........	——	——	2 atoms	1 atom	3 atoms

It is, perhaps, not unworthy of remark that when Soubeiran, Liebig, and Dumas engaged, a few years back, in those inquiries and experiments by which the formation and composition of chloroform was first discovered, their sole and only object was the investigation of a point in philosophical chemistry. They labored for the pure love and extension of knowledge. They had no idea that the substance to which they called the attention of their chemical brethren could or would be turned to any practical purpose, or that it possessed any physiological or therapeutic effects upon animal economy. I mention this to show that the *cui bono* argument against philosophical investigations, on the grounds that there may be at first no apparent practical benefit to be derived from them, has been amply refuted in this, as it has been in many other instances. For I feel assured that the use of chloroform will soon entirely supersede the use of ether; and, from the facility and rapidity of its exhibition, it will be employed as an anæsthetic agent in many cases, and under many circumstances, in which ether would never have been had recourse to. Here, then, we have a substance which, in the first instance, was merely interesting as a matter of scientific curiosity and research, becoming rapidly an object of intense importance, as an agent by which human suffering and agony may be annulled and abolished, under some of the most trying circumstances in which human nature is ever placed.

POSTSCRIPT

Since the above observations were sent to press I have—through the great kindness of Professor Miller and Dr. Duncan—had an opportunity of trying the effects of the inhalation of chloroform, to-day, in three cases of operation in the Royal Infirmary of Edinburgh. A great collection of professional gentlemen and students witnessed the results, and among the number was Professor Dumas, of Paris, the chemist who first ascertained and established the chemical composition of chloroform. He happened to be passing through Edinburgh, engaged along with Dr. Milne Edwards, who accompanied him, in an official investigation for the French Government, and was, in no small degree, rejoiced to witness the wonderful physiological effects of a substance with whose chemical history his own name was so intimately connected.

I append notes, obligingly furnished me by Professor Miller and Dr. Duncan, of the three cases of operation. The two first cases were operated on by Professor Miller; the third, by Dr. Duncan. In applying the chloroform in the first case I used a pocket handkerchief as the inhaling instrument; in the last two I employed a hollow sponge.

"CASE I.—A boy, four or five years old, with necrosis of one of the bones of the forearm. Could speak nothing but Gaelic. No means consequently, of explaining to him what he was required to do. On holding a handkerchief, on which some chloroform had been sprinkled, to his face, he became frightened and wrestled to be away. He was held gently, however, by Dr. Simpson, and obliged to inhale. After a few inspirations he ceased to cry or move, and fell into a sound, snoring sleep. A deep incision was now made down to the diseased bone; and, by the use of the forceps, nearly the whole of the radius, in the state of sequestrum, was extracted. During this operation, and the subsequent examination of the wound by the finger, not the slightest evidence of the suffering of pain was given. He still slept on soundly, and was carried back to his ward in that state. Half an hour afterwards he was found in bed, like a child newly awakened from a refreshing sleep, with a clear, merry eye and placid expression of countenance, wholly unlike what is found to obtain after ordinary etherization. On being questioned by a Gaelic interpreter who was found among the students he stated that he had never felt any pain, and that he felt none now. On being shown his wounded arm, he looked much surprised, but neither cried nor otherwise expressed the slightest alarm.

"CASE II.—A soldier who had an opening in the cheek—the result of exfoliation of the jaw—was next made to inhale. At first he showed some signs of moving his hands too freely; but soon also fell into a state of sleep and snoring. A free incision was made across the lower jaw, and from this the dense adhering integuments were freely dissected all round, so as to raise the soft parts of the cheek. The edges of the opening were then made raw, and the whole line of incision was brought together by several points of suture. This patient had previously undergone two minor operations of a somewhat similar kind; both of them had proved unsuccessful, and he bore them very ill—proving unusually unsteady and complaining bitterly of severe pain. On the present occasion he did not wince or moan in the slightest degree; and on the return of consciousness said that he had felt nothing. His first act, when apparently about half awake, was suddenly to clutch up the sponge with which the chloroform was used and re-adjust it to his mouth, obviously implying that he had found the inhalation from it anything but a disagreeable duty.

"This case was further interesting, as being one of those operations in the region of the mouth, in which it had been deemed impossible to use ether, and certainly it would have been impossible to have performed the operation with any complicated inhaling apparatus applied to the mouth of the patient."

"CASE III.—A young man, of about twenty-five years of age, having necrosis of the first phalanx of the great toe and ulceration of the integuments, the consequence of injury. The ulcerated surface was exceedingly tender to the touch, so much so that he winced whenever the finger was brought near to it; and the slightest pressure made him cry out. After the removal of the dressings, which caused some pain and fretting, the inhalation was commenced, and the patient almost immediately* became insensible and lay perfectly still, while the diseased mass was being removed by amputation of the toe through the middle of the second phalanx. The inhalation was now stopped. The edges of the wound were then brought together with three stitches and the wound dressed. The

---

* Dr. Christison, who was watching the result, informs me that this patient was affected in half a minute.

patient shortly afterwards awoke, looked round him, and gratefully declared his entire and perfect freedom from all pain and uneasiness during the operation."

The whole quantity of chloroform used in these three operations did not exceed half an ounce, and, as Professor Miller afterwards observed to the students that were present, if ether had been used, several ounces of it would have been requisite to produce the same amount of anæsthetic effect.

The following case occurred also to-day, to Mr. Miller, in private practice. The notes of it, and the subsequent remark, are in his own words.

"CASE IV.—A young lady wished to have a tumor (encysted) dissected out from beneath the angle of the jaw. The chloroform was used in small quantity (about a drachm) sprinkled upon a piece of operation sponge. In considerably less than a minute she was sound asleep, sitting easily in a chair, with her eyes shut, and with her ordinary expression of countenance. The tumor was extirpated and a stitch inserted without any pain having been either shown or felt. Her sensations, throughout, as she subsequently stated, had been of the most pleasing nature; and her manageableness during the operation was as perfect as if she had been a wax doll or a lay figure.

"No sickness, vomiting, head-ache, salivation, uneasiness of chest, in any of the cases. Once or twice a tickling cough took place in the first breathings."

I have, up to this date, exhibited the chloroform to about fifty individuals. In not a single instance has the slightest bad result of any kind whatever occurred from its employment.

EDINBURGH, November 15, 1847

Puerperal Fever

Oliver Wendell Holmes

From a Photograph obtained from Dr. Edwin A. Locke and Dr. John
W. Farlow, Librarian of the Boston Medical Library.

OLIVER WENDELL HOLMES
1809–1894

Dr. Holmes was born in the "old gambrel-roofed house" in Cambridge, Massachusetts, August 29, 1809. His father, the Rev. Abiel Holmes, belonged to the old-fashioned Calvinistic school, in which the imaginary horrors of nature were emphasized till every corner and shadow contained some sprite or hobgoblin, but in which also the integrity of the individual and personal responsibility were taught as the foundations of character. His mother, Sarah Wendell, was "a bright, vivacious woman, * * * very cheerful and social." Such a combination might well produce a forceful yet kind and genial nature, capable of writing the essay on puerperal fever and the verse and prose which have touched the hearts of so many.

After a general school education he went to Andover Academy, and from there to Harvard College, in 1825, to become a member of the Class of '29. On graduating he studied law for a short time, but soon abandoned it for medicine. His own account of this change is of interest here. "What determined me to give up law and apply myself to medicine I can hardly say, but I had from the first looked upon that year's study as an experiment. * * * At the end of the first year in the Dane Law School I took up the new study which was to be my final choice."* During this year of law study he had "tasted the intoxicating pleasure of authorship," and, as he puts it, "there is no form of lead-poisoning which more rapidly and thoroughly pervades the blood and bones and marrow than that which reaches the young author through mental contact with type-metal." It was during this year that "Old Ironsides" was written, and being upon a subject of national interest, it brought its author, then only twenty-one years of age, into prominence throughout the United States.

* Farewell Address to the (Harvard) Medical School, delivered in 1882.

His medical studies were begun in a private school conducted by Dr. James Jackson. After attending two courses of lectures in this school his parents found money to send him to Europe to complete his medical studies. The French capital at that time was the continental seat of learning, and in medicine the school of Louis was especially conspicuous in international reputation. Thus in 1833, being twenty-four years of age, Holmes came under those influences which did much to mould his literary and medical character. In Morse's "Life and Letters" is to be found a full and most interesting account of these years,* a summary of which is well expressed in Holmes' own words. He says: " * * * I have more fully learned at least three principles since I have been in Paris: not to take authority when I can have facts; not to guess when I can know; not to think a man must take physic because he is sick"; and again: "My aim has been to qualify myself * * * not for a mere scholar, for a follower after other men's opinions, for a dependent on their authority,—but for the character of a man who has seen and therefore knows; who has thought and therefore has arrived at his own conclusions." (Letter written while a medical student in Paris.) These two quotations, each in its own way, express the motives which actuated him in his professional work. It is this spirit, matured and vigorous, which makes itself evident throughout the puerperal fever essay, both in the thoroughness of his investigation and the powerful exposition of his findings.

On returning from Paris in 1836 he made an unsuccessful attempt to practise in Boston. He seems never to have been fitted by taste or temperament for the life of the practitioner. From 1836 to the year (1847) of his appointment as Parkman Professor of Anatomy and Physiology in the Harvard Medical School he contributed to medical literature many essays, which, together with others published later, have appeared in book form.† The most important of these is the one, here reprinted, on puerperal

* "Life and Letters of O. W. Holmes," by John T. Morse, Jr.; Houghton, Mifflin & Co.

† "Medical Essays," Houghton, Mifflin & Co.

fever. This essay appeared in April, 1843, in *The New England Quarterly Journal of Medicine and Surgery*, a short-lived journal of no great reputation. The idea of investigating the subject occurred to him at a meeting of the Boston Society for Medical Improvement, at which he heard a report and discussion of a fatal case of child-bed fever. The physician holding the autopsy upon this case himself had died within a week of the examination. During that week he had attended several women in confinement, all of which were attacked with puerperal fever. Though first published in an obscure journal with small circulation, the essay contained " * * * real thought" on a "real subject" which "knocks the wind out of somebody or other." In 1852 and 1854 his conclusions were attacked, and on republishing the essay in 1855 he added in reply to these attacks, an introduction which leads one to think that his year in the study of law was not misspent. "I am too much in earnest," he says, "for either humility or vanity, but I do entreat those who hold the keys of life and death to listen to me also for this once. I ask no personal favor, but I beg to be heard in behalf of the women whose lives are at stake, until some stronger voice shall plead for them." In reading the account of this controversy one is struck with the similarity between the difficulties which Harvey, Jenner, and Morton had to meet and those which confronted Holmes. Bitter sarcasm emanated from men in the profession whose high position required an answer. Holmes was thirty-four years of age when his report first appeared. He held no university position.* When his essay was republished with an introduction he was twelve years older, and had been for eight years Professor of Anatomy in the Harvard Medical School, and its Dean from 1847 to 1853. It was during these intervening years that the original essay was attacked in lectures which in 1852 and 1854 were published. Of these attacks he says: "When, by the permission of Providence, I held up to the professional public the damnable facts connected with the conveyance of poison from one young mother's

---

* *Note:* From 1838 to 1840 he had filled the chair of Anatomy and Physiology at Dartmouth College.

chamber to another's—for doing which humble office I desire to be thankful that I have lived, though nothing else should ever come to my life—I had to bear the sneers of those whose position I had assailed, and, as I believe have at last demolished, so that nothing but the ghosts of dead women stir among the ruins." The evidence contained in this essay has been conclusive of the contagiousness of puerperal fever, a fact remarkable when it is remembered that the science of bacteriology was at that time unborn. To prove his point it was necessary to gather facts from professional men who, from the nature of the inquiry, would prefer to have such facts kept in obscurity. He seems, however, to have imbued the investigation with the great humanitarian significance which in truth it possessed. Physicians to whom he appealed caught the spirit of his search and lost the fear of personal exposure and willingly contributed private records which even in that day threatened ruin to their reputation. Out of all this material he formed a record which established beyond question the contagiousness of puerperal fever. As Morse says, "If it were a seed of truth it would grow, while the assault watered it."

Although Dr. Holmes retained for many years the chair of anatomy, his essay on puerperal fever is the only piece of scientific work of any great importance of which there is record. His medical essays and addresses are numerous, however, as will be seen by the bibliographic list printed below. The essay as it appeared originally in 1843 is reprinted here. The Introduction to the edition of 1855 is not given except in the extracts already quoted and that given below. It is, however, an example of clear, logical, earnest argument, and may well be taken as a type of rejoinder in scientific questions. If Holmes experienced "crystalline clairvoyance" when he wrote the "Chambered Nautilus," in writing the essay on "Puerperal Fever" he must have been inspired as are those only who have seen some great truth of nature unfolding before them. Both in the introduction and essay there rings out a clear, forceful, judicial note which one can scarcely believe emanates from the tender-hearted little doctor. In the following extract from the Introduction of the 1855 edition it will be seen that the English is shorn of all unnecessary adornment. "I trust that I have made the issue perfectly distinct and intelligible. And let it be remembered that this is no subject to be smoothed over by nicely adjusted phrases of half assent and half censure divided between the parties. The balance must be struck boldly and the result declared plainly. If I have been hasty, presumptuous, ill-informed, illogical; if my array of facts means nothing; if there is no reason for any caution in the view of these facts; let me be told so on such authority that I must believe it, and I will be silent henceforth, recognizing that my mind is in a state of disorganization * * * * *persons* are nothing in this matter; better that twenty pamphleteers should be silenced, or as many professors unseated, than that one mother's life should be taken. There is no quarrel here between men, but there is deadly incompatibility and exterminating warfare between doctrines. * * * * If I am wrong, let me be put down by such rebuke as no rash declaimer has received since there has been a public opinion in the medical profession of America; if I am right, let doctrines which lead to professional homicide be no longer taught from the chairs of those two great Institutions. Indifference will not do here; our journalists and committees have no right to take up their pages with minute anatomy and tediously detailed cases while it is a question whether or not the 'black death' of child-bed is to be scattered broadcast by the agency of the mother's friend and advisor. Let the men who mould opinions look to it; if there is any voluntary blindness, any interested oversight, any culpable negligence, even, in such a matter, and the facts shall reach the public ear, the pestilence-carrier of the lying-in chamber must look to God for pardon, for man will never forgive him."

Such is the ending to the Introduction of 1855. Bacteriology was soon to come and prove upon far surer grounds the correctness of his conclusions, but before this, antisepsis came to mitigate the ravages and show that it was "cause and effect, the cause being in some way connected with the person" of those in attendance. It is not in place in this sketch to treat of Dr. Holmes' writings in the field of *belles-lettres* beyond mentioning the influence these, as well as his technical essays and addresses, exerted and continue to exert in raising the standard of style in medical literature. Dr. Holmes died at Boston, October 7, 1894, being in his eighty-fifth year.

1843 and 1855

THE CONTAGIOUSNESS OF PUERPERAL FEVER

Note.—This essay appeared first in 1843, in "a short-lived periodical of little note" (Morse), *The New England Quarterly Journal of Medicine*, and was reprinted in the "Medical Essays" published in 1855 by (Ticknor and Fields) Houghton, Mifflin & Co., by whose courtesy it is here reproduced.

In collecting, enforcing, and adding to the evidence accumulated upon this most serious subject, I would not be understood to imply that there exists a doubt in the mind of any well-informed member of the medical profession as to the fact that puerperal fever is sometimes communicated from one person to another, both directly and indirectly. In the present state of our knowledge upon this point I should consider such doubts merely as a proof that the sceptic had either not examined the evidence, or, having examined it, refused to accept its plain and unavoidable consequences. I should be sorry to think, with Dr. Rigby, that it was a case of "oblique vision"; I should be unwilling to force home the *argumentum ad hominem* of Dr. Blundell, but I would not consent to make a *question* of a momentous fact which is no longer to be considered as a subject for trivial discussions, but to be acted upon with silent promptitude. It signifies nothing that wise and experienced practitioners have sometimes doubted the reality of the danger in question; no man has the right to doubt it any longer. No negative facts, no opposing opinions, be they what they may, or whose they may, can form any answer to the series of cases now within the reach of all who choose to explore the records of medical science.

If there are some who conceive that any important end would be answered by recording such opinions, or by collecting the history of all the cases they could find in which no evidence of the influence of contagion existed, I believe they are in error. Suppose a few writers of authority can be found to profess a disbelief in contagion,—and they are very few compared with those who think differently,—is it quite clear that they formed their opinions on a view of all the facts, or is it not apparent that they relied mostly on their own solitary experience? Still further, of those whose names are quoted, is it not true that scarcely a single one could,

by any possibility, have known the half or the tenth of the facts
bearing on the subject which have reached such a frightful amount
within the last few years ?   Again, as to the utility of negative facts,
as we may briefly call them,—instances, namely, in which exposure
has not been followed by disease,—although, like other truths, they
may be worth knowing, I do not see that they are like to shed any
important light upon the subject before us.   Every such instance
requires a good deal of circumstantial explanation before it can
be accepted.   It is not enough that a practitioner should have had
a single case of puerperal fever not followed by others.   It must be
known whether he attended others while this case was in progress,
whether he went directly from one chamber to others, whether he
took any, and what, precautions.   It is important to know that
several women were exposed to infection derived from the patient,
so that allowance may be made for want of predisposition.   Now,
if of negative facts so sifted there could be accumulated a hundred
for every one plain instance of communication here recorded, I trust
it need not be said that we are bound to guard and watch over the
hundredth tenant of our fold, though the ninety and nine may be
sure of escaping the wolf at its entrance.   If any one is disposed,
then, to take a hundred instances of lives endangered or sacrificed
out of those I have mentioned, and make it reasonably clear that
within a similar time and compass *ten thousand* escaped the same
exposure, I shall thank him for his industry, but I must be permitted
to hold to my own practical conclusions, and beg him to adopt or at
least to examine them also.   Children that walk in calico before
open fires are not always burned to death; the instances to the contrary may be worth recording; but by no means if they are to be
used as arguments against woollen frocks and high fenders.

   I am not sure that this paper will escape another remark which
it might be wished were founded in justice.   It may be said that the
facts are too generally known and acknowledged to require any
formal argument or exposition, that there is nothing new in the
positions advanced, and no need of laying additional statements
before the profession.   But on turning to two works, one almost
universally, and the other extensively, appealed to as authority in

this country, I see ample reason to overlook this objection.   In the last edition of Dewees's Treatise on the "Diseases of Females" it is expressly said, "In this country, under no circumstance that puerperal fever has appeared hitherto, does it afford the slightest ground for the belief that it is contagious."   In the "Philadelphia Practice of Midwifery" not one word can be found in the chapter devoted to this disease which would lead the reader to suspect that the idea of contagion had ever been entertained.   It seems proper, therefore, to remind those who are in the habit of referring to these works for guidance that there may possibly be some sources of danger they have slighted or omitted, quite as important as a trifling irregularity of diet, or a confined state of the bowels, and that whatever confidence a physician may have in his own mode of treatment, his services are of questionable value whenever he carries the bane as well as the antidote about his person.

The practical point to be illustrated is the following: *The disease known as puerperal fever is so far contagious as to be frequently carried from patient to patient by physicians and nurses.*

Let me begin by throwing out certain incidental questions, which, without being absolutely essential, would render the subject more complicated, and by making such concessions and assumptions as may be fairly supposed to be without the pale of discussion.

1. It is granted that all the forms of what is called puerperal fever may not be, and probably are not, equally contagious or infectious.   I do not enter into the distinctions which have been drawn by authors, because the facts do not appear to me sufficient to establish any absolute line of demarcation between such forms as may be propagated by contagion and those which are never so propagated.   This general result I shall only support by the authority of Dr. Ramsbotham, who gives, as the result of his experience, that the same symptoms belong to what he calls the infectious and the sporadic forms of the disease, and the opinion of Armstrong in his original Essay.   If others can show any such distinction, I leave it to them to do it.   But there are cases enough that show the prevalence of the disease among the patients of a single practitioner when it was in no degree epidemic, in the proper

sense of the term. I may refer to those of Mr. Roberton and of Dr. Peirson, hereafter to be cited, as examples.

2. I shall not enter into any dispute about the particular *mode* of infection, whether it be by the atmosphere the physician carries about him into the sick-chamber, or by the direct application of the virus to the absorbing surfaces with which his hand comes in contact. Many facts and opinions are in favor of each of these modes of transmission. But it is obvious that, in the majority of cases, it must be impossible to decide by which of these channels the disease is conveyed, from the nature of the intercourse between the physician and the patient.

3. It is not pretended that the contagion of puerperal fever must always be followed by the disease. It is true of all contagious diseases that they frequently spare those who appear to be fully submitted to their influence. Even the vaccine virus, fresh from the subject, fails every day to produce its legitimate effect, though every precaution is taken to insure its action. This is still more remarkably the case with scarlet fever and some other diseases.

4. It is granted that the disease may be produced and variously modified by many causes besides contagion, and more especially by epidemic and endemic influences. But this is not peculiar to the disease in question. There is no doubt that smallpox is propagated to a great extent by contagion, yet it goes through the same periods of periodical increase and diminution which have been remarked in puerperal fever. If the question is asked how we are to reconcile the great variations in the mortality of puerperal fever in different seasons and places with the supposition of contagion, I will answer it by another question from Mr. Farr's letter to the Registrar-General. He makes the statement that "*five* die weekly of smallpox in the metropolis when the disease is not epidemic," and adds, "The problem for solution is, Why do the five deaths become 10, 15, 20, 31, 58, 88, weekly, and then progressively fall through the same measured steps?"

5. I take it for granted that, if it can be shown that great numbers of lives have been and are sacrificed to ignorance or blindness on this point, no other error of which physicians or nurses may be

occasionally suspected will be alleged in palliation of this; but that whenever and wherever they can be shown to carry disease and death instead of health and safety, the common instincts of humanity will silence every attempt to explain away their responsibility.

The treatise of Dr. Gordon, of Aberdeen, was published in the year 1795, being among the earlier special works upon the disease. A part of his testimony has been occasionally copied into other works, but his expressions are so clear, his experience is given with such manly distinctness and disinterested honesty, that it may be quoted as a model which might have been often followed with advantage.

"This disease seized such women only as were visited or delivered by a practitioner, or taken care of by a nurse, who had previously attended patients affected with the disease."

"I had evident proofs of its infectious nature, and that the infection was as readily communicated as that of the smallpox or measles, and operated more speedily than any other infection with which I am acquainted."

"I had evident proofs that every person who had been with a patient in the puerperal fever became charged with an atmosphere of infection, which was communicated to every pregnant woman who happened to come within its sphere. This is not an assertion, but a fact, admitting of demonstration, as may be seen by a perusal of the foregoing table"—referring to a table of seventy-seven cases, in many of which the channel of propagation was evident.

He adds: "It is a disagreeable declaration for me to mention, that I myself was the means of carrying the infection to a great number of women." He then enumerates a number of instances in which the disease was conveyed by midwives and others to the neighboring villages, and declares that "these facts fully prove that the cause of the puerperal fever, of which I treat, was a specific contagion, or infection, altogether unconnected with a noxious constitution of the atmosphere."

But his most terrible evidence is given in these words: "I ARRIVED AT THAT CERTAINTY IN THE MATTER THAT I COULD VENTURE

TO FORETELL WHAT WOMEN WOULD BE AFFECTED WITH THE DISEASE, UPON HEARING BY WHAT MIDWIFE THEY WERE TO BE DELIVERED, OR BY WHAT NURSE THEY WERE TO BE ATTENDED, DURING THEIR LYING-IN: AND ALMOST IN EVERY INSTANCE MY PREDICTION WAS VERIFIED."

Even previously to Gordon, Mr. White, of Manchester, had said: "I am acquainted with two gentlemen in another town, where the whole business of midwifery is divided betwixt them, and it is very remarkable that one of them loses several patients every year of the puerperal fever, and the other never so much as meets with the disorder"—a difference which he seems to attribute to their various modes of treatment.*

Dr. Armstrong has given a number of instances in his Essay on Puerperal Fever of the prevalence of the disease among the patients of a single practitioner. At Sunderland, "in all, forty-three cases occurred from the 1st of January to the 1st of October, when the disease ceased; and of this number, forty were witnessed by Mr. Gregson and his assistant, Mr. Gregory, the remainder having been separately seen by three accoucheurs." There is appended to the London edition of this Essay a letter from Mr. Gregson, in which that gentleman says, in reference to the great number of cases occurring in his practice, "The cause of this I cannot pretend fully to explain, but I should be wanting in common liberality if I were to make any hesitation in asserting that the disease which appeared in my practice was highly contagious, and communicable from one puerperal woman to another." "It is customary among the lower and middle ranks of people to make frequent personal visits to puerperal women resident in the same neighborhood, and I have ample evidence for affirming that the infection of the disease was often carried about in that manner; and, however painful to my feelings, I must in candor declare that it is very probable the contagion was conveyed, in some instances, by myself, though I took every possible care to prevent such a thing from happening the moment that I ascertained that the distemper was infectious." Dr. Armstrong goes on to mention six other instances within

* *On the Management of Lying-in Women*, p. 120.

his knowledge, in which the disease had at different times and places been limited, in the same singular manner, to the practice of individuals, while it existed scarcely, if at all, among the patients of others around them. Two of the gentlemen became so convinced of their conveying the contagion that they withdrew for a time from practice.

I find a brief notice, in an American journal, of another series of cases, first mentioned by Mr. Davies, in the "Medical Repository." This gentleman stated his conviction that the disease is contagious.

"In the autumn of 1822 he met with twelve cases, while his medical friends in the neighborhood did not meet with any, 'or at least very few.' He could attribute this circumstance to no other cause than his having been present at the examination, after death, of two cases, some time previous, and of his having imparted the disease to his patients, notwithstanding every precaution."*

Dr. Gooch says: "It is not uncommon for the greater number of cases to occur in the practice of one man, whilst the other practitioners of the neighborhood, who are not more skilful or more busy, meet with few or none. A practitioner opened the body of a woman who had died of puerperal fever, and continued to wear the same clothes. A lady whom he delivered a few days afterwards was attacked with and died of a similar disease; two more of his lying-in patients, in rapid succession, met with the same fate; struck by the thought that he might have carried contagion in his clothes, he instantly changed them, and met with no more cases of the kind.† A woman in the country who was employed as washerwoman and nurse washed the linen of one who had died of puerperal fever; the next lying-in patient she nursed died of the same disease; a third nursed by her met with the same fate, till the neighborhood, getting afraid of her, ceased to employ her."‡

In the winter of the year 1824, "several instances occurred of its prevalence among the patients of particular practitioners, whilst

* *Philad. Med. Journal* for 1825, p. 408.

† A similar anecdote is related by Sir Benjamin Brodie, of the late Dr. John Clark, *Lancet*, May 2, 1840.

‡ *An Account of Some of the Most Important Diseases Peculiar to Women*, p. 4.

others who were equally busy met with few or none. One instance of this kind was very remarkable. A general practitioner, in large midwifery practice, lost so many patients from puerperal fever that he determined to deliver no more for some time, but that his partner should attend in his place. This plan was pursued for one month, during which not a case of the disease occurred in their practice. The elder practitioner, being then sufficiently recovered, returned to his practice, but the first patient he attended was attacked by the disease and died. A physician who met him in consultation soon afterwards, about a case of a different kind, and who knew nothing of his misfortune, asked him whether puerperal fever was at all prevalent in his neighborhood, on which he burst into tears, and related the above circumstances.

"Among the cases which I saw this season in consultation, four occurred in one month in the practice of one medical man, and all of them terminated fatally."*

Dr. Ramsbotham asserted, in a lecture at the London Hospital, that he had known the disease spread through a particular district, or be confined to the practice of a particular person, almost every patient being attacked with it, while others had not a single case. It seemed capable, he thought, of conveyance, not only by common modes, but through the dress of the attendants upon the patient.†

In a letter to be found in the "London Medical Gazette" for January, 1840, Mr. Roberton, of Manchester, makes the statement which I here give in a somewhat condensed form.

A midwife delivered a woman on the 4th of December, 1830, who died soon after with the symptoms of puerperal fever. In one month from this date the same midwife delivered thirty women, residing in different parts of an extensive suburb, of which number sixteen caught the disease and all died. These were the only cases which had occurred for a considerable time in Manchester. The other midwives connected with the same charitable institution as the woman already mentioned are twenty-five in number, and deliver, on an average, ninety women a week, or about three hun-

* Gooch, *op. cit.*, p. 71.
† *Lond. Med. Gaz.*, May 2, 1835.

dred and eighty a month. None of these women had a case of puerperal fever. "Yet all this time this woman was crossing the other midwives in every direction, scores of the patients of the charity being delivered by them in the very same quarters where her cases of fever were happening."

Mr. Roberton remarks that little more than half the women she delivered during this month took the fever; that on some days all escaped, on others only one or more out of three or four: a circumstance similar to what is seen in other infectious maladies.

Dr. Blundell says: "Those who have never made the experiment can have but a faint conception how difficult it is to obtain the exact truth respecting any occurrence in which feelings and interests are concerned. Omitting particulars, then, I content myself with remarking, generally, that from more than one district I have received accounts of the prevalence of puerperal fever in the practice of some individuals, while its occurrence in that of others, in the same neighborhood, was not observed. Some, as I have been told, have lost ten, twelve, or a greater number of patients, in scarcely broken succession; like their evil genius, the puerperal fever has seemed to stalk behind them wherever they went. Some have deemed it prudent to retire for a time from practice. In fine, that this fever may occur spontaneously, I admit; that its infectious nature may be plausibly disputed, I do not deny; but I add, considerately, that in my own family I had rather that those I esteemed the most should be delivered, unaided, in a stable, by the manger-side, than that they should receive the best help, in the fairest apartment, but exposed to the vapors of this pitiless disease. Gossiping friends, wet-nurses, monthly nurses, the practitioner himself, these are the channels by which, as I suspect, the infection is principally conveyed."*

At a meeting of the Royal Medical and Chirurgical Society Dr. King mentioned that some years since a practitioner at Woolwich lost sixteen patients from puerperal fever in the same year. He was compelled to give up practice for one or two years, his business being divided among the neighboring practitioners. No case of puerperal

* *Lect. on Midwifery*, p. 395.

fever occurred afterwards, neither had any of the neighboring surgeons any cases of this disease.

At the same meeting Mr. Hutchinson mentioned the occurrence of three consecutive cases of puerperal fever, followed subsequently by two others, all in the practice of one accoucheur.*

Dr. Lee makes the following statement: "In the last two weeks of September, 1827, five fatal cases of uterine inflammation came under our observation. All the individuals so attacked had been attended in labor by the same midwife, and no example of a febrile or inflammatory disease of a serious nature occurred during that period among the other patients of the Westminster General Dispensary, who had been attended by the other midwives belonging to that institution."†

The recurrence of long series of cases like those I have cited, reported by those most interested to disbelieve in contagion, scattered along through an interval of half a century, might have been thought sufficient to satisfy the minds of all inquirers that here was something more than a singular coincidence. But if, on a more extended observation, it should be found that the same ominous groups of cases clustering about individual practitioners were observed in a remote country, at different times, and in widely separated regions, it would seem incredible that any should be found too prejudiced or indolent to accept the solemn truth knelled into their ears by the funeral bells from both sides of the ocean—the plain conclusion that the physician and the disease entered, hand in hand, into the chamber of the unsuspecting patient.

That such series of cases have been observed in this country, and in this neighborhood, I proceed to show.

In Dr. Francis's "Notes to Denman's Midwifery" a passage is cited from Dr. Hosack in which he refers to certain puerperal cases which proved fatal to several lying-in women, and in some of which the disease was supposed to be conveyed by the accoucheurs themselves.‡

* *Lancet*, May 2, 1840.
† *Lond. Cyc. of Pract. Med.*, art., "Fever, Puerperal."
‡ *Denman's Midwifery*, p. 673, third Am. ed.

A writer in the "New York Medical and Physical Journal" for October, 1829, in speaking of the occurrence of puerperal fever confined to one man's practice, remarks: "We have known cases of this kind occur, though rarely, in New York."

I mention these little hints about the occurrence of such cases partly because they are the first I have met with in American medical literature, but more especially because they serve to remind us that behind the fearful array of published facts there lies a dark list of similar events, unwritten in the records of science, but long remembered by many a desolated fireside.

Certainly nothing can be more open and explicit than the account given by Dr. Peirson, of Salem, of the cases seen by him. In the first nineteen days of January, 1829, he had five consecutive cases of puerperal fever, every patient he attended being attacked, and the three first cases proving fatal. In March of the same year he had two moderate cases, in June, another case, and in July, another, which proved fatal. "Up to this period," he remarks, "I am not informed that a single case had occurred in the practice of any other physician. Since that period I have had no fatal case in my practice, although I have had several dangerous cases. I have attended in all twenty cases of this disease, of which four have been fatal. I am not aware that there has been any other case in the town of distinct puerperal peritonitis, although I am willing to admit my information may be very defective on this point. I have been told of some 'mixed cases,' and 'morbid affections after delivery.'"*

In the "Quarterly Summary of the Transactions of the College of Physicians of Philadelphia"† may be found some most extraordinary developments respecting a series of cases occurring in the practice of a member of that body.

Dr. Condie called the attention of the Society to the prevalence, at the present time, of puerperal fever of a peculiarly insidious and malignant character. "In the practice of one gentleman extensively engaged as an obstetrician nearly every female he has attended in

* *Remarks on Puerperal Fever*, pp. 12 and 13.

† For May, June, and July, 1842.

confinement, during several weeks past, within the above limits"
(the southern sections and neighboring districts), "had been attacked by the fever."

"An important query presents itself, the doctor observed, in
reference to the particular form of fever now prevalent. Is it,
namely, capable of being propagated by contagion, and is a physician who has been in attendance upon a case of the disease war-
ranted in continuing, without interruption, his practice as an obstetrician ? Dr. C., although not a believer in the contagious character
of many of those affections generally supposed to be propagated
in this manner, has, nevertheless, become convinced by the facts
that have fallen under his notice that the puerperal fever now
prevailing is capable of being communicated by contagion. How,
otherwise, can be explained the very curious circumstance of the
disease in one district being exclusively confined to the practice
of a single physician, a Fellow of this College, extensively engaged
in obstetrical practice, while no instance of the disease has occurred in the patients under the care of any other accoucheur
practising within the same district; scarcely a female that has
been delivered for weeks past has escaped an attack ?"

Dr. Rutter, the practitioner referred to, "observed that, after
the occurrence of a number of cases of the disease in his practice,
he had left the city and remained absent for a week, but, on returning, no article of clothing he then wore having been used by him
before, one of the very first cases of parturition he attended was
followed by an attack of the fever and terminated fatally; he cannot
readily, therefore, believe in the transmission of the disease from
female to female in the person or clothes of the physician."

The meeting at which these remarks were made was held on the
3d of May, 1842. In a letter dated December 20, 1842, addressed
to Dr. Meigs, and to be found in the "Medical Examiner,"* he
speaks of "those horrible cases of puerperal fever, some of which
you did me the favor to see with me during the past summer,"
and talks of his experience in the disease, "now numbering nearly
seventy cases, all of which have occurred within less than a twelve-
month past."

* For January 21, 1843.

And Dr. Meigs asserts, on the same page, "Indeed, I believe that his practice in that department of the profession was greater than that of any other gentleman, which was probably the cause of his seeing a greater number of the cases." This from a professor of midwifery, who some time ago assured a gentleman whom he met in consultation that the night on which they met was the eighteenth in succession that he himself had been summoned from his repose,* seems hardly satisfactory.

I must call the attention of the inquirer most particularly to the Quarterly Report above referred to, and the letters of Dr. Meigs and Dr. Rutter, to be found in the "Medical Examiner." Whatever impression they may produce upon his mind, I trust they will at least convince him that there is some reason for looking into this apparently uninviting subject.

At a meeting of the College of Physicians just mentioned Dr. Warrington stated that a few days after assisting at an autopsy of puerperal peritonitis, in which he laded out the contents of the abdominal cavity with his hands, he was called upon to deliver three women in rapid succession. All of these women were attacked with different forms of what is commonly called puerperal fever. Soon after these he saw two other patients, both on the same day, with the same disease. Of these five patients, two died.

At the same meeting Dr. West mentioned a fact related to him by Dr. Samuel Jackson, of Northumberland. Seven females, delivered by Dr. Jackson in rapid succession, while practising in Northumberland County, were all attacked with puerperal fever, and five of them died. "Women," he said, "who had expected me to attend upon them, now becoming alarmed, removed out of my reach, and others sent for a physician residing several miles distant. These women, as well as those attended by midwives, all did well; nor did we hear of any deaths in child-bed within a radius of fifty miles, excepting two, and these I afterwards ascertained to have been caused by other diseases." He underwent, as he thought, a thorough purification, and still his next patient was attacked with the disease and died. He was led to suspect that the contagion might

* *Medical Examiner* for December 10, 1842.

have been carried in the gloves which he had worn in attendance upon the previous cases. Two months or more after this he had two other cases. He could find nothing to account for these unless it were the instruments for giving enemata, which had been used in two of the former cases and were employed by these patients. When the first case occurred, he was attending and dressing a limb extensively mortified from erysipelas, and went immediately to the accouchement with his clothes and gloves most thoroughly imbued with its effluvia. And here I may mention that this very Dr. Samuel Jackson, of Northumberland, is one of Dr. Dewees's authorities against contagion.

The three following statements are now for the first time given to the public. All of the cases referred to occurred within this State, and two of the three series in Boston and its immediate vicinity.

I. The first is a series of cases which took place during the last spring in a town at some distance from this neighborhood. A physician of that town, Dr. C., had the following consecutive cases:

> No. 1, delivered March 20, died March 24.
> " 2,   "   April 9, " April 14.
> " 3,   "   "   10, "   "   14.
> " 4,   "   "   11, "   "   18.
> " 5,   "   "   27, " May   3.
> " 6,   "   "   28, had some symptoms, recovered.
> " 7,   "   May   8, had some symptoms, also recovered.

These were the only cases attended by this physician during the period referred to. "They were all attended by him until their termination, with the exception of the patient No. 6, who fell into the hands of another physician on the 2d of May." (Dr. C. left town for a few days at this time.) Dr. C. attended cases immediately before and after the above-named periods, none of which, however, presented any peculiar symptoms of the disease.

About the 1st of July he attended another patient in a neighboring village, who died two or three days after delivery.

The first patient, it is stated, was delivered on the 20th of March. "On the 19th Dr. C. made the autopsy of a man who died suddenly, sick only forty-eight hours; had œdema of the thigh and gangrene extending from a little above the ankle into the cavity of the abdomen." Dr. C. wounded himself very slightly in the right hand during the autopsy. The hand was quite painful the night following, during his attendance on the patient No. 1. He did not see this patient after the 20th, being confined to the house, and very sick from the wound just mentioned, from this time until the 3d of April.

Several cases of erysipelas occurred in the house where the autopsy mentioned above took place, soon after the examination. There were also many cases of erysipelas in town at the time of the fatal puerperal cases which have been mentioned.

The nurse who laid out the body of the patient No. 3 was taken on the evening of the same day with sore throat and erysipelas, and died in ten days from the first attack.

The nurse who laid out the body of the patient No. 4 was taken on the day following with symptoms like those of this patient, and died in a week, without any external marks of erysipelas.

"No other cases of similar character with those of Dr. C. occurred in the practice of any of the physicians in the town or vicinity at the time. Deaths following confinement have occurred in the practice of other physicians during the past year, but they were not cases of puerperal fever. No post-mortem examinations were held in any of these puerperal cases."

Some additional statements in this letter are deserving of insertion:

"A physician attended a woman in the immediate neighborhood of the cases numbered 2, 3, and 4. This patient was confined the morning of March 1st, and died on the night of March 7th. It is doubtful whether this should be considered a case of puerperal fever. She had suffered from canker, indigestion, and diarrhœa for a year previous to her delivery. Her complaints were much aggravated for two or three months previous to delivery; she had become greatly emaciated, and weakened to such an extent that it had not been expected that she would long survive her confinement, if indeed she reached that period. Her labor was easy enough; she flowed a good deal, seemed exceedingly prostrated, had ringing in the ears, and other symptoms of exhaustion; the pulse was quick and small. On the second and third day there was some tenderness and tumefaction of the abdomen, which increased somewhat on the fourth and fifth. He had cases in midwifery before and after this, which presented nothing peculiar."

It is also mentioned in the same letter that another physician had a case during the last summer and another last fall, both of which recovered.

Another gentleman reports a case last December, a second case five weeks, and another three weeks, since. All these recovered. A case also occurred very recently in the practice of a physician in the village where the eighth patient of Dr. C. resides, which proved fatal. "This patient had some patches of erysipelas on the legs and arms. The same physician has delivered three cases since, which have all done well. There have been no other cases in this town or its vicinity recently. There have been some few cases of erysipelas." It deserves notice that the partner of Dr. C., who attended the autopsy of the man above mentioned and took an active part in it, who also suffered very slightly from a prick under the thumb-nail received during the examination, had twelve cases of midwifery between March 26th and April 12th, all of which did well, and presented no peculiar symptoms. It should also be stated that during these seventeen days he was in attendance on all the cases of erysipelas in the house where the autopsy had been performed. I owe these facts to the prompt kindness of a gentleman whose intelligence and character are sufficient guaranty for their accuracy.

The two following letters were addressed to my friend Dr. Storer by the gentleman in whose practice the cases of puerperal fever occurred. His name renders it unnecessary to refer more particularly to these gentlemen, who on their part have manifested the most perfect freedom and courtesy in affording these accounts of their painful experience.

"*January* 28, 1843.

II. . . . "The time to which you allude was in 1830. The first case was in February, during a very cold time. She was confined the 4th, and died the 12th. Between the 10th and 28th of this month I attended six women in labor, all of whom did well except the last, as also two who were confined March 1st and 5th. Mrs. E., confined February 28th, sickened, and died March 8th. The next day, 9th, I inspected the body, and the night after attended a lady, Mrs. B., who sickened, and died 16th. The 10th, I attended another, Mrs. G., who sickened, but recovered. March 16th I went from Mrs. G.'s room to attend a Mrs. H., who sickened, and died 21st. The 17th, I inspected Mrs. B. On the 19th, I went directly from Mrs. H.'s room to attend another lady, Mrs. G., who also sickened, and died 22d. While Mrs. B. was sick, on 15th, I went directly from her room a few rods, and attended another woman, who was not sick. Up to 20th of this month I wore the same clothes. I now refused to attend any labor, and did not till April 21st, when, having thoroughly cleansed myself, I resumed my practice, and had no more puerperal fever.

"The cases were not confined to a narrow space. The two nearest were half a mile from each other, and half that distance from my residence. The others were from two to three miles apart, and nearly that distance from my residence. There were no other cases in their immediate vicinity which came to my knowledge. The general health of all the women was pretty good, and all the labors as good as common, except the first. This woman, in consequence of my not arriving in season, and the child being half-born at some time before I arrived, was very much exposed to the cold at the time of confinement, and afterwards, being confined in a very open, cold room. Of the six cases, you perceive only one recovered.

"In the winter of 1817 two of my patients had puerperal fever, one very badly, the other not so badly. Both recovered. One other had swelled leg, or phlegmasia dolens, and one or two others did not recover as well as usual.

"In the summer of 1835 another disastrous period occurred in my practice. July 1st I attended a lady in labor, who was afterwards quite ill and feverish; but at the time I did not consider her case a decided puerperal fever. On the 8th I attended one who did well. On the 12th, one who was seriously sick. This was also an equivocal case, apparently arising from constipation and irritation of the rectum. These women were ten miles apart and five from my residence. On 15th and 20th two who did well. On 25th I attended another. This was a severe labor, and followed by unequivocal puerperal fever, or peritonitis. She recovered. August 2d and 3d, in about twenty-four hours, I attended four persons. Two of them did very well; one was attacked with some of the common symptoms, which, however, subsided in a day or two, and the other had decided puerperal fever, but recovered. This woman resided five miles from me. Up to this time I wore the same coat. All my other clothes had frequently been changed. On 6th, I attended two women, one of whom was not sick at all; but the other, Mrs. L., was afterwards taken ill. On 10th, I attended a lady, who did very well. I had previously changed all my clothes, and had no garment on which had been in a puerperal room. On 12th, I was called to Mrs. S., in labor. While she was ill, I left her to visit Mrs. L., one of the ladies who was confined on 6th. Mrs. L. had been more unwell than usual, but I had not considered her case anything more than common till this visit. I had on a surtout at this visit, which, on my return to Mrs. S., I left in another room. Mrs. S. was delivered on 13th with forceps. These women both died of decided puerperal fever.

"While I attended these women in their fevers I changed my clothes, and washed my hands in a solution of chloride of lime after each visit. I attended seven women in labor during this period, all of whom recovered without sickness.

"In my practice I have had several single cases of puerperal fever, some of whom have died and some have recovered. Until the year 1830 I had no suspicion that the disease could be communicated from one patient to another by a nurse or midwife; but I now think the foregoing facts strongly favor that idea. I was so much convinced of this fact that I adopted the plan before related.

"I believe my own health was as good as usual at each of the above periods. I have no recollection to the contrary.

"I believe I have answered all your questions. I have been more particular on some points perhaps than necessary; but I thought you could form your own opinion better than to take mine. In 1830

I wrote to Dr. Channing a more particular statement of my cases. If I have not answered your questions sufficiently, perhaps Dr. C. may have my letter to him, and you can find your answer there."*

"BOSTON, February 3, 1843.

III. "My DEAR SIR: I received a note from you last evening requesting me to answer certain questions therein proposed, touching the cases of puerperal fever which came under my observation the past summer. It gives me pleasure to comply with your request, so far as it is in my power so to do, but, owing to the hurry in preparing for a journey, the notes of the cases I had then taken were lost or mislaid. The principal *facts*, however, are too vivid upon my recollection to be soon forgotten. I think, therefore, that I shall be able to give you all the information you may require.

"All the cases that occurred in my practice took place between the 7th of May and the 17th of June, 1842.

"They were not confined to any particular part of the city. The first two cases were patients residing at the South End, the next was at the extreme North End, one living in Sea Street and the other in Roxbury. The following is the order in which they occurred:

"CASE 1.—Mrs.—— was confined on the 7th of May, at 5 o'clock, P. M., after a natural labor of six hours. At 12 o'clock at night, on the 9th (thirty-one hours after confinement), she was taken with severe chill, previous to which she was as comfortable as women usually are under the circumstances. She died on the 10th.

"CASE 2.—Mrs.—— was confined on the 10th of June (four weeks after Mrs. C.), at 11 A. M., after a natural, but somewhat severe, labor of five hours. At 7 o'clock, on the morning of the 11th, she had a chill. Died on the 12th.

"CASE 3.—Mrs.——, confined on the 14th of June, was comfortable until the 18th, when symptoms of puerperal fever were manifest. She died on the 20th.

* In a letter to myself this gentleman also stated, "I do not recollect that there was any erysipelas or any other disease particularly prevalent at the time."

"Case 4.—Mrs.——, confined June 17th, at 5 o'clock, a. m., was doing well until the morning of the 19th. She died on the evening of the 21st.

"Case 5.—Mrs.—— was confined with her *fifth* child on the 17th of June, at 6 o'clock in the evening. This patient had been attacked with puerperal fever, at three of her previous confinements, but the disease yielded to depletion and other remedies without difficulty. This time, I regret to say, I was not so fortunate. She was not attacked, as were the other patients, with a chill, but complained of extreme pain in abdomen, and tenderness on pressure, almost from the moment of her confinement. In this, as in the other cases, the disease resisted all remedies, and she died in great distress on the 22d of the same month. Owing to the extreme heat of the season and my own indisposition, none of the subjects were examined after death. Dr. Channing, who was in attendance with me on the three last cases, proposed to have a *post-mortem* examination of the subject of case No. 5, but from some cause which I do not now recollect it was not obtained.

"You wish to know whether I wore the same clothes when attending the different cases. I cannot positively say, but I should think I did not, as the weather became warmer after the first two cases; I therefore think it probable that I made a change of at least a *part* of my dress. I have had no other case of puerperal fever in my own practice for three years, save those above related, and I do not remember to have lost a patient before with this disease. While absent, last July, I visited two patients sick with puerperal fever, with a friend of mine in the country. Both of them recovered.

"The cases that I have recorded were not confined to any particular constitution or temperament, but it seized upon the strong and the weak, the old and the young—one being over forty years, and the youngest under eighteen years of age. . . . If the disease is of an erysipelatous nature, as many suppose, contagionists may perhaps find some ground for their belief in the fact that, for two weeks previous to my first case of puerperal fever, I had been attending a severe case of erysipelas, and the infection may have been conveyed through me to the patient; but, on the other hand, why is not this the case with other physicians, or with the same physician at all times, for since my return from the country I have had a more inveterate case of erysipelas than ever before, and no difficulty whatever has attended any of my midwifery cases?"

I am assured, on unquestionable authority, that "about three years since a gentleman in extensive midwifery business, in a neighboring State, lost in the course of a few weeks eight patients in child-bed, seven of them being undoubted cases of puerperal fever. No other physician of the town lost a single patient of this disease during the same period." And from what I have heard in conversation with some of our most experienced practitioners, I am inclined to think many cases of the kind might be brought to light by extensive inquiry.

This long catalogue of melancholy histories assumes a still darker aspect when we remember how kindly nature deals with the parturient female, when she is not immersed in the virulent atmosphere of an impure lying-in hospital, or poisoned in her chamber by the unsuspected breath of contagion. From all causes together not more than four deaths in a thousand births and miscarriages happened in England and Wales during the period embraced by the first Report of the Registrar-General.* In the second Report the mortality was shown to be about five in one thousand.† In the Dublin Lying-in Hospital, during the seven years of Dr. Collins's mastership, there was one case of puerperal fever to 178 deliveries, or less than six to the thousand, and one death from this disease in 278 cases, or between three and four to the thousand.‡ Yet during this period the disease was endemic in the hospital, and might have gone on to rival the horrors of the pestilence of the Maternité, had not the poison been destroyed by a thorough purification.

In private practice, leaving out of view the cases that are to be ascribed to the self-acting system of propagation, it would seem that the disease must be far from common. Mr. White, of Manchester, says: "Out of the whole number of lying-in patients whom I have delivered (and I may safely call it a great one), I have never lost one, nor to the best of my recollection has one been greatly endangered,

---

* First Report, p. 105. † Second Report, p. 73.

‡ Collins's *Treatise on Midwifery*, p. 228, etc.

by the puerperal, miliary, low nervous, putrid malignant, or milk fever."* Dr. Joseph Clarke informed Dr. Collins that in the course of *forty-five* years' most extensive practice he lost but *four* patients from this disease.† One of the most eminent practitioners of Glasgow who has been engaged in very extensive practice for upwards of a quarter of a century testifies that he never saw more than twelve cases of real puerperal fever.‡

I have myself been told by two gentlemen practising in this city, and having for many years a large midwifery business, that they had neither of them lost a patient from this disease, and by one of them that he had only seen it in consultation with other physicians. In five hundred cases of midwifery, of which Dr. Storer has given an abstract in the first number of this journal, there was only one instance of fatal puerperal peritonitis.

In the view of these facts it does appear a singular coincidence that one man or woman should have ten, twenty, thirty, or seventy cases of this rare disease following his or her footsteps with the keenness of a beagle, through the streets and lanes of a crowded city, while the scores that cross the same paths on the same errands know it only by name. It is a series of similar coincidences which has led us to consider the dagger, the musket, and certain innocent-looking white powders as having some little claim to be regarded as dangerous. It is the practical inattention to similar coincidences which has given rise to the unpleasant but often necessary documents called *indictments*, which has sharpened a form of the cephalotome sometimes employed in the case of adults, and adjusted that modification of the fillet which delivers the world of those who happen to be too much in the way while such striking coincidences are taking place.

I shall now mention a few instances in which the disease appears to have been conveyed by the process of direct inoculation.

Dr. Campbell, of Edinburgh, states that in October, 1821, he assisted at the post-mortem examination of a patient who died with puerperal fever. He carried the pelvic viscera in his pocket to the class-room. The same evening he attended a woman in

* *Op. cit.*, p. 115.   † *Op. cit.*, p. 228.   ‡ *Lancet*, May 4, 1833.

labor without previously changing his clothes; this patient died. The next morning he delivered a woman with the forceps; she died also, and of many others who were seized with the disease within a few weeks, three shared the same fate in succession.

In June, 1823, he assisted some of his pupils at the autopsy of a case of puerperal fever. He was unable to wash his hands with proper care, for want of the necessary accommodations. On getting home he found that two patients required his assistance. He went without further ablution or changing his clothes; both these patients died with puerperal fever.* This same Dr. Campbell is one of Dr. Churchill's authorities against contagion.

Mr. Roberton says that in one instance within his knowledge a practitioner passed the catheter for a patient with puerperal fever late in the evening; the same night he attended a lady who had the symptoms of the disease on the second day. In another instance a surgeon was called while in the act of inspecting the body of a woman who had died of this fever, to attend a labor; within forty-eight hours this patient was seized with the fever.†

On the 16th of March, 1831, a medical practitioner examined the body of a woman who had died a few days after delivery, from puerperal peritonitis. On the evening of the 17th he delivered a patient, who was seized with puerperal fever on the 19th, and died on the 24th. Between this period and the 6th of April the same practitioner attended two other patients, both of whom were attacked with the same disease and died.‡

In the autumn of 1829 a physician was present at the examination of a case of puerperal fever, dissected out the organs, and assisted in sewing up the body. He had scarcely reached home when he was summoned to attend a young lady in labor. In sixteen hours she was attacked with the symptoms of puerperal fever, and narrowly escaped with her life.§

In December, 1830, a midwife, who had attended two fatal cases of puerperal fever at the British Lying-in Hospital, examined

* *Lond. Med. Gazette*, December 10, 1831. † *Ibid.* for January, 1832.
‡ *London Cyc. of Pract. Med.*, art., "Fever, Puerperal."
§ *London Cyc. of Pract. Med.*, art. "Fever Puerperal."

a patient who had just been admitted, to ascertain if labor had commenced. This patient remained two days in the expectation that labor would come on, when she returned home and was then suddenly taken in labor and delivered before she could set out for the hospital. She went on favorably for two days, and was then taken with puerperal fever and died in thirty-six hours.*

"A young practitioner, contrary to advice, examined the body of a patient who had died from puerperal fever; there was no epidemic at the time; the case appeared to be purely sporadic. He delivered three other women shortly afterwards; they all died with puerperal fever, the symptoms of which broke out very soon after labor. The patients of his colleague did well, except one, where he assisted to remove some coagula from the uterus; she was attacked in the same manner as those whom he had attended, and died also." The writer in the "British and Foreign Medical Review," from whom I quote this statement,—and who is no other than Dr. Rigby,—adds: "We trust that this fact alone will forever silence such doubts, and stamp the well-merited epithet of 'criminal,' as above quoted, upon such attempts."†

From the cases given by Mr. Ingleby I select the following: Two gentlemen, after having been engaged in conducting the *post-mortem* examination of a case of puerperal fever, went in the same dress, each respectively, to a case of midwifery. "The one patient was seized with the rigor about thirty hours afterwards. The other patient was seized with a rigor the third morning after delivery. *One recovered, one died.*"‡ One of these same gentlemen attended another woman in the same clothes two days after the autopsy referred to. "The rigor did not take place until the evening of the fifth day from the first visit. *Result fatal.*" These cases belonged to a series of seven, the first of which was thought to have originated in a case of erysipelas. "Several cases of a mild character followed the foregoing seven, and their nature being now most unequivocal, my friend declined visiting all midwifery cases for a time, and there was no recurrence of the disease."

These cases occurred in 1833. Five of them proved fatal. Mr. Ingleby gives another series of seven cases which occurred to a practitioner in 1836, the first of which was also attributed to his having opened several erysipelatous abscesses a short time previously.

I need not refer to the case lately read before this society, in which a physician went, soon after performing an autopsy of a case of puerperal fever, to a woman in labor, who was seized with the same disease and perished. The forfeit of that error has been already paid.

At a meeting of the Medical and Chirurgical Society before referred to, Dr. Merriman related an instance occurring in his own practice, which excites a reasonable suspicion that two lives were sacrificed to a still less dangerous experiment. He was at the examination of a case of puerperal fever at two o'clock in the afternoon. *He took care not to touch the body.* At nine o'clock the same evening he attended a woman in labor; she was so nearly delivered that he had scarcely anything to do. The next morning she had severe rigors, and in forty-eight hours she was a corpse. Her infant had erysipelas and died in two days.*

In connection with the facts which have been stated it seems proper to allude to the dangerous and often fatal effects which have followed from wounds received in the post-mortem examination of patients who have died of puerperal fever. The fact that such wounds are attended with peculiar risk has been long noticed. I find that Chaussier was in the habit of cautioning his students against the danger to which they were exposed in these dissections.†
The head *pharmacien* of the Hôtel Dieu, in his analysis of the fluid effused in puerperal peritonitis, says that practitioners are convinced of its deleterious qualities, and that it is very dangerous to apply it to the denuded skin.‡ Sir Benjamin Brodie speaks of it as being well known that the inoculation of lymph or pus from the peritoneum of a puerperal patient is often attended with danger-

* *Lancet,* May 2, 1840.
† Stein, *L'Art d'Accoucher,* 1794; *Dict. des Sciences Médicales,* art., "Puerperal."
‡ *Journal de Pharmacie,* January, 1836.

ous and even fatal symptoms. Three cases in confirmation of this statement, two of them fatal, have been reported to this society within a few months.

Of about fifty cases of injuries of this kind, of various degrees of severity, which I have collected from different sources, at least twelve were instances of infection from puerperal peritonitis. Some of the others are so stated as to render it probable that they may have been of the same nature. Five other cases were of peritoneal inflammation; three in males. Three were what was called enteritis, in one instance complicated with erysipelas; but it is well known that this term has been often used to signify inflammation of the peritoneum covering the intestines. On the other hand, no case of typhus or typhoid fever is mentioned as giving rise to dangerous consequences, with the exception of the single instance of an undertaker mentioned by Mr. Travers, who seems to have been poisoned by a fluid which exuded from the body. The other accidents were produced by dissection, or some other mode of contact with bodies of patients who had died of various affections. They also differed much in severity, the cases of puerperal origin being among the most formidable and fatal. Now a moment's reflection will show that the number of cases of serious consequences ensuing from the dissection of the bodies of those who had perished of puerperal fever is so vastly disproportioned to the relatively small number of autopsies made in this complaint as compared with typhus or pneumonia (from which last disease not one case of poisoning happened), and still more from all diseases put together, that the conclusion is irresistible that a most fearful morbid poison is often generated in the course of this disease. Whether or not it is *sui generis* confined to this disease, or produced in some others, as, for instance, erysipelas, I need not stop to inquire.

In connection with this may be taken the following statement of Dr. Rigby. "That the discharges from a patient under puerperal fever are in the highest degree contagious we have abundant evidence in the history of lying-in hospitals. The puerperal abscesses are also contagious, and may be communicated to healthy lying-in women by washing with the same sponge; this fact has been repeatedly proved in the Vienna Hospital; but they are equally communicable to women not pregnant; on more than one occasion the women engaged in washing the soiled bed-linen of the General Lying-in Hospital have been attacked with abscess in the fingers or hands, attended with rapidly spreading inflammation of the cellular tissue."*

Now add to all this the undisputed fact that within the walls of lying-in hospitals there is often generated a miasm, palpable as the chlorine used to destroy it, tenacious so as in some cases almost to defy extirpation, deadly in some institutions as the plague; which has killed women in a private hospital of London so fast that they were buried two in one coffin to conceal its horrors; which enabled Tonnellé to record two hundred and twenty-two autopsies at the Maternité of Paris; which has led Dr. Lee to express his deliberate conviction that the loss of life occasioned by these institutions completely defeats the objects of their founders; and out of this train of cumulative evidence, the multiplied groups of cases clustering about individuals, the deadly results of autopsies, the inoculation by fluids from the living patient, the murderous poison of hospitals—does there not result a conclusion that laughs all sophistry to scorn, and renders all argument an insult?

I have had occasion to mention some instances in which there was an apparent relation between puerperal fever and erysipelas. The length to which this paper has extended does not allow me to enter into the consideration of this most important subject. I will only say that the evidence appears to me altogether satisfactory that some most fatal series of puerperal fever have been produced by an infection originating in the matter or effluvia of erysipelas. In evidence of some connection between the two diseases, I need not go back to the older authors, as Pouteau or Gordon, but will content myself with giving the following references, with their dates; from which it will be seen that the testimony has been constantly coming before the profession for the last few years:

* *System of Midwifery*, p. 292.

"London Cyclopædia of Practical Medicine," article *Puerpe-ral Fever*, 1833.

Mr. Ceeley's Account of the Puerperal Fever at Aylesbury, "Lancet," 1835.

Dr. Ramsbotham's Lecture, "London Medical Gazette," 1835.

Mr. Yates Ackerly's Letter in the same journal, 1838.

Mr. Ingleby on Epidemic Puerperal Fever, "Edinburgh Medical and Surgical Journal," 1838.

Mr. Paley's Letter, "London Medical Gazette," 1839.

Remarks at the Medical and Chirurgical Society, "Lancet," 1840.

Dr. Rigby's "System of Midwifery," 1841.

"Nunneley on Erysipelas," a work which contains a large number of references on the subject, 1841.

"British and Foreign Quarterly Review," 1842.

Dr. S. Jackson, of Northumberland, as already quoted from the Summary of the College of Physicians, 1842.

And, lastly, a startling series of cases by Mr. Storrs, of Doncaster, to be found in the "American Journal of the Medical Sciences" for January, 1843.

The relation of puerperal fever with other continued fevers would seem to be remote and rarely obvious. Hey refers to two cases of synochus occurring in the Royal Infirmary of Edinburgh, in women who had attended upon puerperal patients. Dr. Collins refers to several instances in which puerperal fever has appeared to originate from a continued proximity to patients suffering with typhus.*

Such occurrences as those just mentioned, though most important to be remembered and guarded against, hardly attract our notice in the midst of the gloomy facts by which they are surrounded. Of these facts, at the risk of fatiguing repetitions, I have summoned a sufficient number, as I believe, to convince the most incredulous that every attempt to disguise the truth which underlies them all is useless.

It is true that some of the historians of the disease, especially

* *Treatise on Midwifery*, p. 228.

Hulme, Hull, and Leake, in England; Tonnellé, Dugès, and
Baudelocque, in France, profess not to have found puerperal
fever contagious. At the most they give us mere negative facts,
worthless against an extent of evidence which now overlaps the
widest range of doubt, and doubles upon itself in the redundancy
of superfluous demonstration. Examined in detail, this and much
of the show of testimony brought up to stare the daylight of conviction out of countenance, proves to be in a great measure
unmeaning and inapplicable, as might be easily shown were it
necessary. Nor do I feel the necessity of enforcing the conclusion which arises spontaneously from the facts which have been
enumerated, by formally citing the opinions of those grave
authorities who have for the last half-century been sounding the
unwelcome truth it has cost so many lives to establish.

"It is to the British practitioner," says Dr. Rigby, "that we are
indebted for strongly insisting upon this important and dangerous
character of puerperal fever."*

The names of Gordon, John Clarke, Denman, Burns, Young,†
Hamilton,‡ Haighton,§ Good,‖ Waller,¶ Blundell, Gooch, Ramsbotham, Douglas,** Lee, Ingleby, Locock,†† Abercrombie,‡‡
Alison,§§ Travers,‖‖ Rigby, and Watson,¶¶ many of whose writings I have already referred to, may have some influence with
those who prefer the weight of authorities to the simple deductions
of their own reason from the facts laid before them. A few Continental writers have adopted similar conclusions.*** It gives me

* *British and Foreign Med. Rev.* for January, 1842.

† *Encyc. Britannica*, xiii, 467, art., "Medicine."

‡ *Outlines of Midwifery*, p. 109.   § *Oral Lectures*, etc.

‖ *Study of Medicine*, ii, 195.   ¶ *Medical and Physical Journal*, July, 1830.

** *Dublin Hospital Reports* for 1822.

†† *Library of Practical Medicine*, i, 373.

‡‡ *Researches on Diseases of the Stomach*, etc., p. 181.

§§ *Library of Practical Medicine*, i, 96.

‖‖ *Further Researches on Constitutional Irritation*, p. 128.

¶¶ *London Medical Gazette*, February, 1842.

***See *British and Foreign Medical Review*, vol. iii, p. 525, and vol. iv, p. 517.
Also *Ed. Med. and Surg. Journal* for July, 1824, and *American Journal of Med.
Sciences* for January, 1841.

pleasure to remember that, while the doctrine has been unceremoniously discredited in one of the leading journals,* and made very light of by teachers in two of the principal medical schools of this country, Dr. Channing has for many years inculcated, and enforced by examples, the danger to be apprehended and the precautions to be taken in the disease under consideration.

I have no wish to express any harsh feeling with regard to the painful subject which has come before us. If there are any so far excited by the story of these dreadful events that they ask for some word of indignant remonstrance to show that science does not turn the hearts of its followers into ice or stone, let me remind them that such words have been uttered by those who speak with an authority I could not claim.† It is as a lesson rather than as a reproach that I call up the memory of these irreparable errors and wrongs. No tongue can tell the heart-breaking calamity they have caused; they have closed the eyes just opened upon a new world of love and happiness; they have bowed the strength of manhood into the dust; they have cast the helplessness of infancy into the stranger's arms, or bequeathed it, with less cruelty, the death of its dying parent. There is no tone deep enough for regret, and no voice loud enough for warning. The woman about to become a mother, or with her new-born infant upon her bosom, should be the object of trembling care and sympathy wherever she bears her tender burden or stretches her aching limbs. The very outcast of the streets has pity upon her sister in degradation when the seal of promised maternity is impressed upon her. The remorseless vengeance of the law, brought down upon its victim by a machinery as sure as destiny, is arrested in its fall at a word which reveals her transient claim for mercy. The solemn prayer of the liturgy singles out her sorrows from the multiplied trials of life, to plead for her in the hour of peril. God forbid that any member of the profession to which she trusts her life, doubly precious at that eventful period, should hazard it negligently, unadvisedly, or selfishly!

* *Phil. Med. Journal*, vol. xii, p. 364.

† Dr. Blundell and Dr. Rigby in the works already cited.

There may be some among those whom I address who are disposed to ask the question, What course are we to follow in relation to this matter? The facts are before them, and the answer must be left to their own judgment and conscience. If any should care to know my own conclusions, they are the following; and in taking the liberty to state them very freely and broadly, I would ask the inquirer to examine them as freely in the light of the evidence which has been laid before him.

1. A physician holding himself in readiness to attend cases of midwifery should never take any active part in the post-mortem examination of cases of puerperal fever.

2. If a physician is present at such autopsies, he should use thorough ablution, change every article of dress, and allow twenty-four hours or more to elapse before attending to any case of midwifery. It may be well to extend the same caution to cases of simple peritonitis.

3. Similar precautions should be taken after the autopsy or surgical treatment of cases of erysipelas, if the physician is obliged to unite such offices with his obstetrical duties, which is in the highest degree inexpedient.

4. On the occurrence of a single case of puerperal fever in his practice, the physician is is bound to consider the next female he attends in labor, unless some weeks at least have elapsed, as in danger of being infected by him, and it is his duty to take every precaution to diminish her risk of disease and death.

5. If within a short period two cases of puerperal fever happen close to each other, in the practice of the same physician, the disease not existing or prevailing in the neighborhood, he would do wisely to relinquish his obstetrical practice for at least one month, and endeavor to free himself by every available means from any noxious influence he may carry about with him.

6. The occurrence of three or more closely connected cases, in the practice of one individual, no others existing in the neighborhood, and no other sufficient cause being alleged for the coincidence, is *primâ facie* evidence that he is the vehicle of contagion.

7. It is the duty of the physician to take every precaution that

the disease shall not be introduced by nurses or other assistants, by making proper inquiries concerning them, and giving timely warning of every suspected source of danger.

8. Whatever indulgence may be granted to those who have heretofore been the ignorant causes of so much misery, the time has come when the existence of a *private pestilence* in the sphere of a single physician should be looked upon, not as a misfortune, but a crime; and in the knowledge of such occurrences the duties of the practitioner to his profession should give way to his paramount obligations to society.

ADDITIONAL REFERENCES AND CASES

Fifth Annual Report of the Registrar-General of England, 1843. Appendix. Letter from William Farr, Esq.—Several new series of cases are given in the letter of Mr. Storrs, contained in the appendix to this report. Mr. Storrs suggests precautions similar to those I have laid down, and these precautions are strongly enforced by Mr. Farr, who is, therefore, obnoxious to the same criticisms as myself.

Hall and Dexter, in Am. Journal of Med. Sc. for January, 1844.—Cases of puerperal fever seeming to originate in erysipelas.

Elkington, of Birmingham, in Provincial Med. Journal, cited in Am. Journ. Med. Sc. for April, 1844.—Six cases in less than a fortnight, seeming to originate in a case of erysipelas.

West's Reports, in Brit. and For. Med. Review for October, 1845, and January, 1847.—Affection of the arm, resembling malignant pustule, after removing the placenta of a patient who died from puerperal fever. Reference to cases at Würzburg, as proving contagion, and to Keiller's cases in the Monthly Journal for February, 1846, as showing connection of puerperal fever and erysipelas.

Kneeland.—Contagiousness of Puerperal Fever. Am. Jour. Med. Sc., January, 1846. Also, Connection between Puerperal Fever and Epidemic Erysipelas. *Ibid.*, April, 1846.

Robert Storrs.—Contagious Effects of Puerperal Fever on the Male Subject; or on Persons not Child-bearing. (From Provincial Med. and Surg. Journal.) Am. Jour. Med. Sc., January, 1846. Numerous cases. See also Dr. Reid's case in same journal for April, 1846.

Routh's paper in Proc. of Royal Med. Chir. Soc., Am. Jour. Med. Sc., April, 1849, also in B. and F. Med. Chir. Review, April, 1850.

Hill, of Leuchars.—A Series of Cases Illustrating the Contagious Nature of Erysipelas and of Puerperal Fever, and their Intimate Pathological Connection. (From Monthly Journal of Med. Sc.) Am. Jour. Med. Sc., July, 1850.

Skoda on the Causes of Puerperal Fever. (Peritonitis in rabbits, from inoculation with different morbid secretions.) Am. Jour. Med. Sc., October, 1850.

Arneth.—Paper read before the National Academy of Medicine. Annales d'Hygiène, Tome LXV. 2e Partie. (Means of Disinfection proposed by M. "Semmeliveis." (Semmelweiss.) Lotions of chloride of lime and use of nail-brush before admission to lying-in wards. Alleged sudden and great decrease of mortality from puerperal fever. Cause of disease attributed to inoculation with cadaveric matters.) See also *Routh's* paper, mentioned above.

Moir.—Remarks at a meeting of the Edinburgh Medico-chirurgical Society. Refers to cases of Dr. Kellie, of Leith. *Sixteen* in succession, *all fatal.* Also to several instances of individual pupils having had a succession of cases in various quarters of the town, while others, practising as extensively in the same localities, had none. Also to several special cases not mentioned elsewhere. Am. Jour. Med. Sc. for October, 1851. (From New Monthly Journal of Med. Science.)

Simpson.—Observations at a Meeting of the Edinburgh Obstetrical Society. (An "eminent gentleman," according to Dr. Meigs, whose "name is as well known in America as in (his) native land," Obstetrics, Phil., 1852, pp. 368, 375.) The student is referred to this paper for a valuable *résumé* of many of the facts, and the necessary inferences, relating to this subject. Also for another series of cases, Mr. Sidey's, five or six in rapid succession. Dr. Simpson attended the dissection of two of Dr. Sidey's cases, and freely handled the diseased parts. His next four child-bed patients were affected with puerperal fever, and it was the first time he had seen it in practice. As Dr. Simpson is *a gentleman* (Dr. Meigs, as above), and as "a gentleman's hands are clean" (Dr. Meigs' sixth letter), it follows that a gentleman with clean hands may carry the disease. Am. Jour. Med. Sc., October, 1851.

Peddie.—The five or six cases of Dr. Sidey, followed by the four of Dr. Simpson, did not end the series. A practitioner in Leith having examined in Dr. Simpson's house, a portion of the uterus obtained from one of the patients, had immediately afterwards three fatal cases of puerperal fever. Dr. Peddie referred to two distinct series of consecutive cases in his own practice. He had since taken precautions, and not met with any such cases. Am. Jour. Med. Sc., October, 1851.

Copland.—Considers it proved that puerperal fever may be propagated by the hands and the clothes, or either, of a third person, the bed-clothes or body-clothes of a patient. Mentions a new series of cases, one of which he saw, with the practitioner who had attended them. She was *the sixth* he had had within a few days. *All died.* Dr. Copland insisted that contagion had caused these cases; advised precautionary measures, and the practitioner had no other cases for a considerable time. Considers it *criminal,* after the evidence adduced,—which he could have quadrupled,—and the weight of authority brought forward, for a practitioner to be the medium of transmitting contagion and death to his patients. Dr. Copland lays down rules similar to those suggested by myself, and is therefore entitled to the same epithet for so doing. Medical Dictionary, New York, 1852. Article, *Puerperal States and Diseases.*

If there is any appetite for facts so craving as to be yet unappeased,—*lassata, necdum satiata,*—more can be obtained. Dr. Hodge remarks that "the frequency and importance of this singular circumstance (that the disease is occasionally more prevalent with one practitioner than another) has been exceedingly overrated." More than thirty strings of cases, more than two hundred and fifty sufferers from puerperal fever, more than one hundred and thirty deaths, appear as the results of a sparing estimate of such among the facts I have gleaned as could be numerically valued. These facts constitute, we may take it for granted, but a small fraction of those that have actually occurred. The number of them might be greater, but "'t is enough, 't will serve," in Mercutio's modest phrase, so far as frequency is concerned. For a just estimate of the importance of the singular circumstance, it might be proper to consult the languid survivors, the widowed husbands, and the motherless children, as well as "the unfortunate accoucheur."

LIST OF WRITINGS *

The Contagiousness of Puerperal Fever, N. Eng. Q. J. M. and S., Bost., 1842–3, i, 503–530. Also reprint.

Boylston prize dissertations for the years 1836 and 1837, xiv, 371 pp., octavo, Boston, Little and Brown, 1838.

Homeopathy and its Kindred Delusions, 72 pp., 12mo, Boston, W. D. Ticknor, 1842.

The Position and Prospects of the Medical Student, 28 pp., octavo, Boston, J. Putnam, 1844.

An Introductory Lecture, Delivered at the Massachusetts Medical College, 38 pp., octavo, Boston, W. D. Ticknor and Co., 1847.

The Benefactors of the Medical School of Harvard University, 37 pp., octavo, Boston, Ticknor, Reed and Fields, 1850.

Puerperal Fever as a Private Pestilence, 60 pp., octavo, Boston, Ticknor and Fields, 1855.

Valedictory Address (Harvard University), 15 pp., octavo, Boston, D. Clapp, 1858. Reprinted from Boston M. and S. J., 1858, lviii.

Currents and Counter Currents in Medical Science, 48 pp., octavo, Ticknor and Fields, 1860.

Border Lines of Knowledge in Some Provinces of Medical Science, 80 pp., octavo, Boston, Ticknor and Fields, 1862.

Oration Delivered Before the City Authorities of Boston on the Fourth of July, 1863, 60 pp., octavo, Boston, J. E. Farwell and Co., 1863.

The Human Wheel, 15 pp., octavo, Philadelphia, B. F. Palmer, 1863.

Teaching from the Chair and at the Bedside, 45 pp., octavo, Boston, D. Clapp and Son, 1867.

The Medical Profession in Massachusetts: A Lecture, 45 pp., octavo, Boston, J. Wilson and Son, 1869.

The Claims of Dentistry, 35 pp., octavo, Boston, Rand, Avery and Co., 1872.

Mechanism in Thought and Morals, 101 pp., octavo, Boston, J. R. Osgood and Co., 1877.

Dedicatory Address at the Opening of the New Building and Hall of the Boston Medical Library Association, 14 pp., octavo, Cambridge, 1879.

Farewell Address (as) Parkman, Professor of Anatomy in the Medical School of Harvard University, November 28, 1882.

* As they appear in the Surgeon General's Library, Index Catalogue (Washington), and the Index Medicus.

Holmes's article on Puerperal Fever antedates that of Semmelweis, but as the writings of the latter author are classical, references to them are given here—

Semmelweis, Ignaz Philipp, 1818–1865.
Die Aetiologie, der Begriff, und die Prophylaxis des Kindbettfiebers, vi, 543 pp., octavo, Pest, Wien, u. Leipzig, C. A. Hartleben, 1861.
Zwei offene Briefe an Dr. J. Spaeth, Professor der Geburtshilfe an der K. K. Josephs Akademie in Wien und an Hofrath Dr. F. W. Scanzoni, Professor der Geburtshilfe zu Würzburg, 21 pp., 16mo, Pest, G. Emich, 1861.
Zwei offene Briefe an Hofrath Dr. Edward Casp. Jac v. Siebold, Professor der Geburtshilfe zu Göttingen, und an Hofrath Dr. F. W. Scanzoni, Professor der Geburtshilfe zu Würzburg, 40 pp., 16mo, Pest, G. Emich, 1861.
Höchst wichtige Erfahrungen über die Aetiologie der in Gebäranstalten epidemischen Puerperalfieber. Ztschr. d. K. K. Gesellsch. d. Aerzte in Wien, 1847, ii, 242, 1849, v, 64.
A Gyermekágyi lás Kóroktana (etiologie of puerperal fever), Orvosi hetil., Budapest, 1858, ii, 1; 17; 65; 81; 305; 337; 353.

A CATALOGUE OF SELECTED DOVER BOOKS
IN ALL FIELDS OF INTEREST

A CATALOGUE OF SELECTED DOVER BOOKS
IN ALL FIELDS OF INTEREST

WHAT IS SCIENCE?, *N. Campbell*
The role of experiment and measurement, the function of mathematics, the nature of scientific laws, the difference between laws and theories, the limitations of science, and many similarly provocative topics are treated clearly and without technicalities by an eminent scientist. "Still an excellent introduction to scientific philosophy," H. Margenau in *Physics Today*. "A first-rate primer . . . deserves a wide audience," *Scientific American*. 192pp. 5⅜ x 8.
Paperbound $1.25

THE NATURE OF LIGHT AND COLOUR IN THE OPEN AIR, *M. Minnaert*
Why are shadows sometimes blue, sometimes green, or other colors depending on the light and surroundings? What causes mirages? Why do multiple suns and moons appear in the sky? Professor Minnaert explains these unusual phenomena and hundreds of others in simple, easy-to-understand terms based on optical laws and the properties of light and color. No mathematics is required but artists, scientists, students, and everyone fascinated by these "tricks" of nature will find thousands of useful and amazing pieces of information. Hundreds of observational experiments are suggested which require no special equipment. 200 illustrations; 42 photos. xvi + 362pp. 5⅜ x 8.
Paperbound $2.00

THE STRANGE STORY OF THE QUANTUM, AN ACCOUNT FOR THE GENERAL READER OF THE GROWTH OF IDEAS UNDERLYING OUR PRESENT ATOMIC KNOWLEDGE, *B. Hoffmann*
Presents lucidly and expertly, with barest amount of mathematics, the problems and theories which led to modern quantum physics. Dr. Hoffmann begins with the closing years of the 19th century, when certain trifling discrepancies were noticed, and with illuminating analogies and examples takes you through the brilliant concepts of Planck, Einstein, Pauli, Broglie, Bohr, Schroedinger, Heisenberg, Dirac, Sommerfeld, Feynman, etc. This edition includes a new, long postscript carrying the story through 1958. "Of the books attempting an account of the history and contents of our modern atomic physics which have come to my attention, this is the best," H. Margenau, Yale University, in *American Journal of Physics*. 32 tables and line illustrations. Index. 275pp. 5⅜ x 8.
Paperbound $1.75

GREAT IDEAS OF MODERN MATHEMATICS: THEIR NATURE AND USE, *Jagjit Singh*
Reader with only high school math will understand main mathematical ideas of modern physics, astronomy, genetics, psychology, evolution, etc. better than many who use them as tools, but comprehend little of their basic structure. Author uses his wide knowledge of non-mathematical fields in brilliant exposition of differential equations, matrices, group theory, logic, statistics, problems of mathematical foundations, imaginary numbers, vectors, etc. Original publication. 2 appendixes. 2 indexes. 65 ills. 322pp. 5⅜ x 8.
Paperbound $2.00

The Music of the Spheres: The Material Universe — From Atom to Quasar, Simply Explained, *Guy Murchie*
Vast compendium of fact, modern concept and theory, observed and calculated data, historical background guides intelligent layman through the material universe. Brilliant exposition of earth's construction, explanations for moon's craters, atmospheric components of Venus and Mars (with data from recent fly-by's), sun spots, sequences of star birth and death, neighboring galaxies, contributions of Galileo, Tycho Brahe, Kepler, etc.; and (Vol. 2) construction of the atom (describing newly discovered sigma and xi subatomic particles), theories of sound, color and light, space and time, including relativity theory, quantum theory, wave theory, probability theory, work of Newton, Maxwell, Faraday, Einstein, de Broglie, etc. "Best presentation yet offered to the intelligent general reader," *Saturday Review.* Revised (1967). Index. 319 illustrations by the author. Total of xx + 644pp. 5⅜ x 8½.
Vol. 1 Paperbound $2.00, Vol. 2 Paperbound $2.00,
The set $4.00

Four Lectures on Relativity and Space, *Charles Proteus Steinmetz*
Lecture series, given by great mathematician and electrical engineer, generally considered one of the best popular-level expositions of special and general relativity theories and related questions. Steinmetz translates complex mathematical reasoning into language accessible to laymen through analogy, example and comparison. Among topics covered are relativity of motion, location, time; of mass; acceleration; 4-dimensional time-space; geometry of the gravitational field; curvature and bending of space; non-Euclidean geometry. Index. 40 illustrations. x + 142pp. 5⅜ x 8½. Paperbound $1.35

How to Know the Wild Flowers, *Mrs. William Starr Dana*
Classic nature book that has introduced thousands to wonders of American wild flowers. Color-season principle of organization is easy to use, even by those with no botanical training, and the genial, refreshing discussions of history, folklore, uses of over 1,000 native and escape flowers, foliage plants are informative as well as fun to read. Over 170 full-page plates, collected from several editions, may be colored in to make permanent records of finds. Revised to conform with 1950 edition of Gray's Manual of Botany. xlii + 438pp. 5⅜ x 8½. Paperbound $2.00

Manual of the Trees of North America, *Charles Sprague Sargent*
Still unsurpassed as most comprehensive, reliable study of North American tree characteristics, precise locations and distribution. By dean of American dendrologists. Every tree native to U.S., Canada, Alaska; 185 genera, 717 species, described in detail—leaves, flowers, fruit, winterbuds, bark, wood, growth habits, etc. plus discussion of varieties and local variants, immaturity variations. Over 100 keys, including unusual 11-page analytical key to genera, aid in identification. 783 clear illustrations of flowers, fruit, leaves. An unmatched permanent reference work for all nature lovers. Second enlarged (1926) edition. Synopsis of families. Analytical key to genera. Glossary of technical terms. Index. 783 illustrations, 1 map. Total of 982pp. 5⅜ x 8.
Vol. 1 Paperbound $2.25, Vol. 2 Paperbound $2.25,
The set $4.50

IT'S FUN TO MAKE THINGS FROM SCRAP MATERIALS,
Evelyn Glantz Hershoff
What use are empty spools, tin cans, bottle tops? What can be made from rubber bands, clothes pins, paper clips, and buttons? This book provides simply worded instructions and large diagrams showing you how to make cookie cutters, toy trucks, paper turkeys, Halloween masks, telephone sets, aprons, linoleum block- and spatter prints — in all 399 projects! Many are easy enough for young children to figure out for themselves; some challenging enough to entertain adults; all are remarkably ingenious ways to make things from materials that cost pennies or less! Formerly "Scrap Fun for Everyone." Index. 214 illustrations. 373pp. 5⅜ x 8½. Paperbound $1.50

SYMBOLIC LOGIC and THE GAME OF LOGIC, *Lewis Carroll*
"Symbolic Logic" is not concerned with modern symbolic logic, but is instead a collection of over 380 problems posed with charm and imagination, using the syllogism and a fascinating diagrammatic method of drawing conclusions. In "The Game of Logic" Carroll's whimsical imagination devises a logical game played with 2 diagrams and counters (included) to manipulate hundreds of tricky syllogisms. The final section, "Hit or Miss" is a lagniappe of 101 additional puzzles in the delightful Carroll manner. Until this reprint edition, both of these books were rarities costing up to $15 each. Symbolic Logic: Index. xxxi + 199pp. The Game of Logic: 96pp. 2 vols. bound as one. 5⅜ x 8. Paperbound $2.00

MATHEMATICAL PUZZLES OF SAM LOYD, PART I
selected and edited by M. Gardner
Choice puzzles by the greatest American puzzle creator and innovator. Selected from his famous collection, "Cyclopedia of Puzzles," they retain the unique style and historical flavor of the originals. There are posers based on arithmetic, algebra, probability, game theory, route tracing, topology, counter and sliding block, operations research, geometrical dissection. Includes the famous "14-15" puzzle which was a national craze, and his "Horse of a Different Color" which sold millions of copies. 117 of his most ingenious puzzles in all. 120 line drawings and diagrams. Solutions. Selected references. xx + 167pp. 5⅜ x 8. Paperbound $1.00

STRING FIGURES AND HOW TO MAKE THEM, *Caroline Furness Jayne*
107 string figures plus variations selected from the best primitive and modern examples developed by Navajo, Apache, pygmies of Africa, Eskimo, in Europe, Australia, China, etc. The most readily understandable, easy-to-follow book in English on perennially popular recreation. Crystal-clear exposition; step-by-step diagrams. Everyone from kindergarten children to adults looking for unusual diversion will be endlessly amused. Index. Bibliography. Introduction by A. C. Haddon. 17 full-page plates, 960 illustrations. xxiii + 401pp. 5⅜ x 8½. Paperbound $2.00

PAPER FOLDING FOR BEGINNERS, *W. D. Murray and F. J. Rigney*
A delightful introduction to the varied and entertaining Japanese art of origami (paper folding), with a full, crystal-clear text that anticipates every difficulty; over 275 clearly labeled diagrams of all important stages in creation. You get results at each stage, since complex figures are logically developed from simpler ones. 43 different pieces are explained: sailboats, frogs, roosters, etc. 6 photographic plates. 279 diagrams. 95pp. 5⅜ x 8⅜. Paperbound $1.00

PRINCIPLES OF ART HISTORY,
H. Wölfflin
Analyzing such terms as "baroque," "classic," "neoclassic," "primitive," "picturesque," and 164 different works by artists like Botticelli, van Cleve, Dürer, Hobbema, Holbein, Hals, Rembrandt, Titian, Brueghel, Vermeer, and many others, the author establishes the classifications of art history and style on a firm, concrete basis. This classic of art criticism shows what really occurred between the 14th-century primitives and the sophistication of the 18th century in terms of basic attitudes and philosophies. "A remarkable lesson in the art of seeing," *Sat. Rev. of Literature.* Translated from the 7th German edition. 150 illustrations. 254pp. 6⅛ x 9¼.   Paperbound $2.00

PRIMITIVE ART,
Franz Boas
This authoritative and exhaustive work by a great American anthropologist covers the entire gamut of primitive art. Pottery, leatherwork, metal work, stone work, wood, basketry, are treated in detail. Theories of primitive art, historical depth in art history, technical virtuosity, unconscious levels of patterning, symbolism, styles, literature, music, dance, etc. A must book for the interested layman, the anthropologist, artist, handicrafter (hundreds of unusual motifs), and the historian. Over 900 illustrations (50 ceramic vessels, 12 totem poles, etc.). 376pp. 5⅜ x 8.   Paperbound $2.25

THE GENTLEMAN AND CABINET MAKER'S DIRECTOR,
Thomas Chippendale
A reprint of the 1762 catalogue of furniture designs that went on to influence generations of English and Colonial and Early Republic American furniture makers. The 200 plates, most of them full-page sized, show Chippendale's designs for French (Louis XV), Gothic, and Chinese-manner chairs, sofas, canopy and dome beds, cornices, chamber organs, cabinets, shaving tables, commodes, picture frames, frets, candle stands, chimney pieces, decorations, etc. The drawings are all elegant and highly detailed; many include construction diagrams and elevations. A supplement of 24 photographs shows surviving pieces of original and Chippendale-style pieces of furniture. Brief biography of Chippendale by N. I. Bienenstock, editor of *Furniture World.* Reproduced from the 1762 edition. 200 plates, plus 19 photographic plates. vi + 249pp. 9⅛ x 12¼.   Paperbound $3.50

AMERICAN ANTIQUE FURNITURE: A BOOK FOR AMATEURS,
Edgar G. Miller, Jr.
Standard introduction and practical guide to identification of valuable American antique furniture. 2115 illustrations, mostly photographs taken by the author in 148 private homes, are arranged in chronological order in extensive chapters on chairs, sofas, chests, desks, bedsteads, mirrors, tables, clocks, and other articles. Focus is on furniture accessible to the collector, including simpler pieces and a larger than usual coverage of Empire style. Introductory chapters identify structural elements, characteristics of various styles, how to avoid fakes, etc. "We are frequently asked to name some book on American furniture that will meet the requirements of the novice collector, the beginning dealer, and . . . the general public. . . . We believe Mr. Miller's two volumes more completely satisfy this specification than any other work," *Antiques.* Appendix. Index. Total of vi + 1106pp. 7⅞ x 10¾.
Two volume set, paperbound $7.50

THE BAD CHILD'S BOOK OF BEASTS, MORE BEASTS FOR WORSE CHILDREN, and A MORAL ALPHABET, *H. Belloc*
Hardly and anthology of humorous verse has appeared in the last 50 years without at least a couple of these famous nonsense verses. But one must see the entire volumes — with all the delightful original illustrations by Sir Basil Blackwood — to appreciate fully Belloc's charming and witty verses that play so subacidly on the platitudes of life and morals that beset his day — and ours. A great humor classic. Three books in one. Total of 157pp. 5⅜ x 8.
Paperbound $1.00

THE DEVIL'S DICTIONARY, *Ambrose Bierce*
Sardonic and irreverent barbs puncturing the pomposities and absurdities of American politics, business, religion, literature, and arts, by the country's greatest satirist in the classic tradition. Epigrammatic as Shaw, piercing as Swift, American as Mark Twain, Will Rogers, and Fred Allen, Bierce will always remain the favorite of a small coterie of enthusiasts, and of writers and speakers whom he supplies with "some of the most gorgeous witticisms of the English language" (H. L. Mencken). Over 1000 entries in alphabetical order. 144pp. 5⅜ x 8.
Paperbound $1.00

THE COMPLETE NONSENSE OF EDWARD LEAR.
This is the only complete edition of this master of gentle madness available at a popular price. *A Book of Nonsense, Nonsense Songs, More Nonsense Songs and Stories* in their entirety with all the old favorites that have delighted children and adults for years. The Dong With A Luminous Nose, The Jumblies, The Owl and the Pussycat, and hundreds of other bits of wonderful nonsense. 214 limericks, 3 sets of Nonsense Botany, 5 Nonsense Alphabets, 546 drawings by Lear himself, and much more. 320pp. 5⅜ x 8.
Paperbound $1.00

THE WIT AND HUMOR OF OSCAR WILDE, *ed. by Alvin Redman*
Wilde at his most brilliant, in 1000 epigrams exposing weaknesses and hypocrisies of "civilized" society. Divided into 49 categories—sin, wealth, women, America, etc.—to aid writers, speakers. Includes excerpts from his trials, books, plays, criticism. Formerly "The Epigrams of Oscar Wilde." Introduction by Vyvyan Holland, Wilde's only living son. Introductory essay by editor. 260pp. 5⅜ x 8.
Paperbound $1.00

A CHILD'S PRIMER OF NATURAL HISTORY, *Oliver Herford*
Scarcely an anthology of whimsy and humor has appeared in the last 50 years without a contribution from Oliver Herford. Yet the works from which these examples are drawn have been almost impossible to obtain! Here at last are Herford's improbable definitions of a menagerie of familiar and weird animals, each verse illustrated by the author's own drawings. 24 drawings in 2 colors; 24 additional drawings. vii + 95pp. 6½ x 6.
Paperbound $1.00

THE BROWNIES: THEIR BOOK, *Palmer Cox*
The book that made the Brownies a household word. Generations of readers have enjoyed the antics, predicaments and adventures of these jovial sprites, who emerge from the forest at night to play or to come to the aid of a deserving human. Delightful illustrations by the author decorate nearly every page. 24 short verse tales with 266 illustrations. 155pp. 6⅝ x 9¼.
Paperbound $1.50

THE PRINCIPLES OF PSYCHOLOGY,
William James
The full long-course, unabridged, of one of the great classics of Western literature and science. Wonderfully lucid descriptions of human mental activity, the stream of thought, consciousness, time perception, memory, imagination, emotions, reason, abnormal phenomena, and similar topics. Original contributions are integrated with the work of such men as Berkeley, Binet, Mills, Darwin, Hume, Kant, Royce, Schopenhauer, Spinoza, Locke, Descartes, Galton, Wundt, Lotze, Herbart, Fechner, and scores of others. All contrasting interpretations of mental phenomena are examined in detail—introspective analysis, philosophical interpretation, and experimental research. "A classic," *Journal of Consulting Psychology.* "The main lines are as valid as ever," *Psychoanalytical Quarterly.* "Standard reading . . . a classic of interpretation," *Psychiatric Quarterly.* 94 illustrations. 1408pp. 5⅜ x 8.

Vol. 1 Paperbound $2.50, Vol. 2 Paperbound $2.50,
The set $5.00

VISUAL ILLUSIONS: THEIR CAUSES, CHARACTERISTICS AND APPLICATIONS,
M. Luckiesh
"Seeing is deceiving," asserts the author of this introduction to virtually every type of optical illusion known. The text both describes and explains the principles involved in color illusions, figure-ground, distance illusions, etc. 100 photographs, drawings and diagrams prove how easy it is to fool the sense: circles that aren't round, parallel lines that seem to bend, stationary figures that seem to move as you stare at them — illustration after illustration strains our credulity at what we see. Fascinating book from many points of view, from applications for artists, in camouflage, etc. to the psychology of vision. New introduction by William Ittleson, Dept. of Psychology, Queens College. Index. Bibliography. xxi + 252pp. 5⅜ x 8½. Paperbound $1.50

FADS AND FALLACIES IN THE NAME OF SCIENCE,
Martin Gardner
This is the standard account of various cults, quack systems, and delusions which have masqueraded as science: hollow earth fanatics. Reich and orgone sex energy, dianetics, Atlantis, multiple moons, Forteanism, flying saucers, medical fallacies like iridiagnosis, zone therapy, etc. A new chapter has been added on Bridey Murphy, psionics, and other recent manifestations in this field. This is a fair, reasoned appraisal of eccentric theory which provides excellent inoculation against cleverly masked nonsense. "Should be read by everyone, scientist and non-scientist alike," R. T. Birge, Prof. Emeritus of Physics, Univ. of California; Former President, American Physical Society. Index. x + 365pp. 5⅜ x 8. Paperbound $1.85

ILLUSIONS AND DELUSIONS OF THE SUPERNATURAL AND THE OCCULT,
D. H. Rawcliffe
Holds up to rational examination hundreds of persistent delusions including crystal gazing, automatic writing, table turning, mediumistic trances, mental healing, stigmata, lycanthropy, live burial, the Indian Rope Trick, spiritualism, dowsing, telepathy, clairvoyance, ghosts, ESP, etc. The author explains and exposes the mental and physical deceptions involved, making this not only an exposé of supernatural phenomena, but a valuable exposition of characteristic types of abnormal psychology. Originally titled "The Psychology of the Occult." 14 illustrations. Index. 551pp. 5⅜ x 8. Paperbound $2.25

FAIRY TALE COLLECTIONS, *edited by Andrew Lang*
Andrew Lang's fairy tale collections make up the richest shelf-full of traditional children's stories anywhere available. Lang supervised the translation of stories from all over the world—familiar European tales collected by Grimm, animal stories from Negro Africa, myths of primitive Australia, stories from Russia, Hungary, Iceland, Japan, and many other countries. Lang's selection of translations are unusually high; many authorities consider that the most familiar tales find their best versions in these volumes. All collections are richly decorated and illustrated by H. J. Ford and other artists.

THE BLUE FAIRY BOOK. 37 stories. 138 illustrations. ix + 390pp. 5⅜ x 8½.
Paperbound $1.50

THE GREEN FAIRY BOOK. 42 stories. 100 illustrations. xiii + 366pp. 5⅜ x 8½.
Paperbound $1.50

THE BROWN FAIRY BOOK. 32 stories. 50 illustrations, 8 in color. xii + 350pp. 5⅜ x 8½.
Paperbound $1.50

THE BEST TALES OF HOFFMANN, *edited by E. F. Bleiler*
10 stories by E. T. A. Hoffmann, one of the greatest of all writers of fantasy. The tales include "The Golden Flower Pot," "Automata," "A New Year's Eve Adventure," "Nutcracker and the King of Mice," "Sand-Man," and others. Vigorous characterizations of highly eccentric personalities, remarkably imaginative situations, and intensely fast pacing has made these tales popular all over the world for 150 years. Editor's introduction. 7 drawings by Hoffmann. xxxiii + 419pp. 5⅜ x 8½.
Paperbound $2.00

GHOST AND HORROR STORIES OF AMBROSE BIERCE,
edited by E. F. Bleiler
Morbid, eerie, horrifying tales of possessed poets, shabby aristocrats, revived corpses, and haunted malefactors. Widely acknowledged as the best of their kind between Poe and the moderns, reflecting their author's inner torment and bitter view of life. Includes "Damned Thing," "The Middle Toe of the Right Foot," "The Eyes of the Panther," "Visions of the Night," "Moxon's Master," and over a dozen others. Editor's introduction. xxii + 199pp. 5⅜ x 8½.
Paperbound $1.25

THREE GOTHIC NOVELS, *edited by E. F. Bleiler*
Originators of the still popular Gothic novel form, influential in ushering in early 19th-century Romanticism. Horace Walpole's *Castle of Otranto*, William Beckford's *Vathek*, John Polidori's *The Vampyre*, and a *Fragment* by Lord Byron are enjoyable as exciting reading or as documents in the history of English literature. Editor's introduction. xi + 291pp. 5⅜ x 8½.
Paperbound $2.00

BEST GHOST STORIES OF LEFANU, *edited by E. F. Bleiler*
Though admired by such critics as V. S. Pritchett, Charles Dickens and Henry James, ghost stories by the Irish novelist Joseph Sheridan LeFanu have never become as widely known as his detective fiction. About half of the 16 stories in this collection have never before been available in America. Collection includes "Carmilla" (perhaps the best vampire story ever written), "The Haunted Baronet," "The Fortunes of Sir Robert Ardagh," and the classic "Green Tea." Editor's introduction. 7 contemporary illustrations. Portrait of LeFanu. xii + 467pp. 5⅜ x 8.
Paperbound $2.00

EASY-TO-DO ENTERTAINMENTS AND DIVERSIONS WITH COINS, CARDS, STRING, PAPER AND MATCHES, *R. M. Abraham*

Over 300 tricks, games and puzzles will provide young readers with absorbing fun. Sections on card games; paper-folding; tricks with coins, matches and pieces of string; games for the agile; toy-making from common household objects; mathematical recreations; and 50 miscellaneous pastimes. Anyone in charge of groups of youngsters, including hard-pressed parents, and in need of suggestions on how to keep children sensibly amused and quietly content will find this book indispensable. Clear, simple text, copious number of delightful line drawings and illustrative diagrams. Originally titled "Winter Nights' Entertainments." Introduction by Lord Baden Powell. 329 illustrations. v + 186pp. 5⅜ x 8½.   Paperbound $1.00

AN INTRODUCTION TO CHESS MOVES AND TACTICS SIMPLY EXPLAINED, *Leonard Barden*

Beginner's introduction to the royal game. Names, possible moves of the pieces, definitions of essential terms, how games are won, etc. explained in 30-odd pages. With this background you'll be able to sit right down and play. Balance of book teaches strategy — openings, middle game, typical endgame play, and suggestions for improving your game. A sample game is fully analyzed. True middle-level introduction, teaching you all the essentials without oversimplifying or losing you in a maze of detail. 58 figures. 102pp. 5⅜ x 8½.   Paperbound $1.00

LASKER'S MANUAL OF CHESS, *Dr. Emanuel Lasker*

Probably the greatest chess player of modern times, Dr. Emanuel Lasker held the world championship 28 years, independent of passing schools or fashions. This unmatched study of the game, chiefly for intermediate to skilled players, analyzes basic methods, combinations, position play, the aesthetics of chess, dozens of different openings, etc., with constant reference to great modern games. Contains a brilliant exposition of Steinitz's important theories. Introduction by Fred Reinfeld. Tables of Lasker's tournament record. 3 indices. 308 diagrams. 1 photograph. xxx + 349pp. 5⅜ x 8.   Paperbound $2.25

COMBINATIONS: THE HEART OF CHESS, *Irving Chernev*

Step-by-step from simple combinations to complex, this book, by a well-known chess writer, shows you the intricacies of pins, counter-pins, knight forks, and smothered mates. Other chapters show alternate lines of play to those taken in actual championship games; boomerang combinations; classic examples of brilliant combination play by Nimzovich, Rubinstein, Tarrasch, Botvinnik, Alekhine and Capablanca. Index. 356 diagrams. ix + 245pp. 5⅜ x 8½.   Paperbound $1.85

HOW TO SOLVE CHESS PROBLEMS, *K. S. Howard*

Full of practical suggestions for the fan or the beginner — who knows only the moves of the chessmen. Contains preliminary section and 58 two-move, 46 three-move, and 8 four-move problems composed by 27 outstanding American problem creators in the last 30 years. Explanation of all terms and exhaustive index. "Just what is wanted for the student," Brian Harley. 112 problems, solutions. vi + 171pp. 5⅜ x 8.   Paperbound $1.35

SOCIAL THOUGHT FROM LORE TO SCIENCE,
H. E. Barnes and H. Becker
An immense survey of sociological thought and ways of viewing, studying, planning, and reforming society from earliest times to the present. Includes thought on society of preliterate peoples, ancient non-Western cultures, and every great movement in Europe, America, and modern Japan. Analyzes hundreds of great thinkers: Plato, Augustine, Bodin, Vico, Montesquieu, Herder, Comte, Marx, etc. Weighs the contributions of utopians, sophists, fascists and communists; economists, jurists, philosophers, ecclesiastics, and every 19th and 20th century school of scientific sociology, anthropology, and social psychology throughout the world. Combines topical, chronological, and regional approaches, treating the evolution of social thought as a process rather than as a series of mere topics. "Impressive accuracy, competence, and discrimination . . . easily the best single survey," *Nation.* Thoroughly revised, with new material up to 1960. 2 indexes. Over 2200 bibliographical notes. Three volume set. Total of 1586pp. 5⅜ x 8.
Vol. 1 Paperbound $2.75, Vol. 2 Paperbound $2.75, Vol. 3 Paperbound $2.50
The set $8.00

A HISTORY OF HISTORICAL WRITING, *Harry Elmer Barnes*
Virtually the only adequate survey of the whole course of historical writing in a single volume. Surveys developments from the beginnings of historiography in the ancient Near East and the Classical World, up through the Cold War. Covers major historians in detail, shows interrelationship with cultural background, makes clear individual contributions, evaluates and estimates importance; also enormously rich upon minor authors and thinkers who are usually passed over. Packed with scholarship and learning, clear, easily written. Indispensable to every student of history. Revised and enlarged up to 1961. Index and bibliography. xv + 442pp. 5⅜ x 8½. Paperbound $2.50

JOHANN SEBASTIAN BACH, *Philipp Spitta*
The complete and unabridged text of the definitive study of Bach. Written some 70 years ago, it is still unsurpassed for its coverage of nearly all aspects of Bach's life and work. There could hardly be a finer non-technical introduction to Bach's music than the detailed, lucid analyses which Spitta provides for hundreds of individual pieces. 26 solid pages are devoted to the B minor mass, for example, and 30 pages to the glorious St. Matthew Passion. This monumental set also includes a major analysis of the music of the 18th century: Buxtehude, Pachelbel, etc. "Unchallenged as the last word on one of the supreme geniuses of music," John Barkham, *Saturday Review Syndicate.* Total of 1819pp. Heavy cloth binding. 5⅜ x 8.
Two volume set, clothbound $13.50

BEETHOVEN AND HIS NINE SYMPHONIES, *George Grove*
In this modern middle-level classic of musicology Grove not only analyzes all nine of Beethoven's symphonies very thoroughly in terms of their musical structure, but also discusses the circumstances under which they were written, Beethoven's stylistic development, and much other background material. This is an extremely rich book, yet very easily followed; it is highly recommended to anyone seriously interested in music. Over 250 musical passages. Index. viii + 407pp. 5⅜ x 8. Paperbound $2.00

THREE SCIENCE FICTION NOVELS,
John Taine
Acknowledged by many as the best SF writer of the 1920's, Taine (under the name Eric Temple Bell) was also a Professor of Mathematics of considerable renown. Reprinted here are *The Time Stream*, generally considered Taine's best, *The Greatest Game*, a biological-fiction novel, and *The Purple Sapphire*, involving a supercivilization of the past. Taine's stories tie fantastic narratives to frameworks of original and logical scientific concepts. Speculation is often profound on such questions as the nature of time, concept of entropy, cyclical universes, etc. 4 contemporary illustrations. v + 532pp. 5⅜ x 8⅜.

Paperbound $2.00

SEVEN SCIENCE FICTION NOVELS,
H. G. Wells
Full unabridged texts of 7 science-fiction novels of the master. Ranging from biology, physics, chemistry, astronomy, to sociology and other studies, Mr. Wells extrapolates whole worlds of strange and intriguing character. "One will have to go far to match this for entertainment, excitement, and sheer pleasure . . ."*New York Times*. Contents: The Time Machine, The Island of Dr. Moreau, The First Men in the Moon, The Invisible Man, The War of the Worlds, The Food of the Gods, In The Days of the Comet. 1015pp. 5⅜ x 8.

Clothbound $5.00

28 SCIENCE FICTION STORIES OF H. G. WELLS.
Two full, unabridged novels, *Men Like Gods* and *Star Begotten*, plus 26 short stories by the master science-fiction writer of all time! Stories of space, time, invention, exploration, futuristic adventure. Partial contents: *The Country of the Blind, In the Abyss, The Crystal Egg, The Man Who Could Work Miracles, A Story of Days to Come, The Empire of the Ants, The Magic Shop, The Valley of the Spiders, A Story of the Stone Age, Under the Knife, Sea Raiders,* etc. An indispensable collection for the library of anyone interested in science fiction adventure. 928pp. 5⅜ x 8.

Clothbound $4.50

THREE MARTIAN NOVELS,
Edgar Rice Burroughs
Complete, unabridged reprinting, in one volume, of Thuvia, Maid of Mars; Chessmen of Mars; The Master Mind of Mars. Hours of science-fiction adventure by a modern master storyteller. Reset in large clear type for easy reading. 16 illustrations by J. Allen St. John. vi + 490pp. 5⅜ x 8½.

Paperbound $1.85

AN INTELLECTUAL AND CULTURAL HISTORY OF THE WESTERN WORLD,
Harry Elmer Barnes
Monumental 3-volume survey of intellectual development of Europe from primitive cultures to the present day. Every significant product of human intellect traced through history: art, literature, mathematics, physical sciences, medicine, music, technology, social sciences, religions, jurisprudence, education, etc. Presentation is lucid and specific, analyzing in detail specific discoveries, theories, literary works, and so on. Revised (1965) by recognized scholars in specialized fields under the direction of Prof. Barnes. Revised bibliography. Indexes. 24 illustrations. Total of xxix + 1318pp.
Vol. 1 Paperbound $2.00, Vol. 2 Paperbound $2.00, Vol. 3 Paperbound $2.00,

The set $6.00

HEAR ME TALKIN' TO YA, *edited by Nat Shapiro and Nat Hentoff*
In their own words, Louis Armstrong, King Oliver, Fletcher Henderson, Bunk
Johnson, Bix Beiderbecke, Billy Holiday, Fats Waller, Jelly Roll Morton,
Duke Ellington, and many others comment on the origins of jazz in New
Orleans and its growth in Chicago's South Side, Kansas City's jam sessions,
Depression Harlem, and the modernism of the West Coast schools. Taken
from taped conversations, letters, magazine articles, other first-hand sources.
Editors' introduction. xvi + 429pp. 5⅜ x 8½.   Paperbound $2.00

THE JOURNAL OF HENRY D. THOREAU
A 25-year record by the great American observer and critic, as complete a
record of a great man's inner life as is anywhere available. Thoreau's Journals
served him as raw material for his formal pieces, as a place where he could
develop his ideas, as an outlet for his interests in wild life and plants, in
writing as an art, in classics of literature, Walt Whitman and other contemporaries, in politics, slavery, individual's relation to the State, etc. The
Journals present a portrait of a remarkable man, and are an observant social
history. Unabridged republication of 1906 edition, Bradford Torrey and
Francis H. Allen, editors. Illustrations. Total of 1888pp. 8⅜ x 12¼.
                                        Two volume set, clothbound $25.00

A SHAKESPEARIAN GRAMMAR, *E. A. Abbott*
Basic reference to Shakespeare and his contemporaries, explaining through
thousands of quotations from Shakespeare, Jonson, Beaumont and Fletcher,
North's *Plutarch* and other sources the grammatical usage differing from the
modern. First published in 1870 and written by a scholar who spent much of
his life isolating principles of Elizabethan language, the book is unlikely ever
to be superseded. Indexes. xxiv + 511pp. 5⅜ x 8½.   Paperbound $2.75

FOLK-LORE OF SHAKESPEARE, *T. F. Thistelton Dyer*
Classic study, drawing from Shakespeare a large body of references to supernatural beliefs, terminology of falconry and hunting, games and sports, good
luck charms, marriage customs, folk medicines, superstitions about plants,
animals, birds, argot of the underworld, sexual slang of London, proverbs,
drinking customs, weather lore, and much else. From full compilation comes
a mirror of the 17th-century popular mind. Index. ix + 526pp. 5⅜ x 8½.
                                                   Paperbound $2.50

THE NEW VARIORUM SHAKESPEARE, *edited by H. H. Furness*
By far the richest editions of the plays ever produced in any country or
language. Each volume contains complete text (usually First Folio) of the
play, all variants in Quarto and other Folio texts, editorial changes by every
major editor to Furness's own time (1900), footnotes to obscure references or
language, extensive quotes from literature of Shakespearian criticism, essays
on plot sources (often reprinting sources in full), and much more.

HAMLET, *edited by H. H. Furness*
Total of xxvi + 905pp. 5⅜ x 8½.   Two volume set, paperbound $4.75

TWELFTH NIGHT, *edited by H. H. Furness*
Index. xxii + 434pp. 5⅜ x 8½.
                                                   Paperbound $2.25

LA BOHEME BY GIACOMO PUCCINI,
translated and introduced by Ellen H. Bleiler
Complete handbook for the operagoer, with everything needed for full enjoyment except the musical score itself. Complete Italian libretto, with new, modern English line-by-line translation—the only libretto printing all repeats; biography of Puccini; the librettists; background to the opera, Murger's La Boheme, etc.; circumstances of composition and performances; plot summary; and pictorial section of 73 illustrations showing Puccini, famous singers and performances, etc. Large clear type for easy reading. 124pp. 5⅜ x 8½.
Paperbound $1.00

ANTONIO STRADIVARI: HIS LIFE AND WORK (1644-1737),
W. Henry Hill, Arthur F. Hill, and Alfred E. Hill
Still the only book that really delves into life and art of the incomparable Italian craftsman, maker of the finest musical instruments in the world today. The authors, expert violin-makers themselves, discuss Stradivari's ancestry, his construction and finishing techniques, distinguished characteristics of many of his instruments and their locations. Included, too, is story of introduction of his instruments into France, England, first revelation of their supreme merit, and information on his labels, number of instruments made, prices, mystery of ingredients of his varnish, tone of pre-1684 Stradivari violin and changes between 1684 and 1690. An extremely interesting, informative account for all music lovers, from craftsman to concert-goer. Republication of original (1902) edition. New introduction by Sydney Beck, Head of Rare Book and Manuscript Collections, Music Division, New York Public Library. Analytical index by Rembert Wurlitzer. Appendixes. 68 illustrations. 30 full-page plates. 4 in color. xxvi + 315pp. 5⅜ x 8½.
Paperbound $2.25

MUSICAL AUTOGRAPHS FROM MONTEVERDI TO HINDEMITH,
Emanuel Winternitz
For beauty, for intrinsic interest, for perspective on the composer's personality, for subtleties of phrasing, shading, emphasis indicated in the autograph but suppressed in the printed score, the mss. of musical composition are fascinating documents which repay close study in many different ways. This 2-volume work reprints facsimiles of mss. by virtually every major composer, and many minor figures—196 examples in all. A full text points out what can be learned from mss., analyzes each sample. Index. Bibliography. 18 figures. 196 plates. Total of 170pp. of text. 7⅞ x 10¾.
Vol. 1 Paperbound $2.00, Vol. 2 Paperbound $2.00,
The set $4.00

J. S. BACH,
Albert Schweitzer
One of the few great full-length studies of Bach's life and work, and the study upon which Schweitzer's renown as a musicologist rests. On first appearance (1911), revolutionized Bach performance. The only writer on Bach to be musicologist, performing musician, and student of history, theology and philosophy, Schweitzer contributes particularly full sections on history of German Protestant church music, theories on motivic pictorial representations in vocal music, and practical suggestions for performance. Translated by Ernest Newman. Indexes. 5 illustrations. 650 musical examples. Total of xix + 928pp. 5⅜ x 8½.
Vol. 1 Paperbound $2.00, Vol. 2 Paperbound $2.00,
The set $4.00

THE METHODS OF ETHICS, *Henry Sidgwick*
Propounding no organized system of its own, study subjects every major methodological approach to ethics to rigorous, objective analysis. Study discusses and relates ethical thought of Plato, Aristotle, Bentham, Clarke, Butler, Hobbes, Hume, Mill, Spencer, Kant, and dozens of others. Sidgwick retains conclusions from each system which follow from ethical premises, rejecting the faulty. Considered by many in the field to be among the most important treatises on ethical philosophy. Appendix. Index. xlvii + 528pp. 5⅜ x 8½.
Paperbound $2.50

TEUTONIC MYTHOLOGY, *Jakob Grimm*
A milestone in Western culture; the work which established on a modern basis the study of history of religions and comparative religions. 4-volume work assembles and interprets everything available on religious and folkloristic beliefs of Germanic people (including Scandinavians, Anglo-Saxons, etc.). Assembling material from such sources as Tacitus, surviving Old Norse and Icelandic texts, archeological remains, folktales, surviving superstitions, comparative traditions, linguistic analysis, etc. Grimm explores pagan deities, heroes, folklore of nature, religious practices, and every other area of pagan German belief. To this day, the unrivaled, definitive, exhaustive study. Translated by J. S. Stallybrass from 4th (1883) German edition. Indexes. Total of lxxvii + 1887pp. 5⅜ x 8½.   Four volume set, paperbound $10.00

THE I CHING, *translated by James Legge*
Called "The Book of Changes" in English, this is one of the Five Classics edited by Confucius, basic and central to Chinese thought. Explains perhaps the most complex system of divination known, founded on the theory that all things happening at any one time have characteristic features which can be isolated and related. Significant in Oriental studies, in history of religions and philosophy, and also to Jungian psychoanalysis and other areas of modern European thought. Index. Appendixes. 6 plates. xxi + 448pp. 5⅜ x 8½.
Paperbound $2.75

HISTORY OF ANCIENT PHILOSOPHY, *W. Windelband*
One of the clearest, most accurate comprehensive surveys of Greek and Roman philosophy. Discusses ancient philosophy in general, intellectual life in Greece in the 7th and 6th centuries B.C., Thales, Anaximander, Anaximenes, Heraclitus, the Eleatics, Empedocles, Anaxagoras, Leucippus, the Pythagoreans, the Sophists, Socrates, Democritus (20 pages), Plato (50 pages), Aristotle (70 pages), the Peripatetics, Stoics, Epicureans, Sceptics, Neo-platonists, Christian Apologists, etc. 2nd German edition translated by H. E. Cushman. xv + 393pp. 5⅜ x 8.   Paperbound $2.25

THE PALACE OF PLEASURE, *William Painter*
Elizabethan versions of Italian and French novels from *The Decameron*, Cinthio, Straparola, Queen Margaret of Navarre, and other continental sources — the very work that provided Shakespeare and dozens of his contemporaries with many of their plots and sub-plots and, therefore, justly considered one of the most influential books in all English literature. It is also a book that any reader will still enjoy. Total of cviii + 1,224pp.
Three volume set, Paperbound $6.75

THE WONDERFUL WIZARD OF OZ, *L. F. Baum*
All the original W. W. Denslow illustrations in full color—as much a part of
"The Wizard" as Tenniel's drawings are of "Alice in Wonderland." "The
Wizard" is still America's best-loved fairy tale, in which, as the author expresses
it, "The wonderment and joy are retained and the heartaches and nightmares
left out." Now today's young readers can enjoy every word and wonderful picture of the original book. New introduction by Martin Gardner. A Baum
bibliography. 23 full-page color plates. viii + 268pp. 5⅜ x 8.
Paperbound $1.50

THE MARVELOUS LAND OF OZ, *L. F. Baum*
This is the equally enchanting sequel to the "Wizard," continuing the adventures of the Scarecrow and the Tin Woodman. The hero this time is a little
bǒy named Tip, and all the delightful Oz magic is still present. This is the
Oz book with the Animated Saw-Horse, the Woggle-Bug, and Jack Pumpkin-
head. All the original John R. Neill illustrations, 10 in full color. 287pp.
5⅜ x 8.
Paperbound $1.50

ALICE'S ADVENTURES UNDER GROUND, *Lewis Carroll*
The original *Alice in Wonderland*, hand-lettered and illustrated by Carroll
himself, and originally presented as a Christmas gift to a child-friend. Adults
as well as children will enjoy this charming volume, reproduced faithfully
in this Dover edition. While the story is essentially the same, there are slight
changes, and Carroll's spritely drawings present an intriguing alternative to
the famous Tenniel illustrations. One of the most popular books in Dover's
catalogue. Introduction by Martin Gardner. 38 illustrations. 128pp. 5⅜ x 8½.
Paperbound $1.00

THE NURSERY "ALICE," *Lewis Carroll*
While most of us consider *Alice in Wonderland* a story for children of all
ages, Carroll himself felt it was beyond younger children. He therefore provided this simplified version, illustrated with the famous Tenniel drawings
enlarged and colored in delicate tints, for children aged "from Nought to
Five." Dover's edition of this now rare classic is a faithful copy of the 1889
printing, including 20 illustrations by Tenniel, and front and back covers
reproduced in full color. Introduction by Martin Gardner. xxiii + 67pp.
6⅛ x 9¼.
Paperbound $1.50

THE STORY OF KING ARTHUR AND HIS KNIGHTS, *Howard Pyle*
A fast-paced, exciting retelling of the best known Arthurian legends for young
readers by one of America's best story tellers and illustrators. The sword
Excalibur, wooing of Guinevere, Merlin and his downfall, adventures of Sir
Pellias and Gawaine, and others. The pen and ink illustrations are vividly
imagined and wonderfully drawn. 41 illustrations. xviii + 313pp. 6⅛ x 9¼.
Paperbound $1.50

Prices subject to change without notice.

Available at your book dealer or write for free catalogue to Dept. Adsci,
Dover Publications, Inc., 180 Varick St., N.Y., N.Y. 10014. Dover publishes more
than 150 books each year on science, elementary and advanced mathematics,
biology, music, art, literary history, social sciences and other areas.